Praise for *New York Times* bestselling author RaeAnne Thayne

"[Thayne] engages the reader's heart and emotions, inspiring hope and the belief that miracles *are* possible."
—#1 *New York Times* bestselling author Debbie Macomber

"RaeAnne Thayne is quickly becoming one of my favorite authors…. Once you start reading, you aren't going to be able to stop."
—*Fresh Fiction*

"Well-developed characters, plus plenty of raw emotion—and humor—add up to one of [Thayne's] finest books."
—*RT Book Reviews* on *His Second-Chance Family* (4½ stars, Top Pick)

Praise for *USA TODAY* bestselling author Lee Tobin McClain

"*A Family for Easter* by Lee Tobin McClain is a beautiful story of deep friendship, and how it turns into lasting love and brings two families together into one."
—*Harlequin Junkie*

"Everything I look for in a book—it's emotional, tender, and an all-around wonderful story."
—RaeAnne Thayne, *New York Times* bestselling author, on *Low Country Hero*

NEW YORK TIMES BESTSELLING AUTHOR

RaeAnne Thayne

A SOLDIER'S RETURN

 HARLEQUIN®

Recycling programs for this product may not exist in your area.

ISBN-13: 978-1-335-40997-3

A Soldier's Return
First published in 2019.
This edition published in 2021.
Copyright © 2019 by RaeAnne Thayne LLC

Engaged to the Single Mom
First published in 2015.
This edition published in 2021.
Copyright © 2015 by Lee Tobin McClain

All rights reserved. No part of this book may be used or reproduced in any manner whatsoever without written permission except in the case of brief quotations embodied in critical articles and reviews.

This is a work of fiction. Names, characters, places and incidents are either the product of the author's imagination or are used fictitiously. Any resemblance to actual persons, living or dead, businesses, companies, events or locales is entirely coincidental.

This edition published by arrangement with Harlequin Books S.A.

For questions and comments about the quality of this book, please contact us at CustomerService@Harlequin.com.

Harlequin Enterprises ULC
22 Adelaide St. West, 40th Floor
Toronto, Ontario M5H 4E3, Canada
www.Harlequin.com

Printed in U.S.A.

CONTENTS

RaeAnne Thayne finds inspiration in the beautiful northern Utah mountains, where the *New York Times* and *USA TODAY* bestselling author lives with her husband and three children. Her books have won numerous honors, including RITA® Award nominations from Romance Writers of America and a Career Achievement Award from *RT Book Reviews*. RaeAnne loves to hear from readers and can be contacted through her website, raeannethayne.com.

Books by RaeAnne Thayne

Harlequin Special Edition

The Cowboys of Cold Creek

A Cold Creek Christmas Surprise
The Christmas Ranch
A Cold Creek Christmas Story
The Holiday Gift
The Rancher's Christmas Song

The Women of Brambleberry House

A Soldier's Secret
His Second-Chance Family
The Daddy Makeover

HQN

Haven Point

Sugar Pine Trail
The Cottages on Silver Beach
Season of Wonder

Visit the Author Profile page
at Harlequin.com for more titles.

A SOLDIER'S RETURN

RaeAnne Thayne

To Jill Shalvis and Marina Adair.
I love our seaside adventures!

Chapter 1

Some days, a girl reached a point where her best course of action was to run away from her problems.

Melissa Fielding hung up the phone after yet another unproductive discussion with her frustrating ex-husband, drew in a deep, cleansing breath, then threw on her favorite pair of jogging shoes.

Yes, she had a million things to do. The laundry basket spilled over with clothes, she had bills to pay, dirty dishes filled her sink, and she was scheduled to go into the doctor's office where she worked in less than two hours.

None of that mattered right now. She had too much energy seething through her, wave after wave like the sea pounding Cannon Beach during a storm.

Even Brambleberry House, the huge, rambling Victorian where she and her daughter lived in the first-floor apartment, seemed too small right now.

She needed a little good, hard exercise to work some of it off or she would be a stressed, angry mess at work.

She and Cody had been divorced for three years, separated four, but he could still make her more frustrated than anybody else on earth. Fortunately, their seven-year-old daughter, Skye, was at school, so she didn't have to witness her parents arguing yet again.

She yanked open her apartment door to head for the outside door when it opened from the other side. Rosa Galvez, her de facto landlady who ran the three-unit building for her aunt and a friend, walked inside, arms loaded with groceries.

Her friend took one look at Melissa's face and frowned. "Uh-oh. Bad morning?" Rosa asked, her lovely features twisted with concern.

Now that she was off the phone, the heat of Melissa's anger cooled a degree or two, but she could still feel the restless energy spitting and hissing through her like a downed power line.

"You know how it goes. Five minutes on the phone with my ex and I either have to punch something, spend an hour doing yoga or go for a hard run on the beach. I don't have a free hour and punching something would be counterproductive, so a good run is the winner." Melissa took two bags of groceries from Rosa and led the way up the stairs to the other woman's third-floor apartment.

"Run an extra mile or two for me, would you?" Rosa asked.

"Sure thing."

"What does he want this time?"

She sighed. "It's a long story." She didn't want to complain to her friend about Cody. It made her sound bitter and small, and she wasn't, only frustrated at all the broken promises and endless disappointments.

Guilt, an old, unwelcome companion, poked her on the shoulder. Her daughter loved her father despite his failings. Skye couldn't see what Melissa did—that even though Skye was only seven, there was a chance she was more mature than her fun-loving, thrill-chasing father.

She ignored the guilt, reminding herself once more there was nothing she could do about her past mistakes but continue trying to make the best of things for her child's sake.

Rosa opened the door to her wide, window-filled apartment, and Melissa wasn't surprised to find Rosa's much-loved dog, an Irish setter named Fiona, waiting just inside.

"Can I take Fiona on my run?" she asked impulsively, after setting the groceries in the kitchen.

"That would be great!" Rosa exclaimed. "We were going to go on a walk as soon as I put the groceries away, but she would love a run much more. Thank you! Her leash is there on the hook."

At the word *leash*, Fiona loped to the door and did a little circular dance of joy that made more of Melissa's bad mood seep away.

"Let's do this, sweetheart," she said, grabbing the leash from its place by the door and hooking it to Fiona's shamrock-green collar.

"Thank you for this. Have fun." Rosa opened the door for them, and the strong dog just about pulled Melissa toward the stairs. She waved at her friend, then she and the dog hurried outside.

The April morning was one of those rare and precious days along the Oregon Coast when Mother Nature decided it was finally time to get serious about spring. Sunlight gleamed on the water and all the colors seemed saturated and bright from the rains of the preceding few days.

The well-tended gardens of Brambleberry House were overflowing with sweet-smelling flowers—cherry blossoms, magnolia, camellias. It was sheer delight. She inhaled the heavenly aroma, enjoying the undernote of sea and sand and other smells that were inexorable scent-memories of her childhood.

Fiona pulled at the leash, forcing Melissa to pick up her pace. Yes. A good run was exactly the prescription she was writing herself.

As she headed down the path toward the gate that led to the water, she spotted Sonia, the third tenant of Brambleberry House, working in a bed of lavender that hadn't yet burst into bloom.

Sonia was an interesting creature. She wasn't rude, exactly, she simply kept to herself and had done so for the seven months Melissa had lived downstairs from her.

Melissa always felt so guilty when she watched the other woman make her painstaking way up the stairs to her second-floor apartment, often pausing to rest on the landing. She didn't know the nature of Sonia's health issues, but she obviously struggled with something. She walked with a limp, and Rosa had told Melissa once that the other woman had vision issues that precluded driving.

Right after moving in, Melissa had offered to switch apartments with her so Sonia wouldn't have to make the climb, but her offer had been refused.

"I need…the exercise," Sonia had said in her halting, odd cadence. "Going upstairs is good…physical therapy…for me."

Melissa had to admire someone willing to push herself out of her comfort zone, sustained only by the hope that she would grow from the experience.

That was a good life lesson for her. She wasted entirely too much energy dwelling on the painful reality that life hadn't turned out exactly as she planned, that some of her dreams were destined to disappointment.

Like Sonia, maybe it was time she stopped being cranky about things she couldn't control and took any chance that came along to force herself to stretch outside her comfort zone. She needed to learn how to make the best of things, to simply enjoy a gorgeous April day.

"Beautiful morning, isn't it?"

"Lovely," Sonia said with her somewhat lopsided smile. "Hello…Melissa. Hello…Fiona."

She scratched the dog under her chin and was rewarded with one of Fi's doggie grins.

While the Irish setter technically lived with Rosa, the cheerful dog seemed to consider all the occupants of Brambleberry House her particular pack. That shared pet care worked out well for Melissa. Her daughter had been begging for a dog since before the divorce. Skye had been in heaven when they'd moved into Brambleberry House and discovered Rosa had a dog she was more than willing to share. This way, they got the benefits of having a dog without the onus of being responsible for one all the time.

That was yet another thing she had to be grateful for on this beautiful spring day. She had been so blessed to find an open apartment in Brambleberry House when she and Skye returned to Cannon Beach after all those years of wandering. It was almost a little miracle, since the previous tenant had only moved out to get married the week before Melissa returned to her hometown and started looking for a place.

She didn't know if it was fate or kismet or luck or simply somebody watching out for them. She only knew that she and Skye had finally found a place to throw down roots.

She ran hard, accompanied by the sun on her face, the low murmur of the waves, the crunch of sand under her running shoes. All of it helped calm her.

By the time she and Fiona made it the mile and a half to the end of the beach and she'd turned around to head back, the rest of her frustration had abated, and she focused instead on the endorphins from the run and the joy of living in this beautiful place.

She paused for a moment to catch her breath, looking out at the rock formations offshore, the towering haystacks that so defined this part of the Oregon Coast, then the craggy green mountains to the east.

It was so good to be home. She had friends here, connections. Her dad was buried not far from here. Her mom and stepfather were here most of the time, though they had just bought an RV and were spending a few months traveling around the country.

She would have thought being a military wife to Melissa's dad would have cured her mother's wanderlust, but apparently not. They would be back soon.

Melissa didn't envy them. After moving to a new base every few years during her childhood and then following Cody around from continent to continent, she loved being in one place. *This* place. She had missed it more than she even realized, until she finally decided to bring Skye here.

She should have done it years ago instead of trying so hard to stay close to her ex-husband for Skye's sake. She had enjoyed living on Oahu, his home training location, but the cost of living had been prohibitive. Most of her salary as a nurse had gone to housing and the rest to food.

When he decided to move to South America on a whim, she had finally thrown up her hands and opted not to follow him. Instead, she had packed up her daughter for one last move and come home to Cannon Beach.

She started her run again, not wanting to spend more time than she already had that morning dwelling on her mistakes.

It made her sad, wondering if she should have tried harder to make things work, even though she was fully aware both of them had left the marriage long before they finally divorced.

Now wasn't the time to obsess about her failures or the loneliness that kept her up at night.

He had gotten married again. That was what he called to tell her earlier. It had been a spur-of-the-moment decision and they'd gone to St. Croix for their honeymoon, which had been beautiful but expensive. He'd spent so much on the honeymoon, in fact, that he couldn't make that month's child support payment, but he would make it up to her.

He was coming back to Oregon to stay this time, and was willing to finally step up and be the dad he should have been all along. She'd been hearing that story or versions of it for fifteen years. She hoped it would happen, she really did.

Cody wasn't a bad man. She wouldn't have loved him all those years and followed him from country to country to support his dreams if he were. But with the birth of their child, her priorities had changed, while she was afraid his never would.

Enough about Cody. She was genuinely happy for her ex, even if hearing about his new marriage did make her wish she had someone special in her own life.

She sighed again and gripped Fiona's leash. "Come on, Fi. Let's go home."

An odd wind danced across the sand, warmer than the air around it. She almost thought she could hear laughter rippling around her, though she was virtually alone on the beach.

She was hearing things again. Once in a while at the house, she could swear she heard a woman's laugh when no one was there, and a few times she had smelled roses on the stairwell, for no apparent reason.

Maybe the ghost of Brambleberry House had been in the mood for a run today, too. The thought made her smile and she continued heading home.

Few people were out on the beach on this off-season morning, but she did happen to catch sight of a guy running toward her from the opposite direction. He was too far away for her to really see clearly, but she had the random impression of lean strength and fluid grace.

Ridiculous, she told herself. How could she know that from two hundred yards away?

She continued running, intent now only on finishing so she could go into work.

Fiona trotted along beside her in the same rhythm

they had worked out through countless runs like this together. She was aware of the other runner coming closer. He had a dog, too, a small black one who also looked familiar.

They were only fifty feet apart when Fiona, for no apparent reason, suddenly veered in front of Melissa, then stopped stock-still.

With no time to change course or put on the brakes, Melissa toppled over the eighty-pound dog and went flying across the sand. She shoved her hands out to catch her fall instinctively. Her right arm hit sand and she felt a jolt in her shoulder from the impact, but the left one must have made contact with a rock buried beneath the sand, causing a wrenching pain to shoot from her wrist up her arm.

This day just kept getting better and better.

She gasped and flopped over onto her back, cradling the injured wrist as a haze of pain clouded her vision.

Fiona nosed her side as if in apology, and Melissa bit back her instinctive scold. What on earth had gotten into Fiona? They had run together dozens of times. The Irish setter was usually graceful, beautifully trained, and never cut across her path like that.

For about ten seconds, it was all she could do not to writhe around on the ground and howl. She was trying not to cry when she gradually became aware she wasn't alone.

"Are you okay?" a deep male voice asked.

She was covered in sand, grabbing her wrist and whimpering like a baby seal that had lost its mama. Did she *look* okay?

"I'm fine," she lied. "Just a little spill."

She looked up—way, way up—and somehow wasn't

surprised to find the other runner she had spotted a few moments earlier.

Her instincts were right. He *was* great-looking. She had an impression of dark hair and concerned blue eyes that looked familiar. He wore running shorts and a formfitting performance shirt that molded to powerfully defined muscles.

She swallowed and managed to sit up. What kind of weird karma was this? She had just wished for a man in her life, and suddenly a gorgeous one seemed to pop up out of nowhere.

Surely it had to be a coincidence.

Anyway, she might like the idea of a man in her life, but she wasn't at all prepared for the reality of it— especially not a dark-haired, blue-eyed runner who still somehow managed to smell delicious.

He also had a little dog on a leash, a small black schnauzer who was sniffing Fiona like they were old friends.

"Can I give you a hand?"

"Um. Sure."

Still cradling her injured wrist, she reached out with her right hand, and he grasped it firmly and tugged her to her feet. For one odd moment, she could swear she smelled roses above the clean, crisp, masculine scent of him, but that made absolutely no sense.

Was she hallucinating? Maybe she had bonked her head in that gloriously graceful free fall.

"You hurt your wrist," he observed. "Need me to take a look at it? I'm a doctor."

What were the odds that she would fall and injure herself in front of a gorgeous tourist who also happened to be a doctor?

"Isn't that convenient?" she muttered, wondering again at the weird little twist of fate.

He gave her an odd look, half curious and half concerned. Again, she had the strange feeling that she knew him somehow, but she had such a lousy memory for faces and names.

"Melissa. Melissa Blake?"

She narrowed her gaze, more embarrassed at her own lousy memory than anything. He knew her so she obviously had met him before.

"Yes. Actually, it's Melissa Fielding now."

"Oh. Right. You married Cody Fielding, Cannon Beach's celebrity."

And divorced him, she wanted to add. *Don't forget that part.*

"I'm sorry. You know me, but I'm afraid I don't remember your name."

He shrugged. "No reason you should. I was a few years older and I've been gone a long time."

She looked closer. There was something about the shape of his mouth. She had seen it recently on someone else…

"Eli?"

"That's right. Hi, Melissa."

She should have known! All the clues came together. The dog, whom she now recognized as Max, the smart little dog who belonged to Eli's father. The fact that he said he was a doctor. Those startling, searching blue eyes that now seemed unforgettable.

How embarrassing!

In her defense, the last time she had seen Eli Sanderson, he had been eighteen and she had been fifteen. He had graduated from high school and was about to take off across the country to college. The Eli she remembered had been studious and serious. He had kept mostly to himself, more interested in leading the academic decathlon than coming to any sporting events or social functions.

She had been the opposite, always down for a party, as long as it distracted her from the sadness at home in those first years after her father died of brain cancer.

The Eli she remembered had been long and lanky, skinny even. This man, on the other hand, was anything *but* nerdy. He was buff, gorgeous, with lean, masculine features and the kind of shoulders that made a woman want to grab hold and not let go.

Wow. The military had really filled him out.

"I understand you work with my dad," he said.

She worked *for* his father. Melissa was a nurse at Dr. Wendell Sanderson's family medicine clinic. Now she realized why that mouth looked so familiar. She should have picked up on it immediately. His dad's mouth was shaped the same, but somehow that full bottom lip looked very different on Dr. Sanderson Jr.

Her wrist still ached fiercely. "How's your dad?" she asked, trying to divert her attention from it. "I stopped by to see him yesterday after his surgery and was going to call the hospital to check on him today as soon as I finished my run."

"He's good. I was trying to be here before he went under the knife, but my plane was delayed until last night. I did speak to the orthopedic surgeon, who is happy with the outcome so far. Both knee replacements seem to have gone well."

"Oh, good. He won't tolerate being down for long.

I guess that's why it made sense for him to do both at the same time."

"You know him well."

After several months of working for the kindly family medicine doctor, she had gained a solid insight into his personality. Wendell was sweet, patient, genuinely concerned about his patients. He was the best boss she'd ever had.

"Let's take a look at this wrist," Eli said now. Unlike his father, Wendell's son could never be described as kindly or avuncular.

"I'm sure it's fine."

"Again, I'm a doctor. Why don't you let me be the judge of how fine it might be? I saw that nasty tumble and could hear the impact of your fall all the way across the sand. You might have broken something, in which case you're going to want to have it looked at sooner rather than later."

She was strangely reluctant to hand over her wrist— or anything else—to the man and fought the urge to hide her hand behind her back, as if she were caught with a fistful of Oreos in front of an empty cookie jar.

"I can have the radiologist at the clinic x-ray it when I go in to work in an hour."

"Or you can let me take a look at it right now."

She frowned at the implacable set of his jaw. He held his hand out and she sighed. "Ugh. You're as stubborn as your father."

"Thank you. Anytime someone compares me to my father, I take it as a compliment."

He gave his outstretched hand a pointed look, and she frowned again and, cornered, held out her wrist.

The movement made her hurt all over again, and she flushed at the unwilling tears she could feel gather.

His skin was much warmer than she might have expected on a lovely but still cool April morning. Seductively warm. His hands were long-fingered, masculine, much longer than her own, and he wore a sleek Tag Heuer watch.

Her stomach felt hollow, her nerves tight, but she wasn't sure if that was in reaction to the injury or from the unexpected pleasure of skin against skin. He was a doctor taking a look at an injury, she reminded herself, not a sexy guy wanting to hold her hand.

Melissa aimed a glare at Fiona, who had started the whole thing. The dog had planted her haunches in the sand, tail wagging, and seemed to be watching the whole episode with an expression that appeared strangely like amusement.

"It doesn't feel like anything is broken. You can move it, right?"

He held her hand while she wiggled her fingers, then rotated her wrist. It hurt like the devil, but she didn't feel any structural impingement in movement.

"Yes. I told you it wasn't broken. It's already feeling better."

"You can't be completely sure without an X-ray, but I'm all right waiting forty-eight hours or so to check it. I suspect a sprain, but it might be easier to tell in a few days. Do you have a way to splint it? If you don't, I'm sure my dad has something at the office."

"I've got a wrist brace I've worn before when I had carpal tunnel problems."

"You'll want to put that on and have it checked again in a few days. Meanwhile, ice and elevation are your best friends. At least ten minutes every two hours."

As if she had time for that. "I'll do my best. Thanks."

A sudden thought occurred to her, one she was almost afraid to entertain. "How long will you be in town?"

When he was making arrangements to be gone for his surgery, Wendell had hoped Eli might be able to cover for him at the clinic. The last she had heard, though, Eli's hadn't been able to get leave from his military assignment so his father had arranged a substitute doctor through a service in Portland.

Given that Eli was here, she had a feeling all that was about to change—which meant Eli might be her boss for the foreseeable future.

"I'm not sure how much time I can get," he answered now. "That depends on a few things still in play. I'm hoping for a month but I'll be here for the next two to three weeks, at least."

"I see."

She did see, entirely too clearly. This would obviously not be the last she would see of Eli Sanderson.

"I need to go. Thanks for your help," she said quickly.

"I didn't do anything except take a look at your injury. At least promise me you'll raise it up and put some ice on it."

Considering she was scheduled to work at his father's clinic starting in just over an hour and still needed to shower, she wouldn't have time for much self-pampering. "I'll do my best. Thanks."

"How far do you have to go? I can at least help you walk your dog home."

"Fiona isn't my dog. She belongs to my neighbor. We were just sort of exercising each other. And for the record, she's usually very well behaved. I don't quite know what happened earlier, but we'll be fine to make it home on our own. I don't want to disturb your run more than I already have."

"Are you sure?"

"We don't have far to go. I live at Brambleberry House."

His expression registered his surprise. "Wow. You're practically next door to my dad's place."

They couldn't avoid each other, even if they wanted to. She didn't necessarily want to avoid *him*, but considering she was now bedraggled and covered with sand, she was pretty sure he wouldn't be in a hurry to see her again.

"Thanks again for your help. I'll see you later."

"Remember your RICE."

Right. Rest, Ice, Compression, Elevation. The first-aid prescription for injuries like hers. "I'll do my best. Thanks. See you later."

This time as she headed for the house, Fiona trotted along beside her, docile and well behaved.

Melissa's wrist, on the other hand, complained vociferously all the way back to the house. She did her best to ignore it, focusing instead on the unsettling encounter with Dr. Sanderson's only son.

Eli told himself he was only keeping an eye on Melissa as she made her slow way along the beach toward Brambleberry House because he was concerned about her condition, especially whether she had other injuries from her fall she had chosen not to reveal to him.

He was only being a concerned physician, watching over someone who had been hurt while he was nearby.

The explanation rang hollow. He knew it was more than that.

Melissa Blake Fielding had always been a beautiful girl and had fascinated him more than he had wanted to admit to himself or anyone else when he was eighteen and she was only fifteen.

She had been a pretty cheerleader, popular and well-liked—mostly because she always had a smile for everyone, even geeky science students who weren't the greatest at talking to popular, pretty, well-liked cheerleaders.

He had danced with her once at a school dance toward the end of his senior year. She had been there with her date—and future husband—Cody Fielding, who had been ignoring her, as usual.

While his own date had been dancing with her dad, the high school gym teacher and chaperone, Eli had gathered his nerve to ask Melissa to dance, hating that the nicest girl in school had been stuck sitting alone while her jerk of a boyfriend ignored her.

He remembered she had been everything sweet to him during that memorable dance, asking about his plans after graduation.

Did she know her boyfriend and future husband hadn't taken kindly to Eli's nerve in asking Cody's date to dance and had tried to make him pay? He still had a scar above his eyebrow from their subsequent little altercation.

It had been a long time ago. He was a completely

different man than he'd been back then, with wholly different priorities.

He hadn't thought about her in years, at least until his father had mentioned a few months earlier that Melissa was back in town and working for him.

At the time, he had been grieving, lost, more than a little raw. He remembered now that the memory of Melissa had made him smile for the first time in weeks.

Now he had to wonder if that was one of the reasons he had worked hard to arrange things so that he could come home and help his father out during Wendell's recovery from double knee-replacement surgery. On some subconscious level, had he remembered Melissa worked at the clinic and been driven to see her again?

He didn't want to think so. He would be one sorry idiot if that were the case, especially since he didn't have room in his life right now for that kind of complication.

If he *had* given it any thought at all, on any level, he probably would have assumed it wouldn't matter. He was older, she was older. It had been a long time since he'd felt like that awkward, socially inept nerd he'd been in the days when he lived here in Cannon Beach.

He had been deployed most of the last five years and had been through bombings, genocides, refugee disasters. He had seen things he never expected to, had survived things others hadn't.

He could handle this unexpected reunion with a woman he might have had a crush on. He only had to remember that he was no longer that geeky, awkward kid but a well-respected physician now.

In comparison to everything he had been through in the last few years—and especially the horror of six months ago that he was still trying to process—he expected these few weeks of substituting for his father in Cannon Beach to be a walk in the park.

Chapter 2

"You're late." Carmen Marquez, the clinic's receptionist and office manager, gave an arch look over the top of her readers, and Melissa winced but held up her braced wrist.

"I know. It's been a crazy day. I'm sorry. Blame it on this."

"What did you do? Punch somebody?" Tiffany Lowell, one of their certified nursing assistants, gave her a wide-eyed look—though the college student and part-time band front woman wore so much makeup, she had the same expression most of the time.

"I tripped over a big, goofy Irish setter and sprained my wrist. I'm sorry I'm late, but I was on strict orders to rest and put ice on it."

"That's exactly what you should be doing. In fact, it's what Dr. Sanderson would be telling you to do if he were here," Carmen said.

Dr. Sanderson Jr. *had* been the one to give her the instructions, but she wasn't ready to share that interesting bit of gossip with the other women.

"You look like you're either going to puke or pass out," Tiffany observed.

"We don't have any patients scheduled for another half hour," Carmen said with a great deal more sympathy in her voice. "You should at least sit down."

"I'm fine. I need to get ready for the new doctor. He should be coming in today."

Carmen angled her head in a strange way, her mouth pursed and her eyes twinkling. "He's already here. Oh, honey. Have we got a surprise for you."

The butterflies that had been dancing in her stomach since earlier on the beach seemed to pick up their pace. "The substitute doctor is Dr. Sanderson's son, Eli."

"Whoa! Did your fall make you psychic or something?" Tiffany asked with much more respect than she usually awarded Melissa.

"In a way, I guess you could say that. Sort of. I bumped into him on the beach this morning. He was a firsthand witness when I made my graceful face-plant into the sand, and he ended up kindly helping me up."

The memory of the concern in his blue eyes and of his strong fingers holding her hand, his skin warm against hers, made her nerve endings tingle.

She firmly clamped down on the memory. She would have to work closely with him for at least the next few weeks while Wendell recovered. It would be a disaster if she couldn't manage to keep a lid on her unexpected attraction to the man.

"I keep forgetting you grew up in town," Carmen said. "You must know Eli, then."

While Cannon Beach could swarm with tourists during the summer months, it was really a small town at heart. Most permanent residents knew one another.

"We went to school together. He was older. I was a freshman the year he was a senior. I didn't know he was going to be filling in until I bumped into him this morning. Last I heard, we were getting a temp from the Portland agency."

"That's what I heard, too," Carmen said. "I guess we have to roll with what we get."

"I'm pretty sure plenty of women in Cannon Beach will want to roll with Doc Sanderson's son when they see him." Tiffany smirked.

Melissa turned her shocked laugh into a cough. "He told me he wasn't sure until the last minute whether he'd be able to make it back to fill in."

"You know where he's been, right?" Carmen asked.

"Some kind of war zone," Tiffany said.

Wendell had told her something about what his son was doing, how since finishing his internship in emergency medicine several years earlier, Eli had been on a special assignment from the military to work with aid agencies, setting up medical clinics and providing care to desperate, helpless people whose countries were in turmoil. He had been deployed almost constantly over the last five years.

Wendell had been so proud of his son for stepping up, even though his service put him in harm's way time and again. He had also been worried for him.

"He feels things so deeply," her boss had said. "I can't imagine it's easy, the kinds of things he has to see now."

She remembered feeling great sympathy for Eli and

admiration for him, though at the time she had pictured him as the nerdy, scholarly, skinny teenager she remembered, not the buff, gorgeous man she had encountered that morning on the beach.

"One thing I need to ask, though. Maybe you know the answer," Carmen said. "How can he just show up in Cannon Beach and start practicing medicine here? Do I need to check with the licensing board? Doesn't he need an Oregon license or something?"

"Fun and interesting fact. The particular license given to U.S. Army doctors allows them to practice medicine anywhere."

Melissa could feel her vertebrae stiffen and nerves flutter at the deep voice from behind her.

Oh, it was going to be a long two or three weeks if she didn't take control of this ridiculous crush she had suddenly formed for Eli Sanderson.

"I guess that makes sense," Carmen said.

"Yes," he answered. "Think how confusing it would be if an army doc had to go before the licensing board every time he was called to an emergency or had a new assignment."

"That would be a serious pain." Melissa hated the slightly breathless note in her voice. She sounded ridiculous, like the kind of brainless bikini-clad groupies who used to follow the pro surfers on the circuit.

She cleared her throat, wishing she could clear away her nerves as easily.

"Good to know. I'll file that little tidbit away, in case I'm ever on a game show where 'Army Doctors' is a category."

Tiffany snorted, and Eli's mouth quirked up into a little smile, teeth flashing. She had the strangest feeling he hadn't found that many things to smile about lately, though she couldn't have said exactly why she had that impression.

"That would be the most boring game show ever," he said. "Unless you love learning about regulations and protocol."

"I really don't. As long as you can legally see your father's patients, that's all I care about."

"I'll do my best. I know he's been worried about his caseload."

"Your dad is a great doctor, but he worries too much about his patients," Tiffany said.

"Is that possible?" Eli asked.

"He should have worried a little more about himself. He could barely stand up the last few weeks before the surgery."

Tiffany was a bit rough around the edges but like everyone else, she adored Dr. Sanderson and frequently told patients how cool it was that she now worked for the doctor who had delivered her twenty years earlier.

"Your father was so worried about taking time away from his patients he almost didn't have the surgery, though his specialist has been urging him to for months. At least as long as I've been here," Melissa said.

"Longer," Carmen said, her expression exasperated. The older woman liked to mother everyone, even their boss, who was at least two or three years older than the office manager.

"I think he would have continued putting it off and hobbling around if he hadn't injured the right one so badly two weeks ago," Melissa said. "Then the surgery became not only urgent but imperative."

"Everything worked out for the best," Eli said. "I was able to create a gap in my schedule and here I am, at least for a few weeks."

Yes. Here you are.

She had thought him gorgeous in skintight workout clothes. That was nothing compared to the sight of him in khaki slacks, a white exam coat and a crisply ironed button-down shirt a few shades lighter than his blue eyes.

She had been a nurse for years and had never been particularly drawn to a physician, until right this moment.

"How's the wrist?" he asked.

At his words, the pain she had been staving off seemed to rush back. She held up the brace and wriggled her fingers. "Still aches but it's bearable. I agree with you that I should hold off a day or two before I have it x-rayed."

"Did you have any time to put ice on it?"

"A few minutes. Which is the main reason I'm late."

"Good. That's the best thing you can do."

They lapsed into silence and she tried to keep from gawking at him. She loved her job, working with Wendell Sanderson. The man had been nothing but kind to her since the day she'd come back to Cannon Beach. She hated thinking things would be awkward and uncomfortable with Eli here.

She could handle anything for a few weeks, Melissa reminded herself. Even working for a man for whom she had developed a serious thirst.

"Can you give me the charts of those who have appointments today? I'd like to try familiarizing myself with their files."

His words were directed to Carmen yet still provided Melissa the reminder she needed. He was her boss and she couldn't forget that.

"I've already pulled the charts of those coming in this morning. They're on your dad's desk, since I figured you would be setting up in there," the office manager replied. "I'll find the rest and bring them in for you."

"Thank you." He gave the woman a polite smile, and Melissa could swear she felt her ovaries melt.

When he walked back down the hallway toward his office, Melissa slumped into one of the chairs in the waiting room.

Oh, this was not good. At all. She might have silently wished for a man this morning, but in truth she didn't have time for that kind of complication. She had Skye and work and friends, not to mention the online classes she was taking to work toward her nurse practitioner license. There was no room left for her to be stupid about Eli.

"Are you okay?" Carmen asked.

"I will be."

Eventually.

"He seems nice, doesn't he?" Tiffany said. "Dr. Sanderson talks about his son like all the time, but I always pictured him different, somehow. Since he's in the army, I thought he'd have a buzz cut and be all harsh and by the book."

She hadn't pictured him at all, hadn't really given Eli Sanderson much thought over the years. Now she was afraid she would be able to think about little else.

Even her throbbing wrist couldn't seem to distract her.

* * *

"How did your first day go? Any problems or unique diagnoses you think I need to know about?"

Eli adjusted his dad's pillow, giving him a stern look. "Your only job right now is to focus on healing from this surgery. I can take care of your patients, got it? You don't need to worry about them."

"I have no concerns on that front," Wendell assured him. "You're a better doctor than I ever could have dreamed of being at your age."

Eli knew that was far from true. How could it be? His own dreams were haunted by the ghosts of all those he couldn't save. Miri. Justine. Those ghosts at least had names and faces, but there were scores of others who drifted through, anonymous and lost.

He let out a breath, wondering when the hell the sense of guilt and loss would leave him. It had been six months but still felt like yesterday.

He turned his attention back to his father, instead of that war-battered market town.

"Dad, I could never be half the doctor you are. We both know that. I'll be trying my whole life to catch up."

His father rolled his eyes. "We could be here all day patting each other on the back, but I know what I know. And what I know is that you're a damn fine doctor and I'm proud to call you my son. There's no one else on earth I would trust more than you to fill in for me while I'm laid up. When I ask about my patients, it's only because I'm concerned about them, not because I don't think you can care for them the way I would."

His father had been the best doctor Eli knew. Wendell and his genuine concern for his patients had been the main reason Eli had gone to medical school in the first place. He had wanted to help people, to deliver babies and diagnose illnesses and give little kids their first shots.

He had never expected that his first years of practicing medicine would be in a series of emergency shelters and refugee camps, but that was the path he had chosen and he couldn't regret it.

"If I'm not mistaken, that sweet Julia Garrett was supposed to come in today for a prenatal checkup. She and Will had an early-term miscarriage during her last pregnancy, so I've been watching her closely. How did things look today?"

Though he instinctively wanted to tell his father to put all his patients out of his head, Eli knew that wouldn't happen. Wendell wanted to stay current on all the people he had cared for over thirty-five years of practicing in Cannon Beach. Eli had a feeling that was the only way his father would be able to endure the long recovery from his double knee replacement.

"Everything looked good today. The baby measured exactly where she should be at this stage in the pregnancy, the heartbeat sounded strong and steady, and Julia appears healthy and happy. She didn't report any unusual concerns."

"Oh, that's good. This is her fourth pregnancy— fifth, if you count the baby they lost and sixth if you count the fact that her first were twins—and I wanted her to feel confident and comfortable."

As far as Eli was concerned, his father was the iconic family physician. Wendell was dedicated to his patients, compassionate over their troubles and driven to provide them the best possible care. He had delivered some of his own patients—like Will Garrett—and was now delivering the second generation and providing care over their children.

Those patients had saved his father, plucking him out of the deep depression Wendell had fallen into after Eli's mother died following a short but hard-fought battle against breast cancer when Eli was twelve.

They had both been devastated and had dealt with the blow in different ways. Eli had retreated into books, withdrawing from his friends, from baseball, from social activities. His father had done the same, focusing only on his patients and on his son.

The pain of losing Ada Sanderson had eased over the years but hadn't left completely. Eli suspected it never would.

"And how are you, son? I mean, how are you *really*? You haven't talked about what happened with that friend of yours, but I know it still eats at you."

The question, so intuitive, seemed to knock his own knees out from under him. It had always seemed impossible to conceal his inner struggles from his father's gimlet gaze. Still, Eli did his best. He had never told Wendell how close he had been to Justine, or how her death and Miri's had been his fault.

Somehow he managed to summon an expression he hoped resembled a smile. "I'm good. Why wouldn't I be? It's a beautiful time of year to be home in Oregon. I don't remember the last April I was here. I'm not sure what I'm looking forward to more—watching the spring storms churning across the water or savoring the explosion of flowers."

Wendell saw right through him, as usual. His father gave him a searching look even as he shifted on his hospital bed to find a more comfortable position.

"After all the exotic places the army has sent you, are you sure you won't be bored out of your mind treating cold sores and high blood pressure?"

"No. I'm looking forward to that, too, if you want the truth. It will be a nice, calm change of pace. Just what I need to decompress."

"Maybe this will help you figure out whether you're going to stay in the military or settle down somewhere and open a practice. Or maybe join a practice that's already busy with tourists and locals alike."

Since the day Eli finished his residency, Wendell had been after him to become his partner here.

It had always been in his long-range plan, but how could he walk away now, with this heavy sense of responsibility he carried everywhere? He felt the weight of it even more on his shoulders now, after what happened to Justine. She had been dedicated, compassionate, completely driven to help those in turmoil. Her dedication had been silenced forever and she could no longer carry out her work. He had made a vow to carry on in her place.

"Tell me how they have been treating you here," he said to change the subject. "Have you already charmed all the nurses?"

"Not all of them. A few of these nurses have been coming to my office since they were children. I'm afraid they know all my tricks by now."

Wendell was regaling him with a story about the surgeon who had operated on him when Eli heard a slight knock on the door.

A moment later, it was pushed open, and a delicate-looking girl of about seven held the door open while cradling a huge cellophane-wrapped basket in the other.

"Hi, Dr. Sanderson," she said cheerfully, giving his father a winsome smile.

Wendell beamed back at her. "Well, hello there, my dear. Isn't this a lovely surprise?"

She gave a grin, missing her two front teeth, and held up the basket. "This is for you. My mom was busy talking to her friend at the nurses station and I got tired of waiting for her, so I told her I would come by myself. This thing is *heavy*."

"Eli, help my friend Skye out and take that big basket from her before her arms break right off, will you?"

He dutifully rose so he could take the basket out of the girl's arms and set it on the small table next to his father's bed.

While he was occupied, the girl stole his chair, the one right next to Wendell's bedside.

"That stuff is all for you" she said, pointing to the basket. "Even the candy. My mom and I went shopping in three different stores, trying to find all the things you love."

"That is so sweet of you. Your mother is a treasure and so are you, my dear."

She giggled. "My grandma says I'm a pill and too big for my britches."

"I don't doubt that's true," Wendell said.

The girl turned to Eli with a curious look. "Hi," she said brightly. "I'm Skye Fielding. What's your name?"

When she identified herself, he gave her a closer look. Skye Fielding. This had to be Melissa's daughter. He should have picked up the resemblance before she even identified herself. Now he could see she shared the same vivid green eyes with her mother and the same dimple that appeared and disappeared on one side of her mouth.

"This is my son, Elias Alexander Sanderson."

"Whoa. That's a big name. It's…" She counted on her small fingers. "Ten syllables."

Yes. He was fully aware. Try filling out all those letters on military forms designed for guys named Joe Smith. "You can call me Eli," he said.

"Hi, Eli." She settled deeper into his chair, perfectly at home, which he found more amusing than anything he'd seen in a long time. With nowhere else to sit in the room, he leaned against the sink.

"Mom says you got brand-new knees because your old ones hurt you all the time," she said.

"*Old* is the key word there," Wendell muttered.

His father wasn't that old. He was only in his early sixties and vibrant for his age. Why hadn't Wendell started dating and married someone? His father was still a handsome man. Judging by all the flowers and cards in his room, he was fairly popular around town, too. Maybe Eli could work on that while he was home.

"My mom says you have to stay here for two whole weeks!"

She seemed positively aghast at the idea.

"It's not that bad. They have fun things to do all day long. Games and movies and music time. Plus, they serve good food and have free popcorn in the cafeteria."

Eli had a feeling Wendell was trying to convince himself as much as he was the little girl. His father wasn't thrilled about the time that loomed ahead of him in the rehabilitation center, but that was the price for his impatience and desire to do both knees at the same time, when he needed daily therapy and his house wasn't fully accessible.

"Free popcorn! You're lucky. I love popcorn."

"So do I, but if I eat all the free popcorn, I might have a tough time getting back on my feet."

"I guess." She appeared to consider that. "Do you think I could have some now?"

Wendell laughed. "Maybe. You'll have to ask your mom. Where do you think she is?"

"Probably still talking to her friend," Skye said.

A moment later, as if to prove her daughter wrong, Melissa appeared in the doorway, looking slightly frazzled.

He had seen her three times that day, in three different wardrobe changes.

This morning on the beach, she had been wearing running clothes—leggings and a comfortable-looking hoodie, with her hair up in a ponytail. All day he had been aware of her moving around the office in burgundy-colored scrubs and a black cardigan. Tonight, Melissa had changed into jeans and a soft coral sweater and had let her hair down to curl around her shoulders.

He wasn't sure which version he found more attractive. It was a little like being asked to choose among his favorite ice cream flavors.

"Oh," she exclaimed, slightly breathless, with a stern look to her daughter. "Here you are. I didn't know where you went. I was busy talking to Jan and when I turned around, you had completely disappeared."

He could still see the shadows of unease in her expression and felt a wave of sympathy. He didn't have children, but he knew that panicked feeling of not being able to find someone you cared for deeply. He had a flashback of running through a panicked crowd, everyone else screaming and trying to escape the market center while he ran toward the chaos and fear. He closed his eyes, trying to scrub it away and return to the moment.

"I told you two times I was going to carry the basket to room forty-one," Skye informed her mother. "I guess you just didn't hear me."

More of Melissa's fear seemed to seep away and she hugged her child. "I'm sorry, honey. Jan is an old friend of mine from nursing school. I didn't know she was working here. I'm afraid I got a little distracted, catching up with her."

"My arms were too tired to keep holding the basket, so I found the room and gave it myself to Dr. Sanderson."

"I see that. Thanks, kiddo." She ran a hand over her daughter's hair and the sweet, tender familiarity of the gesture sent an odd lump rising in his throat.

The unexpected emotions intensified when she leaned forward and kissed Wendell on the cheek.

"And how are you? How are the new knees?"

His father shrugged, clearly pleased at the visit from Melissa and her daughter. "I can't complain. Though I'm not ready to dance the salsa yet, I can tell they're already less painful than the old ones. They'll be even better once I break them in."

"Don't be in too big of a rush. How many times have I heard you tell your patients that true healing takes time?"

His father made a face. "Do you know how annoying it is to have your own words thrown back in your face?"

She laughed. "It's for your own good."

"I know." He gestured to the brace she wore. "What happened to your wrist?"

Her gaze shifted to Eli, and he thought he saw a soft brush of color soak her cheeks. "It's a long story. Let's just say Fiona was in a strange mood this morning and I fell. But it's feeling much better. Your son checked it out for me."

Whether she had wanted him to or not. She didn't say the words, but he had a feeling she was thinking them.

"That's good to hear. He's a good boy and an excellent doctor. I've been waiting for him to come back so he can meet you."

Oh, no. That sounded entirely too much like matchmaking. He had to cut that off before Wendell got any inappropriate ideas.

"We've met, Dad. You remember. Melissa and I went to high school together for a year, though I'm older. I knew her ex-husband, too."

"My dad got married again and his wife is going to have a baby."

Melissa gave her daughter an exasperated look, and Eli had the feeling she wasn't thrilled with Skye for sharing that particular nugget of information.

"Yes," she said. "We're very happy for them both."

"Sounds like you've got a lot on your plate," Wendell said. "That makes your visit mean even more. A visit would have been enough, you know. You didn't have to bring along a huge care package, so heavy your strong seven-year-old daughter could barely carry it."

"It's only a few things, I promise. The fancy packaging always makes baskets look bigger than they are."

Except for that fleeting glance, she seemed to be avoiding looking at him directly. Why? Had he done something wrong that day in the office? There had been a little awkwardness early on, but Eli had thought by the end of the day they had started to establish a bit of a comfortable rhythm.

Skye nudged the basket closer to Wendell. "Open it. I want to see if you like the stuff we picked out."

"I'm sure I will love everything. It came from you, so of course I will." He smiled at the girl, who beamed back at him.

His father's rapport with both Melissa and her daughter didn't surprise him. Wendell loved people, one reason his staff adored him and his patients returned to him for generations.

"Go on," Skye pressed. "Open it."

He helped his father out by setting the basket on Wendell's lap, then watched as his father went through the contents. There was nothing elaborate, but all the gifts seemed thoughtful and sweet—a paperback mystery he knew Wendell would adore, a book of crossword puzzles, a box of chocolates and a bag of lemon drops, a journal, a soft-looking knit throw that would feel perfect on chilly spring mornings.

His father was delighted with all of it.

"Thank you so very much," he said after he had unearthed each new delight. "How did I ever get so lucky to have you both in my life?"

"We're the lucky ones," Melissa said with a smile.

"I don't have a grandpa and he doesn't have a grand-kid, so Dr. Wendell said we can both pretend we belong to each other," Skye informed Eli.

It warmed his heart that Melissa appeared to watch out for his father. She struck him as someone who couldn't help caring about others. He had witnessed it all day. Even with her own injured wrist, she had been kind and caring to each patient they had seen.

"What are you two up to tonight, besides coming here and making my day?" Wendell asked them.

"We're going to have pizza," Skye informed him. "It's Friday and we always have pizza on Friday. Some-times we make it ourselves and sometimes we order it from a pizza place and sometimes we go out. Tonight we're going out."

"Nice. Where are you heading?"

"We're going to A Slice of Heaven."

"Oh, good choice," Wendell said. "It's one of my favorites. Have you been there yet, son?"

Considering Eli had only been back in town for thirty-six hours and had been working or sleeping for most of that time—or visiting his father—hitting all the local hot spots hadn't exactly been on his priority list. "Not yet."

"You can't miss it. Trust me," his father said.

"You could come with us," Skye offered with that charmer of a smile. "Mom says maybe we can even get cheesy bread. They have the *best* cheesy bread."

"It's been a long day," Melissa said, a trace of defi-ance in her voice. "I need a few carbs to the rescue."

He wanted to suggest she also might need to rest and ice her wrist, but he didn't want to stand in the way of a girl and her carbs.

His father shifted on the bed and yawned, his mouth drawn and his eyes clouding with exhaustion.

"We should go," Melissa said, picking up the hint. "Come on, Skye."

"Do you have to?" Wendell said, though Eli heard the exhaustion in his voice.

"I should go, too, so you can get some rest. That's the best thing for you, in case your doctor hasn't mentioned it."

"He has," Wendell said glumly. "I hate being in this hospital bed."

"You know what they say about doctors making the worst patients. Try to behave yourself. I'll stop by tomorrow."

"Thanks."

His father rolled over, and Eli could tell he was already dozing off. He followed Melissa and her daughter out of the room.

"That was thoughtful of you, bringing a care package to my father," he said when they were out in the hallway. "It obviously touched him."

"Dr. Sanderson has been nothing but kind to us since we moved back to town. It's the very least we can do, giving him a few things to help him pass the time while he's laid up. He's a wonderful man, your father."

"He is."

"Seriously. I've worked with a lot of jerk doctors in my day and your father is a breath of fresh air, as compassionate to his staff as he is to his patients."

"It's always good to hear my own opinion confirmed by those who work closely with him."

"Not gonna lie. He's my favorite of all the doctors I've ever worked with. You have big shoes to fill."

"My feet will never fit in those shoes. Why do you think I haven't come home before now to try? I just have to do my best to stumble along as best I can while I'm here."

That was probably more revealing than he intended, at least judging by the probing look Melissa sent his way. He opted to change the subject. "So you're off to have pizza?"

"Yep. Like I said, we always have pizza on Friday night," Skye told him. "Pizza on Friday, Tacos on Tuesday. The rest of the time, we like to mix things up."

He found it charming that she included herself in the meal-planning process. As precocious as the girl seemed, he wouldn't be surprised if she could fix a gourmet meal all by herself, given the chance.

"That's good. You wouldn't want to be too predictable."

"What are you having for dinner?" Skye asked him.

"I don't know. I haven't crossed that bridge yet. Unfortunately, I do *not* have a pizza-on-Friday tradition, but it sounds good."

More than likely, he would head back to his father's house and make a sandwich or heat up a TV dinner—neither of which sounded very appetizing compared to the carbtastic wonders of A Slice of Heaven.

"You could come with us," Skye suggested.

He glanced at Melissa, who looked taken aback by the invitation. She didn't seem crazy about the idea, yet Eli was surprised at how very much he wanted to accept. The idea of eating alone again at his father's house held no appeal.

"I don't want to impose on your night out together."

"We eat together every night," Skye said. "Besides,

pizza always tastes better when it's shared. It's a scientific fact. Anyway, that's what my mom says."

"Funny. I don't remember learning about that in school."

He sent a sidelong look to Melissa, who shrugged and blushed at the same time.

"You must have missed the breakthrough study. Plus, when you share a pizza, the calories don't count."

"Good to know. I wasn't aware."

"But you've probably had a long day," she said. "Don't let us pressure you into it."

He should gracefully back out of it. She didn't want him there anyway. But he found he wasn't willing to do it. He wanted pizza and he wanted to spend more time with her. Neither craving was necessarily good for him, but that didn't seem to matter.

"I haven't had pizza from A Slice of Heaven in years. Now that you've planted that seed, I'm afraid nothing else will do except that. Thank you for inviting me."

She paused, then gave a smile that seemed only a little forced. "Great. Do you remember where the pizza parlor is?"

"I could probably find it in my sleep. I'll meet you there."

"See you." Skye tugged on her mom's hand. "Let's go. I'm starving!"

She followed her daughter out of the rehab center, and he watched them go for a moment before following closely behind.

As delicious as the wood-fired pizza was at the beloved seaside pizzeria, he found Melissa and her daughter even more appealing.

Chapter 3

In her long and illustrious history of bad ideas, inviting Dr. Eli Sanderson out to grab pizza with them had to rank right up there with the lousy perm she got in seventh grade and losing her virginity to Cody Fielding after the prom her junior year.

Technically, Skye had invited Eli, but Melissa should have figured out a polite way to wiggle out of it, for all of their sakes.

Why *had* Skye invited him along? Her daughter did love Dr. Sanderson Sr., but she usually wasn't so spontaneously open to strangers.

Maybe her daughter had responded, as Melissa did, to that air of loneliness about Eli. She couldn't put her finger on it, but there was just something *sad* about him. A shadow in his eye, a particular set to his mouth.

She had tried hard to teach Skye how important it

was to be kind to others. Okay, maybe she tried to over-compensate a little on her end, knowing her daughter wouldn't receive similar lessons on the rare occasions she was with her dad. Maybe she had tried *too* hard, if Skye was going to go around inviting random gorgeous men to share their Friday-night tradition.

So much for her lectures all day about keeping her head on straight around him. That was fine advice in a professional setting when he was her boss but might be harder to remember in social situations.

It was no big deal. They were only sharing pizza. A Slice of Heaven had notoriously fast service, even on the weekend. With any luck, they could be seated, served and out of there within an hour. Surely she could manage to control her hormones for sixty lousy minutes.

"I like the second Dr. Sanderson," Skye said from the back seat as they drove to the restaurant. "He seems nice…maybe not quite as nice as the first Dr. Sanderson, but better than Dr. Wu or Dr. Charles. Whenever they used to talk to me, they never even looked at me. It's like they didn't think a kid could have anything important to say."

How did a seven-year-old girl become so very perceptive? The doctors in the clinic where Melissa worked in Honolulu before coming back to Cannon Beach had treated *her* that way, too, as if her opinions didn't matter.

"They were very good doctors," she said.

"But are they nice humans?"

That was an excellent question. She hadn't been sorry to leave, though her coworkers had only been one of the reasons she had moved from Honolulu back to

Oregon. Her mother was here, for one thing, and she found she missed being close to Sharon.

And the cost of living had been prohibitive. She had stayed in Hawaii for the last few years mostly because Cody had lived there and she wanted to do all she could to keep Skye's father in her daughter's life. His visitations had become so few and far between as he traveled around on the professional surfer circuit that her efforts had begun to seem laughable. When he had told her the previous summer he was moving again, she had given up trying.

Skye needed a stable home base. Melissa couldn't keep dragging her from town to town, hoping Cody would eventually start paying attention to their child. She had tried for years after the divorce, then decided being closer to her own mother would provide more benefit to her child than infrequent, disappointing visits with her immature father.

Melissa would have loved four or five children, but life hadn't worked out the way she planned. Good thing the one daughter she had was so amazing. Skye was smart and kind and amazingly intuitive for a child.

"Can I play pool tonight at A Slice of Heaven?"

And persistent. Once an idea took root in her head, she could never let it go.

"If there's an empty table, maybe. Otherwise, nope," Melissa said as she pulled into the pizzeria's restaurant, the same answer she gave every time they came.

The people who hung out at the popular restaurant and played at the three tables in the back were serious about the game. They were probably good humans, but they weren't at all patient with a seven-year-old girl just learning how to wield a cue.

Skye sighed as they parked and walked toward the restaurant but she didn't argue, to Melissa's relief. Her wrist was throbbing, and she really wanted to go home and rest it. She would definitely break out the ice pack after her daughter was in bed.

A wave of garlic and the delicious scent of the pizzeria's wood-fired crusts hit the moment Melissa opened the door. Oh, yeah, she suddenly remembered. She was starving. She'd kind of forgotten that while she was talking to Wendell and Eli. Now her stomach growled and she had a fleeting wish that the wisecrack she had made to Eli was true, that none of the calories or carbs of the delicious Slice of Heaven pies counted when they were shared.

Somehow Eli had made it there before they did. He was inside talking to the hostess and daughter of the owner, Gina Salvaticci, who had been a year or two ahead of Melissa. She had never liked her much, she remembered now. Gina had been friends with Cody before Melissa and her family moved to Cannon Beach, and always acted as if she thought Melissa wasn't good enough for him. Since the divorce and Melissa's return to town, she hadn't necessarily warmed to her.

If her father's restaurant didn't serve such good pizza, Melissa would do whatever she could to avoid her. Fortunately, Gina usually wasn't here on Fridays.

But she was here *this Friday*, *and* Gina looked as shocked by the changes in quiet, nerdy Eli Sanderson as Melissa had been and she was obviously flirting with him. She touched his arm as she spoke to him and looked at him from under her half-closed lids, her body facing him and her mouth slightly open.

Melissa felt a sharp kick in her gut, a weird tension, and realized with chagrin that she was jealous of the other woman, even though Eli seemed completely oblivious to any interested body language.

He looked up when they approached. "Here's the rest of my party. You said you had a table ready for us?"

Gina turned and Melissa knew the moment she spotted her. Her gaze narrowed and her hand slid away from Eli. Gina didn't look at all pleased to see another woman joining him.

Melissa couldn't really blame her. A hot doctor coming back to town, even temporarily, was bound to stir up all the single women.

Not *her*. She was willing to entertain a friendship with the man but that was all she could give him. She had no room in her life for anything more, especially not a wandering doctor who would be heading off to the next hot spot on the globe the moment his dad had his knees under him again. Been there, done that, with a man whose career was far more important than his family. She would never even consider it again.

Her priority had to be Skye, and providing her daughter the most stable home life possible, after the chaos of her daughter's earlier years.

She smiled to let the other woman know she wasn't a threat. If Gina was interested in Eli, she should go for it.

"Right this way," Gina said coolly.

She led them back to a fairly good table with a nice view of the sunset.

"Will this be okay for you?" Gina asked. She looked only at Eli when she asked the question. He in turn deferred to Melissa.

"Does this work for you and Skye?" he asked.

"Looks great," she answered. "Thanks."

He reached for the back of a chair and pulled it back. Nobody had held a chair out for her in such a long time, it took Melissa an awkward moment to realize he meant for her to sit there.

"Uh. Thanks."

She *really* needed to get out more.

She sat down and Skye plopped into the seat next to her.

"Can I get a root beer?" she asked.

They had a pretty strict no-soda/low-sugar rule 95 percent of the time, but Melissa tended to relax a bit on pizza night. "One. A small."

"I'll let your server know," Gina said. "Here's a couple of menus," Gina said. "Our special tonight is the arugula and prosciutto with our house-pulled mozzarella."

"Sounds delicious," Eli said. "Thanks."

The next few minutes were spent perusing the menu. Skye ordered her favorite, half cheese, half pepperoni, while Melissa and Eli both ordered the special, along with salads with the house dressing on the side and, of course, an order of their cheesy bread.

"If I can't play pool, can I at least go play the pinball machine?" Skye asked. "I brought all my own quarters."

"All of them? I thought you were saving up for a new scooter like your friend Alice has."

"I am. But Sonia gave me two dollars for helping her pull weeds yesterday, so I put that in my piggy bank and took out six quarters."

Skye reached into her pocket and pulled out change

that jingled as she set it on the table. "I want to see if I can do better than last time we came."

"It's your money. If that's the way you want to spend it, go for it."

"Thanks."

She shoved her chair back and hurried to the row of gaming machines along one wall of the pizzeria. This was an ideal setup, where she could keep an eye on her daughter but didn't have to stand right over her shoulder.

"She seems like a sweet kid," Eli said. "I know my dad thinks so, anyway."

Melissa had made plenty of mistakes in her life—including a disastrous marriage—but her daughter was not among them.

"She's amazing. Kind, compassionate, funny. I won the kid lottery."

He smiled at that and sipped at the beer their server had brought him. "Does she see her father very often?"

All her frustrations from earlier in the day rushed back, and Melissa did her best not to tense.

"Not as often as she'd like. It's been tough to have a relationship when he's always heading to the next beach with the pro surf circuit."

"Must have made it tough on a marriage."

"You could say that."

"How long have you and Cody been divorced?"

"We split up when Skye was three and officially divorced a year later."

"And she's, what, seven now?"

"Yes."

The sense of failure never quite left Melissa, even

after four years. She knew she had no reason to feel guilty, but somehow she couldn't seem to help it.

She didn't tell Eli how hard she had tried to salvage the marriage for her child or how even after it became clear that Cody wouldn't stop cheating, she had chosen to stay in Hawaii, Cody's surfing home base, so her daughter could still see her father.

"Where is he these days?"

"He's coming back to Oregon. His new wife is expecting a baby, and he wants to be closer to his family in Portland so they can help her out."

She wouldn't let herself be bitter about that. When *Melissa* had been pregnant with Skye, Cody hadn't been nearly as solicitous about her needs. He'd been training for a big wave competition, totally focused on it, and couldn't take time away. Instead, they had lived in a crappy studio apartment on the North Shore. He had refused to come back to Oregon, even for her to deliver the baby close to her mom.

Maybe the fact that he was putting his new wife and unborn baby first for once was proof that her ex was finally growing up. She hoped so, but she didn't think anyone could blame her for being skeptical.

"And how long have you been back in Cannon Beach?"

"About seven months. For the past few years, Cody's home base has been Oahu. Last year he moved overseas, so I decided it was time Skye and I came back to be closer to family."

"That's nice. And you live in Brambleberry House."

"For now. We love it there, but I'm saving up to buy a house."

"And going to school, I understand. Carmen or Tiffany mentioned it today."

"I'm working to become a family nurse practitioner," she said as their server set down salads in front of the two of them.

"How's that going?"

"Not going to lie, it's been tough while juggling a full-time job and a child. I still have two years to go. I can do most of the work online, which helps."

"That's terrific. There's such a need for well-trained nurse practitioners right now. Good for you."

The approving look in his eyes sent warmth seeping through her. Going to school and working was tough work, and she had sacrificed sleep and a social life for it, but she was trying to build a solid future for her and her child. All the sacrifices were worthwhile, an investment toward security for Skye.

"What about you? I'm surprised you haven't done the whole family thing yet."

He shrugged, a hint of a shadow in his eyes. "You know how it is. Some guys can handle starting a family while they're in med school, but I wasn't one of them."

"You've been out of med school—what?—five or six years now? There hasn't been a chance in all those years to find somebody you want to make Mrs. Dr. Elias Sanderson?"

"No," he said quickly. Too quickly. The shadows seemed to intensify. Eli Sanderson had secrets. What were they? She had the feeling he had lost someone close to him. Was it a woman?

She wanted to probe, but Skye came back before she could ask a follow-up question.

She was relieved, she told herself. Eli's secrets were

none of her business. He was her employer, at least for the next few weeks. Okay, he might also be becoming a friend. That didn't mean she needed to know everything that had happened to him since the day he had left Cannon Beach for college.

"Your quarters are gone already?" she asked her daughter.

"Pinball is *hard*," Skye complained. "Simon made it look so easy."

Simon was the son of her friends Will and Julia Garrett, twin to Maddie, a girl who sometimes babysat Skye for her. The last time they had come to A Slice of Heaven, their family had been there, too, and Skye had been fascinated, watching the older boy.

"Simon is a teenager, honey. Almost eighteen. He's probably had a lot of practice at it."

She pouted but didn't have time to fret more as their server fortuitously came by just then with their pizzas, fragrant and hot.

They were all too busy the next few moments savoring their meal, which didn't leave a lot of room for talking.

In between bites, Skye kept looking back toward the billiards tables with a wistful look.

"You look like you're wanting to try your hand at pool," Eli said.

"Mom says I can't. It's too busy here on Friday nights. There are people waiting their turn to play."

"My dad has a billiards table in the sunroom," Eli said. "You're welcome to come over and practice a little there before you try to play in the big leagues over here at A Slice of Heaven."

"Thanks," Skye said, eyes wide with excitement.

Melissa tried to hide her frown. She really wished he hadn't said that. Eli would forget he made the offer, but Skye wouldn't.

Her daughter had spent entirely too much time being disappointed by empty promises. She didn't need more.

Maybe she was being too cynical. Maybe he wouldn't forget.

She distracted Skye with their favorite game of I Spy for the rest of the meal, and Eli joined in willingly. He had a unique eye and stumped both her and Skye more than once with the things he observed.

"I'm totally stuffed now," Skye said after two slices. She eased back in her chair and placed her hands over her belly.

Eli chuckled. "That was delicious, wasn't it? The best pizza I've had in a long time. I forgot how delicious the crust here is."

"They have a magic recipe," Melissa said.

"They must, especially if they can make it calorie-free."

His smile made her hormones sigh. Seriously, this was becoming ridiculous.

After they boxed up their leftover pizza, Eli insisted on paying the tab. She would have argued, but her friend Sage and her husband, Eben, part owners of Brambleberry House, came in at that moment and distracted her. By the time she waved goodbye to her friends, the server had already completed the bill.

"Next time is my treat," she said.

"I'll look forward to it," he answered. His words had a ring of sincerity that again warmed her far more than they should.

They walked outside into a lovely April night, rich with the scent of the ocean, with flowers, with new life.

She could hear the low murmur of the waves along with the constant coastal wind that rustled the new leaves of the trees next to the restaurant.

Oh, she had missed it here. She had lived in many beautiful, exotic places since she'd left Cannon Beach, but none of them had been the same. She had lived here longer than anywhere, from the age of thirteen to eighteen. It was home to her.

"That was lovely," he said when they reached their respective vehicles in the parking lot. "The most enjoyable meal I've had in a long time. Thank you for inviting me."

"You're welcome. Thank you for insisting on paying for it."

"Yeah. Thanks," Skye said cheerfully. "It was fun."

Melissa couldn't make a habit of it. She was far too drawn to him.

"Have a good evening, Eli."

Their gazes met, and those shadows prompted her to do something completely uncharacteristic. She stood on tiptoe and kissed his cheek, intending it only as a warm, friendly, welcome-home kind of gesture.

He smelled delicious, of soap and male skin, and it was all she could do not to stand there and inhale.

She forced herself to ease away, regretting the impulse with every passing moment.

"Good night, Melissa. Skye, it was a pleasure. Persuade your mom to take you to my dad's place sometime soon so you can practice your pool game."

"I will! Thanks."

"See you Monday," she said.

"Put some ice on that wrist," he answered, his voice gruff.

She nodded and ushered her daughter to her vehicle. Though her wrist still ached, the injury seemed a lifetime ago.

Chapter 4

Melissa managed to make it through the rest of the weekend without obsessing too much about Eli, mainly because she and Skye spent Saturday running errands, then drove to Portland for the day on Sunday. By Sunday night, the prospect of going back to the clinic and spending the day in his company filled her with nerves.

She managed to push it away by baking strawberry shortcake Sunday evening and texting the other tenants of Brambleberry House, inviting them down to share after Skye was in bed.

Both Rosa and Sonia arrived at the same time, moments after her text went out. The three of them sat out in her screened porch, enjoying the evening breeze and the promise of rain.

"This is…delicious," Sonia said in her slow, halting voice. She gave one of her rare smiles. "Thank you for inviting me."

"You're welcome."

"What brought on your frenzy of baking?" Rosa asked. "Not that I would be complaining, only curious."

Melissa couldn't tell them she had been restless for two days, since leaving Eli at A Slice of Heaven. "We went to the farmers market in Portland yesterday, and the strawberries were so luscious I couldn't resist buying four quarts of them. I have to do something with all those berries."

"Shortcake…was a great choice," Sonia said.

When Melissa offered the invitation, she hadn't really thought their second-floor neighbor would join them, but every once in a while Sonia did the unexpected.

The woman was such a mystery to her. Melissa had tried to gently probe about what medical conditions she had, but Sonia was apparently an expert at the art of deflecting conversation away from herself.

Why did she keep to herself? What secrets lurked beneath her pretty features? Had she been abused? Was she in hiding?

Melissa didn't feel darkness in Sonia's past, only… sadness. She couldn't explain it rationally, it was just a sense. There was a deep sorrow in Sonia. She wished she could get to the bottom of it.

Sometimes she thought becoming a nurse had heightened her compassion for others, giving her instincts she didn't fully understand. Her hunches had been proved right too many times for her to question them any longer, though. Now she simply listened to them.

Fiona, who had trotted down from the third floor with Rosa, lifted her head at that moment and seemed to stare off at nothing in the corner, head cocked as if listening to something only she could hear.

A faint hint of roses seemed to stir in the air, subtle and sly, but that might have been her imagination.

She followed the dog's gaze, then turned back to the other two women. "Do you ever get the feeling we're not the only ones in this house?" she asked impulsively.

"What do you mean?" Sonia asked, brows furrowed. For one brief instant, she looked so panicked that Melissa regretted bringing it up.

"Just… I sometimes feel like the house is alive with memories of the past."

"I know what you mean," Rosa said with her slight Spanish accent. "I never feel like it is malicious or scary."

"No," Melissa said. "I find it comforting, actually. Like somebody is watching over the house and those who live here."

"I don't believe in guardian angels," Sonia said flatly. "I wish I did. At times in my life, I could have used…a guardian angel…or two or twenty."

Her eyes looked haunted, and Melissa wanted to hug her, but she sensed Sonia wouldn't welcome the gesture.

"My grandmother used to say our family is always watching over you, whether you want them to or not."

"Don't you find that a little disturbing?" Melissa asked Rosa.

The other woman laughed and ate more of her strawberry shortcake. "Maybe. My mama's Tio Juan Carlos was crazy. I don't want him anywhere watching over me."

"It's not your crazy great-uncle. I get the feeling it's

someone kind. Does that make me as crazy as Juan Carlos?"

Rosa smiled. "A little. But I am crazy, too. Maybe Abigail, the woman who lived here all her life and died when she was in her nineties, didn't want to leave. She's the one who left the house to my aunt Anna and to Sage Spencer. It could be she's sticking around to keep an eye on things."

"I remember Abigail a little from when we first moved to Cannon Beach," Melissa said. "I like the idea of a sweet older lady keeping watch over the house she loves."

"I do, too," Sonia said. "It's comforting, somehow."

While they finished their strawberry shortcake, they talked about the house and its history, what little Rosa knew from her aunt anyway. Eventually, the conversation drifted to men.

"How are things with the ex-husband?" Rosa asked. "Any updates after your frustration the other day?"

"No. I haven't heard from him."

At Sonia's questioning look, she explained the situation with Cody to the other woman.

"Who was that…good-looking guy I saw you with… yesterday?"

So much for keeping Eli out of her head for five minutes. She fought down a sigh. "That's my new boss. Dr. Sanderson's son, Eli."

"Oh! That's Eli! Wendell…said he might be coming home."

Melissa hadn't realized her neighbor was such good friends with the elder Dr. Sanderson. As far as she knew, Sonia had only visited Dr. Sanderson once since she had been working there. It made sense, though, since he was the best doctor in town.

"If he's that cute, maybe I need to schedule a physical or something," Rosa teased.

"I think...I might be due for a follow-up appointment too," Sonia said.

It was the first joke she had ever heard the other woman make. Rosa looked just as surprised, then grinned. "Maybe we should just drop by the clinic this week to take Melissa out to lunch. We can check him out then."

"Good idea," Sonia said with what could almost be considered a smile.

"You're both terrible. Here. Have some more shortcake."

The conversation drifted to Rosa's work managing her aunt Anna's gift store in town and then to Sonia's plans for the garden.

"This was fun," Rosa said a short time later, stifling a yawn. "But I have to run down to Lincoln City first thing tomorrow to pick up some pottery from one of our suppliers. I had better get to bed."

"Same here," Sonia said. "Thank you for the dessert...and the...conversation."

She rose in her wobbly way.

"It was fun," Melissa said. "We should get together more often. Maybe you two could come for pizza night on Friday. Skye would love hosting a dinner party."

Sonia took on that secretive look she had sometimes. "I won't be here this weekend. But maybe the week after that."

Where do you go? she wanted to ask her secretive neighbor. *And why are you so sad when you return?*

"I'll be gone, too," Rosa said with regret in her eyes. "Fiona and I are going hiking with some friends next weekend."

"No problem. We'll do it another time. Maybe the week after that, then. Put it on your calendars."

"Done," Rosa said with a smile.

"I'll have to look at my…schedule," Sonia said.

She said goodbye to them both, then made her slow way out of the screened porch and to the entryway that led upstairs to her own apartment.

"I hate watching her make that climb," Melissa said. "Why wouldn't she take the ground-floor apartment? It would be so much easier."

"I do not think that one wants the easy," Rosa said, her Spanish accent more pronounced. She stood up, and her dog rose, as well.

"And you don't know anything more about her…issues?" Melissa asked.

"No. She has been in town longer than I have, about four years. Anna said she showed up in town one day and started coming into the gift shop, mainly to pet Conan. That was the dog my aunt and Sage inherited from Abigail, who left them the house. Fiona's sire. One day she asked if Anna knew of any place in town she could rent, and it happened the apartment she lives in now was available. My aunt said she knew of one but it was on the second floor of an old house, and Sonia said it would be perfect. She has been here ever since."

One day Melissa wanted to get to the bottom of Sonia's mystery, though she knew it really wasn't any of her business.

After she said goodbye to Rosa and her dog, she straightened the kitchen, prepped a few things for breakfast in the morning, then headed to her solitary bedroom.

The apartment seemed too quiet and her mind was a tangle, wondering about Cody's plans, about Sonia's secrets, and about the disturbing knowledge that when she awoke, she faced an entire day of working in close proximity to Eli.

She dreamed that night that she was trapped on one of the rock formations off Cannon Beach in the middle of a storm. She was hanging on by her fingernails as waves pounded against the rock and a heavy rain stung her face. She was doing all she could to hold tight, to survive. And then suddenly Eli was there, shirtless but in a white lab coat with a stethoscope around his neck, like something off a sexy doctor calendar.

She might have laughed at her own wild imagination if she hadn't been so into the dream. "I've got you," he murmured in a throaty bedroom voice, and then he lifted her up with those astonishing muscles he had developed since leaving town. A moment later, she was in his arms and he was holding her tightly.

"I won't let you go," he promised gruffly, then his mouth descended and he kissed her fiercely, protectively.

Her alarm went off before she could ask him how they were going to get off the rock and why he needed a stethoscope but not a shirt.

She awoke aroused and restless to a fierce rain pounding the window, as if she had conjured it with her dream.

It took her a moment to figure out where her dream ended and where reality began. What was wrong with her? She had been divorced for three years, separated for longer, and had told herself she was doing just fine putting that part of her life away for now while she devoted her energies to raising Skye.

Since the divorce, she had dated here and there but nothing serious, only for company and a little adult conversation. She hadn't been out at all since she came back to Cannon Beach.

She was lying to herself if she said she didn't miss certain things about having a man in her life. Topping the list would probably be having big, warm muscles to curl up against on a cool, rainy morning when she didn't have to get out of bed for another half hour. She sat up, wrapping her blanket around her, trying to push away the remnants of the dream.

Her wrist inside the brace ached, but it was more a steady ache than the ragged pain she had experienced over the weekend, further proof that it was only a sprain and not a break.

She looked up at the ceiling, listening to the rain click against the window. She didn't have to get Skye up for another hour, so she decided to stretch out some of the kinks in her back and the tumult lingering from that dream with her favorite yoga routine, making concessions to work around her sore wrist.

It did the trick. By the time her alarm went off, signaling it was time to wake up Skye and start their day, she felt much more calm and centered, and that unwanted dream and the feelings it had stirred up inside her mostly subsided.

She would simply ignore whatever was left, she told herself, just as she planned to ignore this inconvenient attraction to Eli.

* * *

The word *ignore* became her watchword over the next week. She managed to put aside her growing attraction to Eli, focusing instead on work and her online coursework and Skye.

She wouldn't exactly call this a good thing, but it helped that the area had been hit with an onslaught of fast-spreading spring viruses and a nasty case of food poisoning from bad potato salad at a spring church potluck.

They were insanely busy all week. Most of her time away from work was spent studying for final exams in the two online classes she had been struggling with, which left her little time to think about anything else.

Her relationship with Eli around the office was cordial and even friendly, but she tried hard not to let the ridiculous crush she was developing on him filter through.

By Friday morning, her wrist was almost completely back to normal except for a few twinges, and Melissa was more than ready for the weekend. It was her late day to go into the office and she decided to again take a quick run after she saw Skye off on the school bus.

She called Rosa to ask if she minded her taking Fiona.

"No!" Her friend said. "You will be doing me a huge favor. My day is shaping up to be a crazy one and I don't know when I will find the time to walk her."

A moment later, she and Fiona were heading out through the beach gate on the edge of the Brambleberry House garden, then running across the sand.

The water was rough this morning, the waves churning with drama. Clouds hung heavy and mist swirled around the haystacks offshore. She wanted to sit on the beach and watch the storm come in, but she had to finish her run in order to make it back for work.

As she and Fiona trotted down the beach, she spotted a few beachcombers and other joggers out. A couple holding hands stopped every once in a while to take selfies of each other and she had to smile. They were in their sixties and acting like newlyweds. For all she knew, they were.

She and Fiona made it to the end of the beach. As she neared home, she spotted a familiar figure running in the opposite direction with a little black schnauzer.

Eli.

This time, she gave him a friendly wave as she approached him, ignoring the nerves suddenly dancing in her stomach. His usually serious expression seemed to ease a little when he spotted her, but she wasn't sure if that was her imagination or not.

He slowed and Max and Fiona sniffed each other happily. "Looks like we're on the same running schedule."

"At least on Fridays. I don't get out as often as I like. The later opening for the office helps since I can go after Skye catches the bus."

"That must make it tough, trying to work out around her schedule."

"It wouldn't be as tough except I'm a wimp and only run when the sun is shining, which hasn't been very often this week."

She didn't want to talk about her sketchy workout habits. She'd done yoga twice. Counting that and her run a week ago when she'd met him on this very beach and today, that made four days in a week. That had to count for something, didn't it? Especially when she had an injury.

"How is your dad?" she asked to change the subject. "When do the doctors say he can go home?"

"He's doing great. The orthopedic doctor says maybe this weekend, but for sure by the middle of the week."

"That's terrific. I can only imagine how tough it must be to have double knee replacements, but I'm sure he'll be happy he did it."

"He already says it's less pain than he was in before."

The sun peeked through the steely clouds to pick up highlights in his hair. She ignored that, too—or at least she tried to tell herself she did.

"How's your wrist?" he asked. "I've been meaning to ask, but things have been so crazy this week as I try to settle in that I keep forgetting."

"It's been a wild week, you're right. You are getting a baptism by fire. We haven't been this busy in a long time."

"How did I get so lucky?"

She smiled. "Maybe all the women in town just want to meet the young, handsome new doctor."

He made a face. "Nice theory. It doesn't explain the food poisoning or the stomach bugs."

"Good point," she said.

Before he could respond, a cry rang out across the beach.

"Help! Please, somebody, help!"

For a split second, Eli went instantly on alert, muscles taut as he scanned the area.

An instant later, he took off at a dead run toward

the older couple Melissa had seen earlier. Max wanted to chase after him, thinking it was a game, but Melissa took a moment to secure both dog leashes. As she sprinted after Eli, she saw the woman was kneeling beside the prone figure of her male companion, who was lying just at the spot where the baby breakers licked at the sand.

"What happened?" Eli was asking as he turned the man over to keep his mouth and nose out of the sand and the incoming tide.

"He was just standing there and then he fell over, unconscious. Please. What's happening?"

The man didn't appear to be breathing and his features had a gray cast to them. Melissa suspected a heart attack, but she didn't say so to the woman.

"What can I do?" she asked Eli.

"Help me move him up the beach, out of the water," Eli said urgently. The two of them tugged the unresponsive man six or seven feet up, just far enough that he wouldn't continue being splashed by the incoming breakers.

"Call 911," Eli instructed to Melissa as he started doing a quick first-aid assessment.

Adrenaline pumping, Melissa pulled out her phone and did as he asked.

"Does your husband have any history of heart trouble?" she asked while waiting for the dispatcher to answer.

"No. None," she said.

"Nine-one-one. What's your emergency?"

"We've got a nonresponsive male approximately sixty-five years old…"

"Sixty-seven," the woman said, her gaze fixed on Eli and her husband.

"Sixty-seven. He has no history of heart trouble but apparently collapsed about one to two minutes ago. Dr. Eli Sanderson is here attending to the patient, currently starting CPR. We are on Cannon Beach, near the water's edge about three hundred yards south of the access point near Gower Street. We're going to need emergency assistance and transport to the hospital."

"Okay. Please stay on the line. I'm going to contact paramedics. We'll get them to your location as soon as we can."

"Thank you."

"He's a doctor?" The man's wife was staring at Eli with astonishment filtering through her shock and terror.

"He is. And I'm a nurse. It's lucky we were here."

"Not luck," the woman said faintly. "It's a miracle. We were going to go up to Ecola State Park this morning beachcombing, but when we were in the car, something told me to come here instead."

They hadn't saved the man yet. She wasn't willing to go that far. "My name is Melissa and this is Eli." Though that adrenaline was still pumping through her, she spoke as patiently as she could manage. The woman would have plenty of time to break down later, after the paramedics took over the situation, but right now it was important to keep her as calm as possible under the circumstances.

"Ma'am, what's your name and what is your husband's name?"

"Carol," she said faintly. "Carol Stewart. This is my husband Jim. We're from Idaho. The Lewiston area.

We've been here for three days and are supposed to go home tomorrow. Today is our w-wedding anniversary."

Oh, she really hoped Eli and the paramedics could resuscitate the man. It would be utterly tragic for Carol to lose her husband on their anniversary.

"How long have you been married?"

"Th-three years. Three amazing years. It's a second marriage for both of us. We were high school sweethearts but went our separate ways after graduation. I got divorced ten years ago and his first wife died about five years ago, and we reconnected on social media."

"Is your husband on any medication?"

"High blood pressure and reflux medication. I can't remember which one, but I have the information on my phone."

"You can give it to the paramedics when they arrive."

Carol gave a distracted nod, her hands over her mouth as she watched Eli continue compressions without any visible response. "Oh, what's happening?"

Before she could answer, the dispatcher returned to the line. "Okay. I have paramedics on the way. They should be there shortly. I'll stay on the line with you until they arrive."

"Thank you. I'm going to hand you over to the patient's wife so she can answer any questions about his medical history for you to pass on to the emergency department at the hospital."

She turned to the other woman and handed over her phone. "Carol, take a deep breath, okay? I need to help Dr. Sanderson right now and someone has to stay on the line with the dispatcher until the paramedics get here. Will you do that for your husband?"

Melissa could see shock and panic were beginning to take over as the reality of the situation seemed to be becoming more clear. The other woman had turned as pale as the clouds, and her breathing seemed shallow and rapid. Carol took one deep, shuddering breath and then another, and appeared to regain some of her composure.

"I… Yes. I think so. Hello?"

When she was certain Carol wasn't going to fall over, offering them an additional patient to deal with, Melissa knelt beside Eli, who was giving rescue breaths.

"Any response?" she asked quietly.

He returned to his chest compressions without pause. "Not yet," he said, his voice grim.

"Do you need me to take over and give you a break?"

"Not with your bad wrist. I'll continue compressions, but it would help if you handle the respirations."

She moved to the man's head and the two of them worked together, with Eli counting out his compressions, then pausing for her to give two breaths.

She wasn't sure how long they worked together. It seemed like forever but was probably only five or six minutes before she spotted paramedics racing toward them across the sand.

In the summertime, this beach would have had lifeguards who could have helped with the emergency rescue, but the lifeguard stations had personnel only during the weekends in May, then daily from June to August.

She knew both the paramedics, she realized as they approached. One, Tim Cortez, had gone to high school with both her and Eli and the other was a newcomer to town but someone she had actually socialized with a few times at gatherings, Tyler Howell.

She had found him entirely too much like her ex-husband, with that same reckless edge, and had declined his invitation to go out. Fortunately, he hadn't been offended and they had remained friends.

Two more paramedics she didn't know were close behind them.

"Hey, Melissa. Hey, Eli," Tim said as they rolled up. "What's going on?"

Eli was still counting compressions so Melissa spoke up to give the situation report. "We've got a sixty-seven-year-old man, Jim Stewart, with no history of heart trouble, on blood pressure and reflux medication. He collapsed about seven minutes ago and has been unresponsive since then but has been receiving CPR since about a minute or so after he fell over."

"Lucky for this guy, you two were close by," Tim said. "We've got the AED now. You want to do the honors, Eli?"

"I'll keep doing CPR while you set it up," Eli said.

A moment later, the paramedics had the automated external defibrillator ready. Eli stopped compressions while they unbuttoned the man's shirt and attached the leads.

Seconds later, Eli turned on the machine and followed the voice commands. A medical degree wasn't at all necessary to run an AED, but Melissa was glad she didn't have to do it.

The man shook a little when the electrical pulse went through him, shocking his heart.

When it was safe, the machine ordered them to check his pulse, and Eli felt for it. He grabbed a stethoscope that one of the paramedics handed over and listened for a heartbeat.

"Nothing," he said grimly. "We're going to have to do another round."

He resumed compressions while waiting for the machine to power up again, then stood back to allow the paramedics to reattach the leads and went through the process again.

Again, Jim's body shook, and Carol let out a little moan. Melissa went to her and put her arm around her as Eli again searched for a pulse.

"I've got something," he said, his voice containing more emotion than Melissa had heard since they had rushed to the man.

He listened with the stethoscope. "Yeah. It's getting stronger."

Both paramedics looked stunned, and Melissa couldn't blame them. She hadn't expected Jim to survive, either. Not really. If she were honest, she had suspected a massive heart attack, possibly even the kind they called the widow-maker.

"Nice work, Doc," Tyler said. He fastened an oxygen mask over Jim's mouth and nose.

Eli stood out of their way and let the two paramedics load Jim onto a gurney. Beside her, Carol was shaking.

"That's good, isn't it? That his heart is working again?"

She didn't want to give the woman false hope. Her husband wasn't out of the woods yet, not by a long shot, though he was starting to regain consciousness.

"Yes. So far, so good. The nearest hospital is up the coast in Seaside, about a fifteen-minute drive from here. That's where the paramedics will take him first.

From there, they may decide he will need to go to Portland."

"Can I ride in the ambulance with him?"

She looked at Tyler, who nodded.

"I'm going to give you my contact info," Melissa said. "Where is your phone? I can enter it in for you. When you need a ride back to Cannon Beach, either to go to your hotel or to get your vehicle or whatever, you call me. I'll come pick you up and bring you back here."

The other woman burst into tears and hugged first Melissa and then Eli. "You've been so kind," she said as she quickly handed over her phone to Melissa. "Thank you. Thank you so much for what you've done. You're a miracle. Both of you. A miracle!"

Melissa was typing the last number of her contact info into Carol's phone when the paramedics started carrying the gurney since the usual wheels wouldn't work well on the sand.

"Let us know how things go with you."

"I will. Thank you."

A moment later, she and Eli stood alone.

"You didn't ride with him," she observed, a little surprised.

"The paramedics had things under control, and I would have just been in the way while they do their thing. I can put my ego aside enough to be sure that the cardiac specialist at the hospital is in a better position to treat Jim than I would be right now."

They both walked to where the dogs were tied up, and Melissa could feel her knees tremble in reaction.

"That was a little more excitement than you probably bargained for this morning," Eli said as he gripped Max's leash.

She patted Fiona's soft fur, wishing she could kneel right there in the sand and bury her face in it for a moment while she regained her composure.

"I would say the same to you. Way to step up, Dr. Sanderson."

"Part of the job description. You help where you can."

"It's more than that for you, isn't it? Even if you weren't a doctor, you're the kind of guy who would jump in and help in any emergency. You must get that from your dad."

He looked surprised by her words and, she wanted to think, pleased, as well. "I don't know about that. I do know that was probably enough of a workout for me today. I'm going to be buzzed on endorphins for at least another hour or two."

"Same here. I need to go." She smiled a little. "I'm supposed to be at work in an hour, and my boss won't be happy if I'm late."

"Sounds like a jerk."

"He's okay," she said.

There was far more she wanted to say, but she didn't trust herself. She had just watched him work tirelessly to save a man's life and she wasn't sure she had the words to convey how much that had moved her.

Chapter 5

His hands were shaking.

Eli gripped Max's leash with one hand and shoved the other in his pocket, hoping to hell Melissa didn't notice.

They had just saved a man's life, and the reaction to that overwhelmed and humbled him.

This wasn't the first time he had saved someone's life. He had been a combat physician and had worked in some nasty hot spots all over the world. For several years, his focus had been refugee camps and providing help and education in war-torn villages, where his patients were usually light on hope and heavy on physical ills from all they had endured.

His efforts weren't always successful.

Too often, there was nothing he could do.

He knew that was the reason for his physical reaction now that the crisis had passed.

Somehow he had traveled back in his memory to the last time he had performed CPR on someone. When he had desperately tried to revive Justine even as he watched her life seep away.

He hadn't really expected Jim to survive. CPR didn't always work and even AED machines couldn't always shock a person's heart back after it had sustained significant damage.

He didn't know what Jim's chances were for long-term recovery, but at least his heart was beating on its own now. Eli had to be grateful for that.

He tried to blink away the image of Justine, of Miri, of those others who had been injured in that suicide bombing, but they remained burned in his mind.

That time, the outcome had been far different. Miri had died instantly. He had known the moment he had raced onto the scene. Justine had survived only moments, conscious and in agony for perhaps thirty seconds after he arrived, until she stopped breathing.

Despite all his efforts, despite the full hour of compressions he had done as they transported her to the makeshift refugee-center hospital. He had done CPR long after his arms started to burn with agony and his back muscles cramped.

The hell of it was, he had known almost from the beginning that she would not survive, and still he had tried. How could he have done anything else?

He let out a slow breath, aware of the cold, hollow ache in his stomach.

"You okay?" Melissa asked as they approached Brambleberry House, her forehead wrinkling with concern as she studied him.

"Fine."

She gave him a searching look but didn't call him on his short answer, which she had to know was a lie. "I'm glad you are, because I'm a wreck," she said instead, with a ragged-sounding little laugh.

"Why?"

"I only wanted to take my favorite dog out for a run. I never expected to play a small part in saving someone's life."

"Not a small part," he corrected. "You were fantastic. You kept Carol calm, focused the dispatcher and helped with rescue breathing when I needed it. We made an excellent team."

She looked surprised and pleased at the completely warranted praise. "Thanks. I'm just glad I was there so I could help. I think the remainder of today is going to seem a little anticlimactic, don't you?

"Probably."

"If only I could persuade my ogre of a boss to give me the rest the day off."

"If only he wasn't such a jerk and you didn't have a full caseload of patients today, he probably would have been happy to give you some time off."

"I guess we'll never know," she said as they reached the beach-access gate leading into the Brambleberry House gardens.

Her humor made him smile. For some reason he didn't quite understand, that made him feel guilty about Justine and Miri all over again. It didn't seem right that he could smile and joke with a beautiful woman who made him desperately want to forget.

Some of his emotional turmoil must have shown on his features.

"Are you sure you're okay? You don't seem as happy

as I might have expected, considering a very fortunate man is alive because of you."

He didn't speak for a long moment, unable to articulate the morass of emotions inside him. He should make some excuse and be on his way. If he wanted to stop at the hospital in Seaside before seeing patients, he had to hurry.

Still, he wanted to confide in her, for reasons he didn't wholly understand.

"This morning seemed to dredge up some things," he confided. "The last patient I performed CPR on didn't make it."

"Oh, Eli," she said. Her expression was drenched with compassion. "I'm sorry. That must be tough. But I can honestly say, seeing you in action today, I'm positive you did everything you could."

Had he? He wanted to think so but wasn't sure he would ever be convinced of that.

"You understand that not every battle we fight as health care professionals can or should be won," she went on softly.

"Yeah. I know. There have been plenty of times when I've had to accept I can't change the inevitable and that it is not in the patient's best interest to try." He paused. "It's harder when it's someone you know.

"The person you lost was someone you cared about."

He didn't know how she could possibly know that, yet she spoke the words as a quiet statement, not a question.

"Yes." He was appalled when emotions welled up in his throat, making it impossible for him to force any more words out around them.

"I'm sorry," she murmured again. She placed her hand on his arm in a small gesture of comfort.

"Thanks," he answered, more touched by her compassion than he could ever say. "I thought I had dealt with it, but apparently not."

"You didn't show your reaction when it mattered, in the heat of the moment, when you had work to do. I was right there beside you and had no idea what you were going through. You were professional, composed, in full command of the situation. I imagine that's something they teach you in the military. Do what has to be done when it matters, then react later."

"I guess."

"Was it another soldier you lost?"

He gripped Max's leash a little more tightly. "Justine was an aid worker. She was from a small town outside Paris, a doctor with Doctors Without Borders, in the last refugee camp where I was helping out. We…became friends."

More than friends, but he didn't want to tell Melissa that now.

"She died in a suicide bombing at a market square along with fifteen others." Including Miri. Sweet, smiling, innocent Miri. "I was a few hundred yards away when it happened, first on the scene."

"Oh, Eli. I'm so sorry. That must have been so difficult."

He acknowledged her sympathy with a nod. "It was. The situations aren't the same at all, except for the CPR part. For some reason, that brought everything back."

"Will you be okay?"

He forced his features into a smile, wishing he

hadn't brought the subject up at all. "I'm fine. Thanks for worrying about me."

"In your professional opinion, Dr. Sanderson, is it appropriate for us to hug? I could sure use one, after everything that's happened this morning."

He didn't consider himself necessarily a physical person, but he really craved the comfort of Melissa's arms right about now. "I could use one, actually."

He wrapped his arms around her and she sagged against him with a little sigh, wrapping her arms around his waist.

It felt so damn good, warm and personal and kind. He had needed a hug for a long time.

He and Justine hadn't been in love. She was more concerned with saving humanity than starting up a relationship with him or anyone else. Still, their relationship had been a bright, happy spot in a miserable situation, and her death had filled him with a complex mix of guilt, grief and deep regret that her shining light to the world had been extinguished.

Melissa's arms tightened around him and she rested her head against his chest, soft and sweet and vulnerable.

After a few more moments, his sadness seemed to trickle away, replaced by something far more dangerous.

Maybe this hug between them wasn't such a good idea. His body was suddenly reminding him that he was still very much alive, and he could think of several excellent ways to reinforce that.

She made a soft, breathy sound and his groin tightened. He'd had a thing for Melissa for a long time.

Having her in his arms now was better than anything he could have imagined.

And he shouldn't be here.

"I should, uh, probably go," he said.

She sighed and stepped away, and he instantly wanted to gather her close again. It was only a simple embrace. Why did it fill him with such peace?

"I'm proud of what you did. You saved a man's life, and I was honored to be part of it." She smiled a little and, before he realized what she intended, she stood on tiptoe and kissed the corner of his mouth.

For a moment, he stood frozen, stunned into immobility. Her lips were soft and tasted like strawberries and cream, his very favorite dessert. He felt her breath on his skin, warm and delicious, and the heat of her where she stood close to him.

More.

That little taste wasn't enough. Not by a long shot. She eased her mouth away after that first little brush of her lips against his. He wasn't fully aware of moving his mouth to more fully meet hers, but he must have. One moment her lips were barely touching the edge of his mouth, the next he had turned his head so that he could capture her mouth in a true kiss.

She made a little sound in her throat, a gasp or a sigh, he wasn't sure which, and her breath seemed to catch, then she kissed him back. Her arms were still around his waist from their hug and now they tightened, pulling him closer.

She was the most delicious thing he'd ever tasted, and the sweetness of her kiss and the incredible *rightness* of her arms around him seemed to wash over Eli like cleansing, healing rain. He kissed her with an urgency bordering on desperation, afraid he would never have the chance again to stand with her between the ocean and a flower garden, afraid he would never again know a kiss like this, one that moved him to his soul.

He should *not* be doing this.

The thought whispered to him over and over, quietly at first, then with increasing intensity.

She worked for him. For his father, technically, but right now for him. This was highly inappropriate, and he needed to stop this moment.

He started to pull away, but she made a soft, sexy little sound and pressed her body against him, as if she couldn't bear to let him go. It was like a match held to dry kindling, the only spark needed for him to ignite. He deepened the kiss, pulling her tightly against him.

He wanted her more than he remembered wanting anything in a long time.

All week as they had worked together, he had been trying not to admit that to himself. He had forced himself to view her strictly as a colleague, a nurse whose dedication and abilities he admired.

Now he could admit he had been lying to himself. Now, with her here in his arms, he could no longer deny it. He saw her as far more than that.

He had a thing for Melissa Fielding and had from the time he was eighteen. She had been the prettiest girl in town, with her big green eyes and her generous smile and the kindness that had always been part of her.

He couldn't have her then because she had eyes only for the jock and popular kid, Cody Fielding.

He couldn't have her now because of a hundred different reasons, mostly because he couldn't be the kind of man she needed.

All those reasons he needed to put a stop to this now, before things skyrocketed out of control, raced through his brain, and he tried to find the strength to heed the warnings. He couldn't do it. She felt too damn right in his arms, as perfect and lovely as a spring morning on Cannon Beach.

She was the one who finally pulled away, easing her mouth slowly from his, her breathing ragged and her eyes dazed and aroused.

A mischievous wind seemed to slide around them, warm and rose scented, though that didn't make sense since it was too early for roses in the Brambleberry House gardens by about a month.

Eli lowered his arms from around her, the magnitude of what had just happened hitting him like a huge Japanese glass fishing ball dropped from the highest branches of the big pine tree on the edge of the garden.

He had just kissed Melissa Blake Fielding—and not a simple kiss, either, but a hot, passionate, open-mouthed kiss that couldn't be mistaken for anything but what it was. A clear declaration that he wanted her.

"That was…not supposed to happen." Her voice sounded breathless, thready, sexy as hell.

"Agreed." He ran a hand through his hair, not sure how to respond.

"I'm not completely sure what *did* happen," she admitted. "I meant to just kiss you on the cheek and then somehow…things sort of exploded."

He had wanted them to explode. Something about the emotional turmoil of the morning had lowered all his defenses, allowing heat and aching hunger to filter through.

"We have both just been through something intense.

Sometimes when that happens, when adrenaline spikes and then crashes, people can react in strange ways."

"That must be it." She didn't look particularly convinced and he couldn't blame her. He had been through plenty of intense things in the military and had never used that as an excuse to tangle tongues with anybody else.

"It was extremely inappropriate of me to kiss you," he said, his voice stiff.

"Was it?" She blinked, clearly at a loss to understand what he meant.

He sighed and took a step farther away, though he knew the opposite side of the beach wouldn't be far enough to make him want her less.

"Technically, I'm your boss. You work for me. In some corners, this might be considered workplace harassment."

She stiffened. "We are not in the workplace right now. And for the record, you did not harass me. I kissed you first."

"A kiss on the cheek. And then I turned it into something else."

"I wanted you to," she admitted. "I kissed you right back. Did you miss that part?"

He frowned. "It still shouldn't have happened."

"Maybe not, but nobody harassed anybody. And technically, I work for your father, not you. You're just the substitute doctor."

He gave a half laugh, not sure whether to be relieved or offended. "You're right. I'm leaving again as soon as my dad is on his feet."

Her features froze for a moment, then she gave a

tight smile. "End of story, then. It happened, we can't change it, so let's just move on from here."

He sighed, not knowing what else to say. "Right. Well, I apologize for any inappropriateness on my part and promise it won't happen again."

Again, she offered that tight smile. "Great. Now I really do need to get going. You might not be justified in firing me because of the way I kiss, but you could if I'm an hour late to work."

"This morning's events more than excuse your tardiness."

"I'll let you try to get that one past Carmen and Tiffany," she said. "I'll see you at work."

He waited until she and her neighbor's dog moved out of sight before he gripped Max's leash and hurried toward his father's house, wishing he had time for a quick jump in the cold Pacific before he headed into the office.

Chapter 6

Though she wanted to find a nearby bench in the beautiful gardens at Brambleberry House and just collapse into a brainless, quivering heap, Melissa forced herself to keep walking toward the house, afraid Eli somehow might be watching.

The kiss they had just shared had shaken her to her core. The heat of it, the intensity behind it, the emotions stirring around inside her. Who would have guessed that Eli could kiss a woman until she couldn't think straight?

Her knees were trembling like she'd just run a marathon, and it was taking every ounce of concentration she had to stay on the path and not to wander blindly into the lilac bushes.

Oh. My. Word.

Dr. Sanderson Jr. packed one heck of a wallop in

his kiss. She had been so very tempted to stay there in his arms for the rest of the day and simply savor the magic of it.

He was right, though. Their kiss was a mistake that never should have happened. At the first touch of his hard mouth on hers, she should have come to her senses and realized what a disaster this was.

She still wasn't sure why she hadn't done exactly that. Maybe it was the adrenaline crash from working on Jim, or maybe it was the highly inappropriate dreams she was still having about him, or maybe it had simply been the result of the long week of doing her best to fight her attraction to him.

Regardless, their kiss *had* happened. How on earth was she supposed to face him at work all day without remembering the taste of his mouth or the salty, musky scent of him, or the safety and security she found in his arms?

She had a serious crush on the man. This morning hadn't exactly helped her gain control of it, first watching him save a life and then sharing that amazing kiss.

As she headed with Fiona toward the house, Rosa walked out on the back porch to greet her. She could tell immediately that her friend had seen her and Eli together at the bottom of the garden. She must have been sitting here when they walked up, with a clear view down to the garden to the beach-access gate.

The only thing she could do was own it. "Yes. Okay. I just kissed my boss. We're both determined to forget about it. I would appreciate if you would try to do the same."

Rosa gave a laugh that she tried to disguise as a

cough. "All right. Enough said. It's none of my business anyway."

Okay, she probably shouldn't have said anything. Now she'd only made things worse by bringing attention to the kiss, like in high school when girls used to walk into class and announce to everyone that they had a new pimple.

"Sorry," she mumbled.

"Nothing to apologize for. I only came for my dog so you did not have to walk her up the stairs."

"Thanks. You have no idea what kind of morning it's been. Eli and I happened upon a tourist who collapsed from a heart attack."

"Is that what the paramedics were doing? I heard the sirens and worried. How is he?"

"Better than he would have been if we hadn't been there. Eli gave him CPR, then shocked him with the AED and he came back. It was amazing to see."

"I can imagine. Good for Eli."

"The kiss you saw. That was kind of a crazy reaction to what happened. The adrenaline rush and everything. We shouldn't have… It won't happen again."

"We are not going to talk about that, though." Rosa smiled and Melissa felt a wave of gratitude for her.

"When do you leave for your hiking trip?" she asked.

"The plan was to take off tonight and be back tomorrow night, but my friend just texted me and had an emergency in the family, so now we're leaving tomorrow and will be back Sunday night. Fiona will be here until then, just in case you need her."

"I might. Thanks."

Fiona tugged at her leash, obviously wanting to be

home, and Rosa gave the dog an exasperated look. "I'd better get her some water, then we've got to head into the office. Have a good day."

"Same to you."

As Rosa and Fiona headed up the stairs to her apartment, Melissa opened the door to her own.

Inside, she fought the urge to collapse on her bed for a few hours. Or maybe the rest of the day.

Rosa had wished her a good day. She had a feeling it would be anything *but* good. How on earth was she supposed to make it through, especially having to face Eli again after that stunning kiss?

She could do it. She had tackled tough things before and she could do it again.

No matter how difficult.

By some miracle, she and Eli managed to get through the day's appointments at the clinic without too much awkwardness between them.

Melissa had decided on a strategy of avoidance. Though it was tough, she tried to pretend their kiss had never happened, that they hadn't spent a glorious five minutes with their mouths tangled together and his arms tightly around her.

It was one of the toughest things she'd ever had to do. Every time she passed him in the hall or shared an exam room with him while he spoke with a patient, she had to actively struggle to keep from staring at his mouth and remembering the heat and magic of their embrace.

The only saving grace was the clinic's caseload. They were both busy with patients all day and didn't have time for small talk. She almost made it through her shift without being alone with him, until she waved goodbye to Carmen and Tiffany and headed out to the parking lot at the end of the day, only to find Eli walking out just ahead of her. She almost turned around to go back inside but couldn't think on her feet quickly enough to come up with an excuse.

She found her urge to flee annoying and demeaning. So they'd shared a kiss. That didn't mean she had to be uncomfortable around him for the rest of his time here in Cannon Beach.

She put on a cheerful smile. She could do this. "Do you have big plans for the weekend?" she asked, then instantly regretted the question. She did *not* want him thinking she was hinting that they should get together or something.

He shook his head. "Dad is hoping he'll be ready to come home soon, so I'll probably be busy making sure the house is ready for him. What about you?"

"Not really. Skye and I are running into Portland tonight to take Carol's things to her. The hotel has already packed them all up for her."

"That's very nice of you."

"It's the least I can do."

Jim had been airlifted to the hospital in Portland and Carol had flown with him, unwilling to leave his side even long enough to come back to Cannon Beach for their suitcases.

"What's the latest? Have you heard? When I talked to Carol earlier, she told me he was likely going to need a quadruple bypass."

"Then you know as much as I do. The surgery won't be until tomorrow, from what I understand. I feel good about his chances, but it's too early to say if he's out of the woods."

"At least he *has* a chance. He wouldn't have, if not for you."

"And you," Eli said.

It was a shared bond between them, one she never would have expected when she awoke that morning.

He smiled a little, more with his eyes than his mouth. Melissa fought a shiver. She also wouldn't have expected that kiss.

Why had he kissed her? And would it happen again?

She cleared her throat. "I'd better go. Skye will be waiting for me at the babysitter's."

"Right. Pizza night. Tell her I meant my invitation of the other day. The two of you are welcome to come to my dad's house so she can shoot some pool. Nobody else is using it. Who knows, maybe she can turn into a pool shark and start fleecing all the tourists over at A Slice of Heaven."

"You're a bad influence on my child," she said, shaking her head. And on *her*, she wanted to add, giving her all kinds of ideas she didn't need complicating her world right now.

She had a weekend away from him to regain her perspective, and the sooner she started the better chance she would have of putting that kiss out of her head.

She gave him a wave and had started to climb into her SUV when another vehicle pulled into the parking lot—a flashy red convertible carrying two people, a blond male and a darker-haired, more petite female.

She paused, ready to explain that the clinic was closed. The convertible pulled up next to her. When the driver pulled off his sunglasses and climbed out with athletic grace, Melissa let out an involuntary gasp.

"Cody! What…what are you doing here?"

Her ex-husband beamed his trademark smile that had appeared on surfing magazine covers for more than a decade. "I told you I was working on coming back to Oregon. And here I am."

"I didn't realize you meant you were coming back immediately."

"I wanted to surprise you, Missy."

"I'm surprised, all right." She couldn't have been more surprised if he'd come back to town with tattoos covering his face like a Maori warrior. "Are you… moving back to Cannon Beach?"

"No. We're just here hanging out with my buddy Ace. You remember him, don't you?"

"Oh, yes." Ace had been a jerk in high school and now had a string of used car lots along the coast. From what she heard, he was *still* a jerk.

"We're going to settle in Portland, near my folks. Since I lost my sponsorship, I need to find a more reliable paycheck. Got that baby on the way and all. My dad's been pushing me to join his office and this seemed as good a time as any."

Now he wanted to be financially stable? For the five years they had been married, he had been perfectly content to let her support them with her nursing career.

"You're going into real estate." She tried to process that shocking information, but it was too much for her brain, after the day she'd had.

"I guess I have to pass some kind of class and stuff before I can actually do any selling. But I'm going to start small and see where it goes."

Knowing her ex as she did, she had no doubt he would probably be brilliant at it. Cody had always been good at convincing people he had exactly what they needed.

After her dad died, Cody had been so sweet and attentive, making her feel like the most important person on earth. She had been grieving and lost, and he had helped remind her the world could still have laughter and ice cream and sweetness.

"You know how you've been bugging me to spend more time with Skye. This is my chance! We're moving into one of my dad's rentals in Portland and working out of his office there. We'll only be a few hours away."

"Great."

"Amalia can't wait to meet her. She's been asking every day."

"Amalia."

"My wife. That's one of the reasons I stopped by before we go out to dinner with Ace and his wife. I want you to meet her. Babe, get out here."

A young woman who looked to be in her early twenties rose from the passenger seat of the convertible with a grace that matched Cody's. She was dark and petite, tanned and fit and gorgeous. And very, very pregnant.

"Oh." The word escaped before Melissa could swallow it down.

Cody glowed like *he* was the pregnant one. He held out a hand to the woman, who moved to his side looking elegant and beautiful—so different from the way Melissa had looked when she was pregnant with Skye, when her ankles had disappeared and all the baby weight had somehow settled in her hips and butt.

"This is Amalia. I met her in Brazil. She doesn't speak much English."

"Hello, Amalia."

"'Ello." The woman's voice was low and throaty and exotic, though she looked nervous. Cody didn't speak a word of Portuguese, as far as she knew. If his new wife didn't speak much English, Melissa had to wonder how they communicated.

"Like I said, she's been dying to meet Skye. Where is she?"

"Not here," she said, pointing out the obvious. "This is my workplace. She's at the babysitter's."

"Oh. Right." He gave a little laugh. "I should have realized that. Where does the babysitter live? I can go see her there."

Skye would be thrilled to see her father. She adored him despite his chronic negligence.

"It would be better if I picked her up. Why don't you meet me at Brambleberry House in about an hour. Do you remember where that is?"

"I think so. Sounds good."

He started to lead his wife back to the car, then apparently noticed Eli, still waiting and watching the scene beside his father's Lexus SUV.

Cody's gaze narrowed. "You look familiar. Have we met?"

Eli coughed politely. "Yeah. Eli Sanderson. We went to school together. You and some buddies ambushed me in the parking lot once during a school dance."

Cody let out a rough laugh. "You're kidding me. Why would I do that?"

Eli shrugged. "You apparently weren't very happy with me for asking Melissa to dance."

"Kind of a dick move, dude, asking another guy's date to dance with you."

"Sometimes. In this case, I guess I figured you wouldn't care, since you had been ignoring her all night."

Cody laughed out loud at that. "I was an ass in high school. I hope there are no hard feelings."

He was *still* an ass, on many levels. She couldn't believe it had taken her so many years to figure it out.

"Why would there be?" Eli said coolly. "It was a long time ago."

She had completely forgotten about that school dance. As usual, Cody had abandoned her in the corner while he talked to his friends. She might as well have been invisible for all the attention her date paid her that night. That wasn't a unique situation. Even now, she wasn't quite sure why she had put up with it for so long.

"Anyway, we're staying the night at Ace's guesthouse, but I was hoping we could take Skye back to Portland with us tomorrow."

"Why?"

"We're buying some things for the new little munchkin, and I figured she might like to be involved in the whole baby thing."

As usual, he didn't think about anyone but himself. He didn't consider that she might have plans with her daughter. They were just supposed to drop everything for him.

According to the Gospel of Cody, the world revolved around him and always would. She hated thinking of the years she had wasted trying to make things different.

She glanced at the pregnant young woman beside him, who looked at Cody like he was the sun and the moon and the stars, all wrapped up in one perfect man.

She wanted to tell him to forget it, that she and Skye would be busy, but her daughter truly did adore her father and she would be sad to miss the chance to spend time with him.

"I'm sure she will be happy to see you."

The truth was, Cody wasn't necessarily a bad father. He did love their daughter, she just didn't come first, the way a child should.

"Perfect. We thought we would leave about eleven."

"I'll have her ready."

"Maybe we'll just wait until then to have Ami meet her. Save us time tonight, since we have to get ready for dinner. Does that work?"

"It should be fine."

"Thanks, Missy. This is gonna be great. You'll see."

With that use of the nickname she hated, he helped his pregnant young wife into the passenger seat of his impractical little red sports car, hopped into the driver's seat and pulled out of the parking lot, leaving Melissa feeling as if she had just been pounded by heavy surf against a seawall.

She closed her eyes for a moment, then opened them, wishing she could have dealt with that encounter alone, without any witnesses.

"Well, that seems like a pretty sucky way to start a weekend."

Eli's dry tone surprised a laugh out of her. "Congratulations, Dr. Sanderson. You officially get the understatement-of-the-week award."

"I was talking about me. It's tough being confronted with the guy who once tried to beat me up."

"Tried to?"

"I was tougher than I looked even when I was a tall, awkward geek."

He had *never* been awkward. She remembered that now, too late.

"I studied jujitsu from about age nine and had a few moves that still serve me well." He studied her. "I take it you're not exactly jumping for joy about your ex-husband's return. Is it the pregnant new wife?"

"No. Not exactly. Skye will be thrilled about having a new sibling to love and she'll be over the moon that she might see Cody more often. She loves her father."

"That's the important thing then, isn't it?"

His words struck with the ring of truth. "Yes. Thanks for the reminder."

He studied her for a moment, blue eyes glinting in the fading sunlight. "You've got your hands full tonight and don't need a trip to Portland. Why don't you let me take care of Jim and Carol's suitcases tonight?"

"I offered. It doesn't seem right to hand off the duty to you simply because it's become inconvenient."

"I don't mind. Max loves riding in the car, and it will give me the chance to check on my patient."

He was such a good man. Why couldn't she have seen past the skinny geekiness when she had been in high school instead of being drawn to the macho, sexy surfer type? She could have avoided so much heartache.

"That's very kind of you. They were staying at The Sea Urchin. The innkeeper has already packed up their suitcases for them. Thank you, Eli."

"It's no problem," he assured her. He gave her a

smile that almost reached his eyes this time, and she surrendered even more of her heart to him.

He made it extremely difficult to resist him, and she was completely failing at the task.

"Didn't you say he was coming at eleven? That was forty minutes ago. Where is he? Do you think he forgot?"

Melissa could feel the muscles in her jaw ache and forced herself to unclench her teeth. "He'll be here," she assured her daughter, though she wasn't at all positive that was the truth.

As she looked at Skye watching anxiously out the window, Melissa was painfully reminded of all the nights she had waited for Cody to come home or call from the road when he said he would.

Cody was great at making promises and lousy at keeping them.

"He'll be here," she said again. "Let me text him again and see where he is."

She quickly shot off a text, only refraining from swearing at him by the same superhuman effort she was using to keep from grinding her molars.

It took him several long moments to reply.

Running late. Waves too good this AM at Indian Beach. On way now.

That was more of an explanation than she used to get from him but still not enough to placate a girl who adored him.

"Looks like he's on his way. Do you have everything you need to sleep over? Pajamas, a change of clothes, your emergency phone, some snacks, coloring paper and pens, your American Girl doll?"

"Yep. Got it all." Skye gave her gap-toothed grin, and Melissa's heart gave another sharp tug. She loved this kind, funny, creative little person with all her heart.

Her daughter was growing up. What would the future hold for this sweet, openhearted child?

"Why don't you practice your reading with me for a few more minutes while we wait?"

"Okay." Skye picked up the book she was reading about a feisty girl who resembled her greatly. They were both laughing at the girl's antics when the doorbell rang.

"That's him!" Skye exclaimed. She dropped the book and raced to the door eagerly.

It was, indeed, her father. Cody walked in with his exotically beautiful bride silently following along.

"Great place." Cody gave an admiring look around the big Victorian, with its high ceilings, transom windows and extensive woodwork. "I remember this from when that old biddy Abigail What's-Her-Name lived here. She never liked me."

"It's been a good apartment for us. The other tenants are wonderful and the landlords have been more than accommodating. It has worked out really well while I continue trying to save up enough for our own place."

"When you're serious about looking, make sure you let me help you. Who knows? I might even discount my commission."

She dug her nails into her palms and forced a smile, when what she really wanted to do was roll her eyes and remind him that if he were more dependable with child support, she could have bought a house when she first came back to town.

"Wow. Thanks. You might want to get your real estate license before you go around making that kind of generous offer."

"Working on it. Working on it. You ready, Skyester?"

"Yep." She threw her arms around Melissa's waist. "Bye, Mommy. Love you."

"Bye, sweetie."

"I'll bring her back tomorrow afternoon. Not sure what time. I was thinking we could maybe hit a baseball game in the afternoon."

No problem. She had nothing else to do but sit around and simply wait for him to drop off their child whenever he felt like it.

"Sounds like fun," she said, forcing another smile. "When you figure out your plans, I would appreciate a text or call so I know roughly when to expect you."

"You got it. Thanks, Missy."

He picked up Skye's suitcase and the booster seat she claimed she didn't need anymore but legally did because she was small for her age. At least Cody didn't argue about that as he led the way back to his flashy convertible. The booster seat barely fit in the minuscule back seat.

She stood on the sidewalk, watching as he helped Skye buckle in, opened the door for his new wife, then climbed in himself.

As Cody backed out of the driveway, Melissa whispered a prayer that her baby girl would be okay, then headed into her empty apartment.

Her remaining chores went quickly, especially without Skye to distract her with hugs and stories and eager attempts to help.

At loose ends, she couldn't seem to focus on her own book or on the television series she was working her way through on Netflix. If only her mother were in town, they could go for a long lunch somewhere, something they never seemed to have time to do.

She needed physical activity but couldn't summon the energy required for a run. After dithering for a few more moments, she finally decided to take a walk to deliver one of the loaves of banana nut bread she and Skye had made earlier that morning to her friends Will and Julia Garrett.

On impulse, she texted Rosa at work, asking if she was still around and, if so, could Melissa borrow Fiona for a walk.

Rosa immediately texted back a big YES with four exclamation points. Then she added, Both of us would thank you for that.

She smiled a little through her glum mood, grateful all over again that her wanderings had led her back here to this beautiful house and new friends.

She had a key to Rosa's apartment, and Fiona jumped around excitedly when Melissa reached for her leash by the door.

"I'm taking a treat to the neighbors," she informed the dog. "You can only come along if you promise to behave yourself. They've got that handsome Labrador who is nothing but trouble."

Fiona shook her head as if she disagreed, which made Melissa truly smile for the first time since she had watched a red convertible drive down the road.

As she and Fiona walked down the stairs, she momentarily thought about inviting Sonia along, then remembered the second-floor tenant was out of town on one of the mysterious trips she took.

Every few months, an anonymous-looking car-service limousine would pick her up and Sonia would slip inside carrying a suitcase, then would return again by another limousine three or four days later.

Rosa had once asked her where she went, but Sonia, as usual, gave vague answers. She had offered some excuse about having to go away on a family matter, then had quickly changed the subject.

Considering she claimed she had no family, that excuse made no sense, but neither she nor Rosa had wanted to interrogate her about it.

The April afternoon was sunny and lovely, perfect for walking, with a sweet-smelling breeze dancing through the Brambleberry House gardens and the sound of waves in the distance.

She wanted to enjoy it and was annoyed with herself that she couldn't seem to shake this blue mood.

Unfortunately, when she and Fiona walked the three blocks to Julia and Will's beautifully restored home, nobody answered the door. She knocked several times but received no answer.

Too bad. She should have called first to make sure they were home. She could always freeze the banana bread, she supposed, though it was never quite as good as when it was fresh out of the oven.

She took a different way home, not realizing until she was almost to it that her route took her directly past Wendell Sanderson's house. She wouldn't have intentionally come this way, but apparently her subconscious had other ideas.

A sharp bark greeted them, and Fiona immediately started wagging her tail and straining at the leash when she spotted Max just inside the garden gate…in the company of Wendell's entirely too appealing son.

She really should have taken another way. Oh, she hoped he didn't think she was staking out the house in the hopes of seeing him.

She couldn't just walk on past, as much as she wanted to. Eli watched her approach, a screwdriver in his hand and an expression on his features she couldn't decipher.

"Hi," he said.

She gestured to the gate. He was installing some kind of locking mechanism, she realized. "This looks fun."

"Since my dad's surgery, Max has decided he's the canine version of Houdini. He's learned how to open the latch and take off."

The dog looked inordinately proud of himself.

"Oh, how sweet. I bet he's letting himself out so he can go look for your dad!"

"That is entirely possible. Or maybe he just doesn't enjoy my company."

That is not *possible*, she wanted to say, but didn't have the nerve.

"How is your dad? When is he coming home?"

"Not as early as he'd hoped. He's been doing so well, we thought he might be cleared to come home tomorrow, but I guess yesterday he had a little tumble during physical therapy."

"Oh, no!"

"He seems to be all right, but the doctor at the rehab

center wants to keep him until at least Monday or Tuesday, to be safe."

"I'm sorry. That must be disheartening for both of you, especially if he thought he was going home sooner."

On impulse, she held out the loaf of banana bread. "Will you take this to him? Skye and I made it this morning for Julia Garrett and her family, but they're not home. Your dad particularly enjoys our banana nut bread."

Eli looked astonished. "Thanks. That's very kind of you, but are you sure you don't want to save it and give it to your friend later?"

"Banana bread is best when it's fresh. When Skye gets home from Portland, we'll make another batch."

"Portland. I forgot she was going with her dad. How are you holding up?"

"Super," she lied. "Except I couldn't stand how quiet my house was, so I borrowed my neighbor's dog and went for a walk so I wouldn't have to be alone there."

He smiled a little at that and patted Fiona, who gazed up at him with adoration.

She had been holding back her emotions all day, but the kindness in his eyes seemed to send them bubbling over. To her great and everlasting dismay she sniffled a little, a tear dripping down her cheek.

"Hey now. It's okay," Eli said, looking slightly panicky. "She won't be gone long."

"I know. She'll be back tomorrow."

Melissa felt so stupid! It was only an overnight visit. Fiona licked at her hand and it was the absolute last straw. She sniffled again and before she knew it, Eli had set the loaf of banana nut bread on top of the gate and reached for her, pulling her against his hard muscles.

"It's okay," he said again.

"She's never been away from me. Not one single night. She's seven years old and she's never slept somewhere she couldn't call out to me. Her father has taken her before but only for a few hours at a time. He doesn't know that she needs a night-light on and she has bad dreams if she eats too much sugar past eight, and when she wakes up, she does this sweet little stretchy thing."

"He'll figure all that out. The important parts anyway."

She let out a sigh, wishing she could stay here the rest of the evening so he could help keep her nerves away. "I know. You're right."

"Cody loves Skye, right? You said as much yesterday."

"He does. He doesn't always do things the same as I would, but that doesn't mean he doesn't love her."

"They will be fine. Skye strikes me as a clever girl. If there are any problems, she can always give you a call to come get her."

This was dangerous, being close to him like this. She couldn't help remembering their kiss the day before, and the way she had flung her arms around his neck and surrendered to her overpowering attraction toward him.

Holding him like this, being close to him and hearing his heartbeat against her cheek, was entirely too risky. It was making her think all kinds of wild thoughts. She was aware of a soft tenderness blooming to life inside her like the spring growth all around them. He was so kind, so concerned about her feelings. He made her feel like she mattered.

How was she supposed to resist that?

She had to. He was leaving again. He'd told her so himself. She couldn't afford to lose her heart to a man destined to break it into a thousand pieces.

Though it made her ache inside to do it, she forced herself to step away. "Thank you. I'm sorry you had to talk me down off the ledge."

"You're welcome. Anytime." He studied her. "You know what you need tonight? A distraction."

For one crazy second, her mind went into some completely inappropriate directions. She could come up with some pretty delicious ways to distract herself involving him, but she had a feeling that wasn't what he was talking about. "What did you have in mind?"

"Tiffany from work and her band are playing at The Haystacks tavern tonight. She gave me a flyer yesterday on her way out the door. I was thinking it would be nice to support her."

Melissa tried not to wince at the suggestion. She adored the young CNA for many reasons, but her musical ability wasn't among them.

"You haven't heard her sing, have you?"

"Is it that bad?"

"Taste can be such a subjective thing."

"In other words, you hate it."

"I don't hate it, exactly. Her band's style is what you might call an acquired taste."

"Well, hers isn't supposed to be the only band. According to the flyer, there are two other bands playing after hers. Who knows, we might get lucky and one might even be tolerable. What do you say?"

Why was he asking her? Because he felt sorry for

her? Was he only being kind, or did he also dislike being alone on a Saturday night?

Did his reasons really matter? She didn't want to stay at home by herself watching television and feeling sorry for herself. He was offering a perfect distraction. If she didn't go, she would be alone all evening, without even Fiona for company, since Rosa was leaving town.

"I suppose it would mean a lot to Tiffany if we both came out to listen to her."

"There you go. A night on the town, plus supporting a coworker. You can't lose."

She wouldn't go that far. There was always the chance she would end up letting down her guard too much and inadvertently reveal the big crush she had on her boss.

She would simply have to be careful that didn't happen. The benefits of getting out of the house offset the small risk that she might make a fool of herself.

"What time?"

"Does eight work?"

"Yes. It's a d—" She caught herself before she said a word that rhymed with eight. This was *not* at date. They were simply two coworkers going out on the town to support someone else who worked with them.

"Deal. It's a deal," she improvised quickly. "Eight works for me."

"Perfect. I'll pick you up then."

"Great. Meantime, I hope your dad enjoys the banana nut bread. If you're lucky, he might even share some with you."

"I'll keep my fingers crossed."

She smiled, grabbed Fiona's leash and headed back toward Brambleberry House, feeling much better about the world than she had a few moments earlier.

Chapter 7

As he drove up to the big, sprawling Victorian house where Melissa lived with her daughter, Eli was aware of a vague sense of danger.

He knew it was ridiculous. He had been in war zones, for heaven's sake, in countless hair-raising circumstances. He had operated on people with bullets flying, had jumped out of helicopters into uncertain territory, had tried to provide medical care in villages where he knew armed hostiles were hiding out.

Yeah, those things had been terrifying. Melissa Blake Fielding posed an entirely different sort of threat.

The woman got to him. She always had. He'd had a thing for her all those years ago when he was in high school, and apparently the intervening years had done nothing to work it out of his system.

This wasn't a date, despite the flowers on the seat

next to him. They were friends and coworkers, he reminded himself. He had no intention of making things more complicated with her.

Sure, he liked her. The pretty cheerleader she had been in school had grown into a woman of strength and substance, someone who showed compassion and kindness to everyone.

She hadn't kissed him out of kindness. His abdominal muscles tightened at the memory of her sweet response the day before and the eagerness of her mouth against his. She had been as into the kiss as he was. He knew he hadn't misread the signs.

That didn't change the fact that he never should have let things go as far as they had.

Melissa had become an indispensable part of his father's practice. His father had told him how very much he relied on her. Eli had no business coming into town for a few weeks and messing with the status quo simply because he wanted something.

This wasn't a date, and he needed to remember that he wasn't the kind of man she needed. He couldn't be that man. She needed someone focused on home and family, not somebody who was simply marking time until he could go back and finish the job he had left undone overseas.

He found deep satisfaction working for the Army Medical Corps. He was helping other people and making a difference in the world, in whatever small way he could. Since Justine and Miri had died in that market square, however, his responsibilities had taken on vital urgency. Justine had been a dedicated physician, passionate about providing care to the desperate and helpless. He felt driven to continue her work.

Her life had held purpose and direction. Her death—
and Miri's—had been meaningless, the result of a
cruel, fruitless act of violence. He was the trained
military officer, and he should have picked up on the
signs of unrest they had seen when they entered that
village. He should never have let her go to the market
that day. Instead, he had ignored his instincts and she
had died as a result.

Because of him, she would no longer be able to help
anyone, and he felt a sacred obligation to continue his
own work in her memory. What else could he do?

He wasn't free to let himself fall for Melissa, no
matter how attracted he was to her. It wouldn't be fair
to either of them.

He wasn't in love with her. They'd only kissed once,
for heaven's sake. She was his coworker and his friend.

He was half-tempted to throw the flowers his father
had insisted he bring into the garbage can over there,
but that would be wasteful. Friends could bring friends
flowers. That didn't mean this was a date.

With that reminder firmly in his head, he walked
up the porch steps of Brambleberry House and rang
the doorbell just as another woman trotted down the
steps carrying a backpack, with Fiona the Irish setter
on her leash.

The woman was pretty, with warm brown eyes and
wavy dark hair. She stopped and smiled at him, eyes
widening a little when she spotted the flowers. He tried
not to flush but had a feeling he wasn't very successful.

"Hello. You must be Dr. Sanderson's son. Eli, right?
The army doctor."

What had she heard about him? And from whom?
Had Melissa mentioned his name? He sighed, annoyed

with himself. This wasn't junior high. It didn't matter if Melissa had mentioned him to her friend or not.

"That's right."

"Nice to meet you. I'm Rosa Galvez. I live upstairs, third floor."

"Any relation to Anna Galvez?" he asked as he petted the dog with his free hand.

Rosa nodded. "She's my aunt, sort of. I was adopted by her brother and his wife, anyway, when I was a teenager."

He sensed a definite story there, especially when the warmth in her eyes seemed to fade a little.

"Anna was always kind to me when I used to go into her gift shop. I understand you're running the place now."

"That's right. I love it," Rosa said. "How is your father doing?"

He couldn't go anywhere in town without people asking him that question, but Eli didn't mind. It was further proof of how beloved Wendell was around Cannon Beach.

"Okay. He had a little setback yesterday, but he should be home soon. The knees are better than ever, he says. Soon he'll be ready to chase all the ladies again."

She smiled. "Give him my best, will you? I like him very much. Your father, he is truly a good man and a good doctor."

"I'll tell him. Thank you."

"You are here to see my friend Melissa, no?"

"Yes. That's right." He found her trace of Spanish accent completely charming.

"Her doorbell is that one."

"Thanks."

She paused and appeared to be debating whether to add something. In the end, she gave a quick glance at Melissa's doorbell, then looked back at him. "I am glad you are here for Melissa tonight. She is having a struggle right now. It is hard to share a daughter."

"I imagine it would be."

"Thank you for being her friend. I am glad to know Dr. Sanderson's son is a good man like his father."

Was he? He was completely positive his father wouldn't have kissed one of his nurses until neither of them could think straight.

Fiona tugged on the leash before he could answer, and Rosa laughed a little. "I have to run. We are off on a little adventure and she is a little excited about it."

"Safe travels," he said.

"Thank you."

She hurried down the steps toward an SUV parked next to Melissa's vehicle, loaded her dog and backpack quickly and backed out.

At least the unexpected conversation had helped put the evening in perspective. Melissa needed a morale boost, and he was glad he had the chance to offer one.

He rang the doorbell, his hands tightening around the flowers in his hand.

When Melissa opened the door, his breath seemed to catch in his chest and, for a crazy moment, he forgot why he was there.

Friends, Eli reminded himself. They were only friends.

"Hi."

"Hi, yourself."

He couldn't think what to say for a long moment, then he remembered the flowers. "Here. These are for you. Peonies from my dad's garden. He was thrilled with the banana bread. It's one of his favorites. When I told him we were going to listen to Tiffany tonight, he insisted I cut some flowers to pay you back for the bread. They were my mom's favorite. The peonies, I mean."

Okay, he was babbling. He never babbled.

She looked touched by the gesture. "He showed me a picture of your mother once. I wish I'd known her. She had the kindest eyes."

He felt the pang he always did when he remembered his mother, the ache that had become a part of him after all these years. "She did."

"How old were you when she died?"

"Twelve."

"I'm sorry. That must have been rough. I was fourteen when I lost my dad. The pain never quite goes away, does it?"

He shook his head, aware of yet another thread tugging him toward her. They both knew the void left behind from losing a parent at a young age.

He didn't know what to do with this soft tenderness unfurling inside him so he focused on the flowers, instead. "Anyway, the vase is from my dad. He made it in ceramics class at the rehab center. He wanted you to keep it."

Her features softened. "I'll cherish it even more, then. It's lovely. I have to tell you, I adore your father. If only he were thirty years younger!"

"Not the first time I've heard that phrase since I've been back in Cannon Beach," he said ruefully. His father was quite popular with women of all ages in town.

Somehow Wendell managed to make every woman feel like she was the most important one in his world.

"Come in a moment while I find somewhere for these and grab my purse." She opened the door, and he followed her into the apartment.

He didn't know what the apartment had looked like before she moved in, but it was clear Melissa and her daughter had turned the space into a home. A large dollhouse stood in one corner, with a baseball bat propped against it and several stuffed animals on the roof, as if keeping watch. The room was cheery and open, with splashes of color from prints on the wall and bright pillows on the sofa and chairs.

"What a great view," he said, immediately drawn to the wall of windows facing the ocean.

"Killer, isn't it?" She moved to stand beside him and admired the rugged coastline outside the sunroom. "This is my favorite spot in the house. Sometimes I can't believe I really live here."

He glanced down at her features, pretty and open and genuine, and had to battle down a fierce urge to kiss her again. It would be so easy. He only had to close the small space between them and lean his head down just so. He could almost taste her, fresh and sweet as ripe strawberries.

His head dipped slightly, but he checked the movement just before he would have followed through on the powerful urge.

No. They were friends. That was all they could ever be. Melissa had enough complications in her life right now with her ex-husband moving back. She didn't need somebody with Eli's kind of baggage.

He was aware of her small swallow, of the way her

gaze shifted from his eyes to his mouth and back again so quickly he wondered if he had imagined it.

It wasn't a good idea to be here alone with her in her warm, comfortable apartment. Not when she was everything he wanted and everything he couldn't have.

"We should go."

Was that disappointment he saw in her eyes? No. He was imagining that, too.

"We should. We wouldn't want to miss Tiffany in all her glory. Just give me a minute."

"Great."

He turned back to the window, hoping he had the strength to keep his hands off her all night.

She wasn't sure why, but Eli Sanderson seemed as uncomfortable as she felt as they walked into The Haystacks tavern.

Why? If she was the reason, what had she done to make him so edgy?

She had a feeling he was regretting whatever impulse had prompted him to invite her out tonight to hear Tiffany's band. She should have backed out when she had the chance. She could have made up some excuse, but she had been so grateful for the distraction she hadn't really thought through how awkward Eli might find it to spend time socially, after their heated kiss the day before.

It was too late now. He had invited her and she had accepted. The only thing she could do now was to make the best of it and try to relax and enjoy herself.

"Have you been here before?" she asked.

He looked around the tavern, with its brick walls and weathered plank bar. "Not recently. I may have stopped in with friends a time or two when I would come back to town during college, but I didn't have a lot of time for barhopping."

The Haystacks was one of those rare drinking establishments that didn't try to be trendy or hip. Its simple unpretentiousness made it popular with tourists and locals alike.

"It's not a bad place. They host some fun events, and on Saturday nights they feature all local musicians."

The place was already crowded and Tiffany's band was setting up on the small stage in the corner of the tavern. Eli managed to find them a table near the stage. He pulled a chair out for her and waited until she was settled before he sat across from her.

"I probably should warn you, I'm not much of a drinker," he admitted. "I've seen too many guys who spent every moment of their R & R hammered."

"You might change your mind and order a drink once the music starts."

He laughed roughly, a sound that seemed to ripple down her spine. "You've built it up so much, I can't wait."

"I shouldn't have said that. I'm sorry. Tiffany actually has an excellent voice. I'm just not sure Puddle of Love is the best venue for her talent."

"Her band is called Puddle of Love."

"I tried to warn you. It's not that bad. I'll be quiet and let you judge for yourself."

She ordered a mojito while Eli ordered one of the locally brewed ales.

She waved at a few people she knew from his father's practice and another couple who had gone to high school with her.

Their order came quickly. She sipped at her drink, then sat back in her chair. "Now that you've been here a week, what do you think?" she asked, making conversation. "Are you ready to stick around in Cannon Beach and go into practice with your dad?"

He shifted. "How did you know he was lobbying hard for that?"

She shrugged. "Lucky guess. I know how proud he is of you and how thrilled he is to have you back. It makes sense that he would want to make it permanent. He said your term of service is done but you're considering signing up for another few years."

He sipped at his beer, his gaze focused on the band setting up.

"Do you love the military that much?" She had to ask.

"It's not that I love it, necessarily. But I know I'm making a difference. I feel a certain…responsibility to continue doing what I'm doing."

"You could make a difference here, too."

"You make it sound so easy."

"Why isn't it?"

He was quiet, sipping at his beer again. "It's complicated."

"Doesn't seem like it to me."

"I'm good at what I do. I don't say that to be cocky, but there's something very fulfilling in knowing I'm helping people who have very few options available to them."

"I can see that."

"To be honest, I'm also not sure I'm ready to settle in one place. The idea of seeing the same patients day after day for the rest of my life seems so…final."

To her, that sounded like a dream come true. She yearned for roots. She had gone to nursing school before she and Cody were married and had barely earned her license before he decided it was time to move to Hawaii, where she had to retake her license requirements. They had lived in a half-dozen places during the five years they were married and she had to become relicensed three times.

She had loved staying in one place and having the chance to get to know their patients a little better.

She supposed everybody had different needs.

Before he could respond, Stew Peters, who ran the bar, went to the microphone. "Hey, everybody. Thanks for coming out. As you all know, it's locals' night tonight. Performing for the first time here at The Haystacks, give it up for Puddle of Love."

She and Eli clapped with enthusiasm as Tiffany took to the stage, looking far different from the young woman Melissa had seen the day before, leaving the office in blue scrubs and a ponytail. Oddly, she also didn't resemble the leather-clad, big-haired rocker Melissa had seen fronting the band the last time she had seen them, at a little dive in Manzanita before Christmas.

This time she was dressed in a simple flowered dress, with her multicolored hair pulled back in a modest headband. Except for the multiple piercings and the vivid hair, she looked like a coed who had stopped into the bar between classes.

She took the microphone and the band behind her started up. As Melissa looked closer, she noticed several significant changes. The drummer was the same, but the guy on lead guitar and the girl playing bass were new to the band.

Tiffany's look and the band personnel weren't the only changes. She could tell after the first few bars. Puddle of Love had mellowed their sound significantly, cutting down on the screaming, angry lyrics and allowing Tiffany's strong contralto voice to come through.

By the time her friend finished the first song, Melissa was clapping along with the rest of the tavern crowd.

"I feel like I missed something here," he leaned in to say when there was a break in the music. "Were you deliberately trying to give me low expectations? They sound great to me."

"This isn't the same Puddle of Love I've heard before, trust me. This is Puddle of Love 2.0."

"I like it."

"So do I."

They both settled in to enjoy the music, mostly covers of rock ballads that somehow sounded evocative and unique with Tiffany's voice. When the set finished, the medical assistant walked through the crowd, greeting people she must have known, until she came to their table.

She looked impossibly young. "You guys came. Wow! I never thought you would."

"I'm glad I got to hear you before I leave town," Eli said. "That was terrific. You've got a gift."

The nurse's aide looked at Melissa.

"I enjoyed every minute of it," she said honestly.

"Thanks, you guys. Seriously, thanks. I like working for your dad—it's a good job—but I kind of feel like I need to take a break from everything and put all my energy into this, you know?"

Melissa remembered being young and passionate, ready to put all her faith into helping her husband follow his dreams.

What about her own dreams? What had she wanted?

"My parents think I'm crazy," Tiffany said with a little laugh. "Do you really think we're good enough to go for it anyway?"

She asked the question of Eli, who looked uncomfortable at being put on the spot. "I'm, uh, probably not the best person to ask. I'm not very musical."

"But you know what you like, right? I saw you getting into the groove."

He looked to Melissa for help, and she tried to tell herself they weren't really a team even when it felt like they were.

"You guys were terrific, Tiff. Seriously. If this is what you really love, I say give it a try. You'll have another chance to get into nursing school, and you've already got your nursing assistant certification to help support you while you follow your dream."

As she spoke the words, she was fully aware of how hypocritical they were. She had given the same advice to Cody, to follow his dream and go for it, then had resented him for devoting all his time and energy to it.

It was too easy to fall into the trap of blaming all the problems in their marriage on his immaturity and lack of commitment. She held a fair share of the responsibility, had been completely unprepared when hard reality hadn't matched up to her rosy expectations.

Tiffany didn't need to hear that right now. Her friend

glowed. "You're the best. Both of you! Are you guys staying for the next group? Glass Army is pretty good."

Melissa glanced over at Eli, who shrugged. "We've paid the cover. Might as well get our money's worth."

"Cool." Tiffany looked over her shoulder to where the drummer was gesturing to her. "Looks like J.P. needs me. Thanks again for coming. I'll see you guys Monday."

She gave Eli a radiant smile, hugged Melissa and returned to her bandmates.

Melissa sighed. "Did somebody just warp time in here? Because I feel about twenty years older than I did when we walked in."

He smiled. "I know what you mean. But for the record, you don't look a day older than Tiffany."

She told herself not to read anything into that. She picked up her drink again, determined to ignore the heat sizzling between them and focus on the music.

Chapter 8

His date-who-wasn't-a-date was a little tipsy. She wasn't precisely drunk—she had only had two and a half mojitos over the past two hours—but he could tell she had let down some of her barriers and seemed more soft and relaxed than he'd seen her since he'd come back to town.

She yawned in the middle of a conversation about which band she preferred—Tiffany's, obviously—and he smiled a little. "We should probably get you home. It's late."

"I don't want to go home," she declared with a hint of defiance in her voice. "It's too quiet there."

The bar didn't close for another hour, but without the live music it had lost most of its appeal for him. Other than The Haystacks, the options for late-night entertainment in Cannon Beach weren't exactly what anyone could call extensive.

"I guess you're right, though," she said with a sigh. "We can't stay here all night."

She rose and started gathering her purse and the jacket she had brought along. She walked out to his dad's SUV with her usual elegant grace, but stumbled a bit when she reached to open the door.

"Here. Let me," he said.

She gave him a broad smile, another hint that she might not be completely sober. "You're just as sweet as your father. Don't tell him I said so."

"I won't," he promised. He made sure she had her seat belt on securely before walking around the vehicle, climbing in and starting it up.

"Oh, look at that dog," she exclaimed as they passed a late-night dog walker with a large yellow Lab on a leash. "I wish I had a dog. Too bad I can't borrow Fiona, but Rosa took her with her out of town. Everyone is gone."

She seemed genuinely sad, but that might have been the mojitos talking.

"Do you want to borrow Max for the night? I'm sure he would be happy to have a sleepover."

She leaned back in the leather seat. "Maybe." She closed her eyes. "He's so cute. He can sleep on the floor by my bed and warn me if any bad guys come around."

He had to smile a little at that and hope he didn't fall into that category. "He can be pretty fierce."

"That's what I need. A fierce dog like Max to protect me."

The idea of telling her he thought she needed a worn-out army doctor sounded ridiculous so he said nothing. "I'll stop at my dad's place and grab Max for you, and I can swing by in the morning to pick him up. Does that work?"

"You are the best boss ever. I mean it. The best!"

He couldn't help the laugh that escaped. For some reason, she gazed at him, an arrested expression on her features.

"I wish you would do that more often," she said.

"What?" The word seemed to hang between them, shimmering on the air.

"Laugh. I like it so much."

He caught his breath, aware of a strange tug, a softness lodged somewhere under his breastbone. This was dangerous territory, indeed. This woman threatened him in ways he wasn't at all prepared to handle.

"I'll keep that in mind," he murmured.

She smiled and closed her eyes, leaning against the leather seat back. A few moments later she was asleep, her hands tucked under her cheek like a child's.

At a stoplight, he looked over, captivated by her. In some ways, she resembled the sweet-faced cheerleader he'd had a thing for back in the day, but he could see now that was an illusion. She was so much more. She had grown into a woman of character and substance, her world changed and shaped by life.

At his father's house, he paused in the driveway for a moment, wondering if it was a stupid idea to loan her Max for the night. She would be fine without him and might find the dog more trouble than he was worth. But Eli had promised. If she would find some solace and comfort from having another creature in the house, Eli wasn't about to stand in the way.

As for Max, the dog would probably treat the whole thing as a fun adventure. He'd been at loose ends with

Wendell in the rehab center and would probably enjoy being needed again.

Max trotted up to him as soon as Eli walked inside, making it an easy matter to scoop up the schnauzer, his food and water bowls, his leash and his favorite blanket. He carried all of it back to his dad's vehicle.

Melissa was still asleep, her breathing soft and measured. After another moment's hesitation, he set the dog and all his comfort supplies on the back seat, then reversed out of the driveway to head the short distance up the hill to Brambleberry House.

If anything, Melissa seemed to have fallen more deeply asleep, snuggling into the leather of the seat. He turned off the engine, reluctant to wake her. He could see Max was snoring away in the back seat, too. Apparently, Eli's company wasn't very scintillating to anyone.

He smiled ruefully and sat for a moment in the stillness of the vehicle. The rest of the world seemed far away right now, as if the two of them and Max were alone here in this quiet, cozy little haven.

Outside the windows, he could see the glitter of stars overhead and the lights of Arch Cape to the south, twinkling against the darkness. A strange, unexpected sense of peace seemed to settle over him like a light, warm mist.

The night was lovely, the sound of waves soothing and familiar. Little by little, he could feel the tension in his shoulders and spine begin to ease.

This…

This was the calm he had been yearning to find since he returned to town. How odd, that he would discover it here in his father's vehicle with a snoring dog in the back seat and a beautiful sleeping woman in the front.

He wasn't going to argue with it. He was just going to soak it in while he had the chance.

Eli closed his eyes, feeling more tension trickle away. He hadn't even realized how tightly wound he had been, yet he found something unbelievably comforting about being here with her. He couldn't have explained it; he only knew she soothed something inside him that had been restless and angry for months and allowed him to set down the twin burdens of guilt and grief for a moment.

Like Max and Melissa, there was a chance he may have fallen asleep, too. He didn't intend to, but the day had been a long one and he felt so very relaxed here beside her.

He awoke sometime later, disoriented and stiff from the uncomfortable position.

Something was different. He opened his eyes and realized with some degree of wonder that she was in his arms.

How had that happened? He hadn't moved, was still behind the wheel, but now he held a woman against him. Her arms were around him, her head resting in the crook of his elbow, and he cradled her against him like a child.

He looked down at her lovely features, tucked against his chest, and was astonished at how absolutely right she felt in his arms.

No. This wasn't right at all. Hadn't he been telling himself all night how he couldn't be the kind of man she needed?

None of that seemed to matter, not here in the darkness. Here, he could admit the truth he had been running from since he'd returned to town.

He was falling for her.

More accurately, he supposed, he was finally allowing himself to acknowledge that he had fallen for her a long time ago and simply had been biding his time, waiting for life and circumstances to bring them together again.

He didn't want to admit it, even to himself. What good would it do? There was no happy-ever-after in the stars for them. He had obligations elsewhere.

His heart ached at knowing this was all they could ever have, these few stolen moments together in his father's SUV in the darkness while the waves pounded relentlessly against the sand.

He wasn't sure if his sudden tension communicated itself to her or if he made some sound or perhaps the dog did, but she began to stir in his arms. She opened her eyes, and for one startling moment there was a blazing joy in her expression, as if she were exactly where she wanted to be, then she seemed to blink a few times and the expression was replaced with confusion and uncertainty.

"Eli. Wh-what are you doing here?" She sat up a little and pulled back to the passenger side of the vehicle, hands in her hair. "What am *I* doing here?"

"We went to see Puddle of Love, remember? Then we stayed for the next group and the next, and there's a chance you may have had a little too much to drink. You fell asleep as I was driving you home. I waited in the driveway for you to wake up but I must have fallen asleep, as well."

She looked out the window, where a light, misty rain had started to fall.

"Okay. That's embarrassing."

"For you or for me? You at least had a moderate degree of alcohol consumption for an excuse. I had one beer all night."

She looked around. "Alcohol or not, I'm still not sure what we're doing *here* in your SUV in the middle of the night. And how did Max get here?"

Quite clearly, he was the one who should be embarrassed about the situation. "You, uh, didn't want to sleep alone tonight so I offered to bring Max up to stay with you."

She shook her head, massaging her forehead. "Well, that will go down in history as one of the most awkward episodes I've ever had with a coworker."

She glanced at the clock on the dashboard. "Is it really after one?"

"Yes. If it's any consolation, I think we only dozed off for an hour or so."

"I should probably go inside. Either that or go down to the beach and dig a giant hole in the sand to climb into."

"You have no reason to be embarrassed, Melissa. Seriously. It was kind of sweet, actually."

He shouldn't have said that. He knew it the moment the words were out. She gazed at him, her blond curls tousled and her eyes soft and her mouth parted slightly. It was all he could do not to yank her back into his arms.

"I'll walk you in," he said, a little more gruffly than he intended.

"Thanks."

"Would you still like Max to stay with you for the night? I can take him home if you'd rather not bother."

She looked at the dog in the back seat, who was beaming at her with that goofy look of his. "I'd like to say no, but I would actually appreciate his company. Having him here might help the house not feel as empty."

He opened the rear door for Max, and the dog trotted up the sidewalk as if he owned the place. Eli grabbed Max's blanket, leash and bowls.

As they walked toward the house, she pulled out her key. "I'm suddenly starving. Are you hungry? I've got stuff on hand to make an omelet, if you want."

He was torn between his conviction that it wasn't a very good idea to spend more time with her and his overwhelming desire to do exactly that.

As if to seal the deal, his stomach suddenly growled and he realized dinner had been hours ago, before he picked her up to go to The Haystacks. He had nibbled a bit on bar snacks, but apparently that wasn't enough.

"There you go," she said with a winsome smile. "Come in."

"I can grab a sandwich at home."

"I'm not super talented in the kitchen, but I do make a mean omelet. They're kind of a specialty of mine. Come on. It's the least I can do, after you were kind enough to let me sleep in your car."

It would be rude to refuse, he told himself. Plus, he wanted to make sure she would be okay on her own without her daughter.

"An omelet does sound good right now."

She smiled and unlocked the door. "It will hit the spot. Trust me."

He did. He trusted her more than any woman in a long time.

The question was, did he trust himself?

What had seemed like a brilliant idea while the two of them were standing outside on her porch suddenly lost a great deal of its shine once they walked inside her apartment.

Melissa was having a hard enough time resisting the man. Sharing late-night snacks alone in her kitchen when there was a chance she might still be slightly buzzed could very well be more temptation than she could resist.

She was still trying to deal with how perfect it had seemed to wake up in his arms. She had felt safe and warm and cared for, though she knew that was ridiculous. How had she ended up there? She still wasn't quite sure. He had explained that she had fallen asleep in the vehicle on the way home from the tavern, but that didn't really explain how she had gone from sitting on her side of the vehicle to being cradled so tenderly in his arms.

Had she snored? Drooled? Done anything else completely mortifying? She had no idea. She also didn't understand how he had *let* her keep sleeping when he could have awakened her the moment he pulled up outside Brambleberry House. Why hadn't he just honked the horn or shouted in her ear? He could have just opened the door and pushed her out, for that matter.

Still, waking up in his arms had felt completely right, somehow.

She was falling for him and she had no idea what to do about it. She knew perfectly well it would only end up in heartbreak for her. He had made it clear he was leaving at the first opportunity. Under other circumstances, she might have followed after him and used her own skills to help those in need.

That was utterly impossible at this stage of her life. She had a daughter. They were settling into life here in Oregon. She didn't have the freedom to let herself fall for someone whose heart was somewhere else. Been there, done that.

She swallowed. She had invited him for an omelet, which was the least she could do after he had been so sweet about trying to distract her from being upset about Skye spending the night with her father.

So she had slept in his arms for a few moments and had awakened with a powerful urge to kiss the dark shadow of his jaw and pull his mouth to hers. She hadn't done that, which meant she had more self-control than she gave herself credit.

She only had to keep her hands off him for the ten minutes it would take her to fix him an omelet and the ten minutes it would take him to eat it. She could handle that.

She led the way into the kitchen, flipping on lights as she went, and quickly tied on an apron.

"This won't take long," she promised him.

"I can help."

"There's not much to do. I suppose you could cut the peppers while I do the onions."

"Sure."

She pulled a green pepper out of the refrigerator, pointed him to the cutting board and handed him a knife, then put on the food-grade gloves she used so onion juice didn't seep into her skin.

After sniffing around it, Max settled into the corner on the pillow Skye kept there for Fiona's visits, and a comfortable silence filled the kitchen, broken only by the sounds of chopping.

She was the first to break it.

"Who is Miri?"

His knife came down hard on the cutting board, and if she hadn't been watching him she might have missed the sudden bleak look that he quickly blinked away.

"How do you…know about Miri?"

"I'm not sure. I think you may have said her name in your sleep. I thought maybe I'd dreamed it, but obviously not."

He let out a breath and then another, and she could tell the question had upset him.

"I'm sorry. I shouldn't have said anything. I was only curious. You don't have to tell me."

He turned his attention to briskly cutting the peppers. Any smaller and they would disappear in the omelet. After a moment, she took them from him and added them along with her chopped onions to the sizzling oil in the omelet pan.

The smells made her mouth water even as her attention remained focused on him.

"I told you about Justine the other day."

"Your doctor friend who died in the suicide bombing. Or was she more than a friend?"

"I'm not sure what we were," he admitted, confirming her suspicion. "We had dated a few times, if you can call it dating when you're in a war zone, surrounded by people facing starvation and violence."

"You said she was there with Doctors without Borders. What was your role? Can you talk about it?"

He hesitated for a moment, and she wondered if she had overstepped, then he spoke. "For the last twelve months, I've been deployed to the Middle East, providing medical care in various refugee camps and setting up clinics in small struggling villages trying to recover from decades of unrest."

"Not an easy task."

"I've been deployed most of the last five years. After the first tour, I asked to go back. It had its challenges but there were many rewards. These are courageous people who have already lost so much, facing truly horrible circumstances."

Every time she heard about people living in rough conditions like Eli was talking about, Melissa regretted her propensity to feel sorry that her life hadn't turned out the way she'd planned. She had so many amazing things in her world. She had a job she loved, good friends, a great apartment next to one of the most beautiful beaches in the world. No, things weren't perfect, but on the whole, her life was extraordinary.

"We were trying to improve conditions," Eli said. "I like to think we were making progress. Justine was absolutely dedicated to the cause and was a real inspiration to everyone."

Features pensive, Eli pulled Max onto his lap and scratched the schnauzer beneath his chin. "As you can imagine, the camp had more than its share of orphaned children."

"How sad." She didn't like thinking about children who had no one to love them.

"There was one in particular who always wanted to help the aid workers. She used to ask to sweep the floor of the medical clinic."

"Miri."

"Yes. She was about seven or eight, the sweetest girl, with a huge smile."

He let out a soft, tortured sigh. "Everyone in the camp watched over her, but she and Justine had a special bond. Miri used to bring her little bouquets of flowery weeds or pretty rocks she'd found. Justine wanted to adopt her, take her back to France with her, and was trying to put the wheels in motion."

She wanted to say how wonderful that such sweetness could survive the horrors of war, but she sensed she didn't want to hear what was coming next. She could see by the tension in his shoulders and the way he gripped his hands tightly together that the rest of the story wasn't as tender.

"What happened?"

She flipped the omelet, wishing she hadn't asked any questions and started them down this grim road.

"One day, Justine asked me to go with her to a village about five or six kilometers away from the camp to help with a clinic for pregnant women and children. A routine trip, we both thought, something we'd done a dozen times in other villages. It was well within my mission as part of a PRT, Provincial Reconstruction Team, trying to help these war-torn areas rebuild." He paused. "She thought it would be fun to take Miri with us. The girl was very good at putting villagers at ease and convincing them to trust us."

He was silent, his eyes haunted by memories she couldn't begin to guess at.

"I didn't want to, but it made both of them happy so I relented. I liked to see them smile. Miri had started doing it more and more, especially when all three of us were together."

"What happened?"

"It was market day and the area was busy. We didn't stop working all morning and saw maybe twenty women, but then things began to slow down a little. I… Miri and Justine decided to walk to the market square to grab some lunch for us and look at some of the local goods on sale. I should have said no, that we should stick together. I'd been uneasy all day, feeling a weird energy."

"Would Justine have stayed behind simply because you asked her to?"

He made a face. "Probably not. She was fiercely independent. If I had told her I had a weird feeling, she would have laughed at me and called me *Monsieur Poule Mouillée.*"

"Mr. Wet Hen," she said, smiling at his quite excellent French accent. Hers wasn't great, but she understood better than she could speak from studying it in school.

"I told myself I was imagining things. There was no potential threat. Why would there be? We were aid workers. I stayed behind at the clinic and didn't go with them because I was too busy showering all my knowledge on the village's young, inexperienced midwife. I had just about run out of things to yammer on about when we heard the blast."

"Oh, Eli."

His features were grim. "Apparently, there were still opposition forces in the area angry that the leadership of this village would accept foreign aid workers. They killed fifteen villagers at a peaceful market square for no reason, along with a sweet orphan girl who only wanted to help."

"Miri," she whispered, heart aching for the devastation she heard in his voice.

"She died instantly. Justine was conscious and in agony for only a moment after I arrived on scene. I tried to stabilize her, but she'd lost too much blood and the shock was too great. She went into cardiac arrest. I told you I did CPR while we tried to call for help but... It was too late. I couldn't save either of them."

She had no words, nothing that could comfort this sort of deep pain.

"Miri was only a girl, with a future that was much brighter than it had been a few months earlier, before Justine came into her life. I hate knowing that future was wiped out because of me."

"Why do you blame yourself?"

"I could have made other choices. I shouldn't have let them go into the market alone. I should have been with them. We should have taken more protection with us."

"Could any of those things have stopped what happened?"

He looked helplessly at her and she knew the answer. No. He would have been a target, too.

She removed the omelet from the stove to a plate, choosing her words with care. "You can't blame yourself, Eli. You didn't plant the explosives and you couldn't have known someone else would. You were there to help people."

"I know that intellectually. Convincing my emotions isn't quite as easy."

The torment on his features broke her heart. She was

a nurse, driven to ease suffering where she saw it, and she hated knowing she couldn't help him.

She couldn't resist going to him and wrapping her arms around his waist. She wanted to tell him not to blame himself, that she understood he had been there to help others and he couldn't hold himself responsible for the evil actions of a few, but she knew that would be cold comfort.

Still, something in her touch must have calmed him, as she hoped. After a few moments, she felt some of the tension in his muscles seep away. He returned her hug with a grateful embrace before he stepped away.

"I'm sorry. I keep thinking I've dealt with it. It was six months ago and most of the time I'm fine. Every once in a while, I let down my guard and the memories wash over me like a flash flood."

"I'm glad I was here to keep them from drowning you."

"So am I." He gestured to the table. "But I hate to waste a good omelet, especially when you've gone to all the trouble to make it. Should we eat?"

For all the sadness of his story, she found the meal surprisingly restful. They spoke of mutual acquaintances and some of the changes that had come over the town in the years since both of them had lived here. She didn't want their time together to end, but the long day finally caught up with her and she couldn't hold back a yawn.

He glanced at his watch, shook his head and rose. "I should go. It's nearly two. Thank you for the omelet and the evening. I enjoyed both."

"Thank *you*. I forgot all about missing Skye."

He shrugged into his jacket and headed for the door. She walked him there, with Max trotting at their heels.

"If you want to take Max home with you, I should be okay. I feel silly I was ever worried about being alone. This house just feels so big when I'm the only one here, especially when I know Sonia and Rosa aren't in town."

"Keep him until Skye gets home, if you want. He's good company. To be honest, you're better company to him than I will probably be. He's been lonely, I'm afraid. I think he misses my dad. And I'll be at the rehab center most of the day, so he would be alone otherwise."

He planned to spend his Sunday with his father, which filled her with a soft tenderness. "You're a very sweet man, Eli."

He raised an eyebrow. "Why? Because I have a good relationship with my dad?"

"You care. Too many people who have been through what you have would harden their soul against letting in any kind of softer feelings, but you haven't. You care about your father, you cared about Jim the other day on the beach, you care about our patients and about your refugee patients thousands of miles away."

She had to kiss him. Though she knew it was potentially dangerous, she couldn't resist rising on her tiptoes and pressing her mouth to his.

He remained frozen for one breathless moment, and then he lowered his mouth to hers and kissed her as she realized both of them had been craving all night.

It was raw and hot, his mouth searching hers, his body pressed against her. She realized as his arms tightened around her that she had been fooling herself. She hadn't kissed him out of tenderness or empathy but because she had been craving his kiss since those magical moments the day before, outside the beach gate.

She made a soft sound and wrapped her arms around his neck, her mouth angled to allow him better access. Her breasts ached where they were pressed against him. *Everything* ached.

His mouth was urgent and demanding on hers, and the hunger in it aroused her.

He wanted her.

She didn't need to feel the hard nudge of his arousal against her to sense it in his hands and his mouth and his body. They were alone in the house. She could take him by the hand and tug him into her bedroom, and they could spend the rest of this rainy, misty night wrapped together, pushing away the shadows.

The temptation consumed her. How easy it would be to take that step. It had been so very long since she had felt wanted and needed and cherished like this.

And then what? If she and Eli spent the night together, where would that leave them? He was still committed to leaving. He had just told her all his reasons for it. He was driven to continue the work he had been doing, providing medical care to people in need. She understood now that he was motivated by a complicated tangle of guilt and grief and obligation. She also understood that she would be a fool to think she would be enough to keep him here.

Her heart would be broken. Just like her marriage—which she had known even as she was saying *I do* was a mistake that never should have happened—it would be her own stupid fault.

One the best ways she had found to discipline Skye on the rare occasions her daughter misbehaved was to redirect, to encourage her to make a better choice. Those words, *make a better choice*, were often all she needed to say when Skye was throwing one of her rare tantrums or doing something Melissa had told her not to do.

She needed to listen to her own advice to her daughter. She had no hope of creating happiness in life if she made choices she knew from the outset would only lead to heartbreak and pain.

She couldn't make love with him, as much as she ached to feel his arms around her all night long, to learn all his secrets and explore that delicious body.

It would leave her too vulnerable. She was already half in love with the man. Spending what was left of the night together would push her headlong the rest of the way.

She had entrusted her heart and her life to one man who put something else ahead of her. Fixing her mistake had cost her dearly, and her child would pay the price for that the rest of her life, forever separated from one parent or the other through the tangled maze of custody and visitations.

She couldn't wander blindly into a similar situation. When he walked away to return to the military and the life that gave him such purpose and meaning, Melissa was very much afraid she would never put back together the pieces of her shattered heart.

She didn't want to end the kiss. She wanted to stay right here forever, with his warm, sexy mouth teasing out all her secrets. Just a few more moments…

He was finally the one who broke the embrace. He eased his mouth away and rested his forehead against hers.

She thought she smelled roses again, but this time the scent was wistful and almost sad.

"Didn't we say we weren't going to do this again?" he said, his forehead pressed to hers.

She wanted to make some smart response but couldn't think of anything. "Kisses don't count in the middle of the night."

"I think that's when they count the most."

After a moment, he stepped away, eyes haunted with regret. "I need to go, before I forget all the reasons why I can't stay."

Her chest ached and she wished with all her heart that things could be different, that she could be the woman for him.

"What about Max?" he asked.

Already the house seemed to echo with emptiness. For all that the ghosts of Brambleberry House seemed friendly enough, she wasn't sure she was strong enough to face them alone tonight. "He's here and he seems comfortable enough. If you don't mind, I'll keep him overnight."

"No problem."

He looked as if he had other things he wanted to say, but Eli finally headed for the door. When he opened it, Melissa saw the light rain of earlier had turned into a steady downpour. It matched her sudden mood— dank, dark, dismal.

"Good night," he said with one last, backward look that seemed filled with regret.

Was he regretting that he had to leave?

Or regretting that they both knew he couldn't stay?

After he walked out into the night, Melissa locked the door behind him, then went through her apartment turning off lights, grateful for Max's company as he followed along behind her.

Her heart ached as she thought of the story Eli had told and the sadness behind it. He must have cared about the woman very much to shoulder such a burden six months later. This Justine person must have been remarkable. Not the kind of woman who basically fell apart simply because her daughter was spending the night with her father.

She had learned to be tough after the divorce, and she needed to call on that strength. Something told her she would need all the courage she could find after Eli left Cannon Beach once more.

Chapter 9

The next day, Sunday, she rose early despite her late night and took Max for a run along the beach. He didn't have Fiona's loping grade but toddled along beside her so cheerfully, it warmed her heart.

The day had turned cooler from the rain of the night before, with more precipitation predicted for later that evening. April could be fickle on the coast, with the rare warm, pleasant day often giving way to a spring snowstorm.

Things weren't supposed to be that drastic, but it was definitely cold enough first thing in the morning that she was grateful for her jacket.

They didn't bump into Eli, as she had half hoped and half feared. All in all, it was the most uneventful run she'd had on the beach in what felt like forever.

As if to remind her of previous fun times, her wrist

ached more than it had in days as she and Max returned to the house. She ignored it and spent the rest of the morning trying not to watch the clock as she finished some of her coursework for her online nurse practitioner classes.

She had just hit Send on another assignment when Max suddenly scampered to the front door just moments before it opened.

"Mommy! Hi! Where are you, Mommy?"

She hurried out to the entryway to find Skye and Cody standing just inside the door. Skye must have used her key to come in.

"You're back! Hi, honey."

"Hi, Mommy." Skye hugged her but didn't stop frowning. "Hey, why do you have Dr. Sanderson's dog? Hi, Max!"

"He's babysitting me," she said. Skye giggled while Cody looked on, confused.

She didn't bother to explain to him. "How did things go?" she asked instead.

She didn't necessarily want Skye to rant about how miserable she'd been overnight. Melissa didn't want to think she was that small-minded.

Still, when her daughter beamed, Melissa had to smile through clenched teeth.

"So fun," Skye said. "We went to a baseball game last night and they had fireworks and everything. Then we had pizza and this morning we went to the store. We were going to go to another baseball game but decided not to. I got to see Grandma and Grandpa Fielding, too. Did you know they have a swimming pool at their new house?"

Her in-laws had only recently moved to Portland from Manzanita and she hadn't been to their house yet.

"I didn't know that. How fun."

Skye made a face. "Dad said it was too cold to go swimming, plus I didn't take my suit."

"Next time, though," Cody promised.

"Do we want to set up the next visit?" she asked her ex.

Cody looked a little distracted, as if he hadn't thought past this one. "I don't know what my schedule's going to look like next week. We might be heading down to Cali. What about two weeks from now?"

She forced a smile. "That could work. Just let me know."

"Thanks, Missy. Hey, Skye-ster. Thanks for hanging with me. I've got to run."

"Okay. Bye, Dad."

"Sorry to leave so fast. Amalia didn't do well on the drive here. She's a bit carsick so I'd better get her back to the city."

"No problem. Next time I could meet you halfway."

"That would be great. You're the best, Miss. Thanks!"

She waved him off, proud of herself for taking the high road this time. It made things go so much more smoothly when she tried to be the adult in their interactions.

After he hurried down the steps, she smiled at her daughter, who was busy petting Max.

"Why is he really here?"

"I wanted some company last night. The house was pretty empty since everyone but me was gone for the night."

"Even Fiona?"

"She went with Rosa on a hiking trip out of town. So, yes, it was just me."

"We should get our own dog."

It was not a new request. Skye had been pushing for their own dog since they had moved from Hawaii.

"Maybe when we get into our own house. I'm so glad you had a great time with your father and Amalia. Is she nice?"

"Really nice. She doesn't say much, but she's trying to learn English. She taught me a little Portuguese. That's what they speak in Brazil, not Brazilian, did you know that?"

"That I did know."

"I don't know why. It's weird, if you ask me. But she taught me how to say hello—*olá*, which kind of sounds like *hola*. And goodbye is *adeus*, which also sounds like *adios*. Thank you is *obrigada*. Dad would say *obrigado* but I'm not sure why. It was fun, except I missed you a ton. Maybe you could come next time."

Wouldn't that be delightful? She swallowed a groan and chose her words carefully. "That's sweet of you, honey, but it's important for you to enjoy your special time with your dad and new stepmom. And soon you'll have a new baby brother to love. You get plenty of time with me."

"I guess. I still missed you."

"I missed you, too. So much, I had to borrow Max here to keep me company."

"I wish we didn't have to give him back."

"I know, honey. But you like sleeping in your own bed and I'm sure Max does, too."

"I guess."

Melissa didn't want to fall into the trap of trying to compete with her ex for most fun parent, but she'd been without her daughter for an entire day and wanted to have a little fun with her while she could. "Why don't you go get your kite and we can take Max home, then fly your kite on that good stretch of beach by Dr. Sanderson's house."

Skye had been begging her to take the kite out for several weeks and she latched onto the idea with enthusiasm. "Yay! I'll go get it."

She skipped to her room, leaving Melissa to gather up the dog's things and try not to be nervous at the idea of seeing Eli again.

As he finished putting together the lift recliner he had purchased that morning, Eli wasn't sure whether his father would be happy about the gift or would accuse him of trying to turn Wendell into an old man before his time.

His father was recovering from a double knee replacement. Nobody would think less of him for using anything that might make his life a little more comfortable. And after all his father did for his patients around town, didn't he deserve a comfortable chair at the end of the day that he could get into and out of without pain?

It was a good argument, if Eli did say so himself. Whether his father would buy into it was another story entirely.

He pulled the chair into the corner where his father's beat-up old recliner held pride of place. He would never dare to get rid of the thing, but he could at least offer this one as an alternative. If nothing else, Max would probably like it.

He looked around automatically for the dog, then remembered. Max had spent the night with Melissa.

Lucky dog.

He pushed the dangerous thought away as he settled into the recliner to check it out. He couldn't think about her like that.

How had she made it through the night? It had taken all his strength that morning not to walk up to Brambleberry House to check on her.

That hadn't stopped him from thinking about her all day. Their hot, intense kiss had haunted him, kept him awake most of the night.

What was he going to do about this attraction to her?

Absolutely nothing.

What could come of it? She deserved better than a long-distance relationship, and that was all he could offer her right now. He was leaving town as soon as his father was back on his legs. Eli had had an email just that morning from his commanding officer, asking when he would be back and whether he was ready to take off again to return to his job overseas.

For one crazy moment, Eli had been tempted to tell Dr. Flores that he was done, he wasn't going to re-up but would continue serving the National Guard, available when his country needed him.

He knew the woman would be disappointed but wouldn't think less of him. Many—in fact, most—army doctors didn't stay in as long as he had, at least not on active duty. His initial commitment had only been two years, but the work had been so fulfilling he hadn't been able to walk away then.

Could he walk away now? That was the million-dollar question. Before Justine and Miri died, he had been thinking about going into private practice while retaining his military benefits by serving in the Guard. That was the course most in the Army Medical Corps eventually took.

Since that horrible day in that dusty market town, he had felt driven to do more, try harder, dedicate himself more fully.

He owed both of them. Didn't he? He hadn't been able to save Justine, but he could help those she had cared about.

That left little place in his world for someone like Melissa, who had finally found her own place to belong here in Cannon Beach.

While he might accept that intellectually, it hadn't stopped him from thinking about her all day, remembering their kiss and feeling comforted all over again when he remembered the sweet way she had wrapped her arms around him in her kitchen, offering solace and concern.

He had it bad for Melissa Fielding. That was the plain truth. He was all tangled up over her and didn't know how to unravel the silken cords around his heart.

The doorbell startled him out of his thoughts, and it took him a minute to figure out how to work the control of the chair enough to put the footrest down so he could get out.

When he opened the door, he was greeted first by a familiar woof, and then by a grin and wave from a young curly-haired girl.

"Hi, the other Dr. Sanderson."

He was as charmed by Skye as he was by her

mother, even though her bright smile reminded him so painfully of Miri. "Hi there, the other Ms. Fielding."

She grinned. "Mom said we had to take Max back to you today, even though I really, really, really wanted to keep him."

He glanced at Skye's mother and felt that peculiar tug in his gut that had also become familiar since he'd come back to town, the one he felt only around Melissa. He wanted to tell the girl she could keep the dog for another night, but he had a feeling Melissa would not appreciate his offer.

"Thank you. Both of you."

"Thanks for loaning him," Melissa said. "He was wonderful company, weren't you, Max?"

The dog yipped as if agreeing with her.

"Here's his stuff." Skye handed over the bowls and blanket he had taken to Brambleberry House the night before.

"Thanks." He took them and set them inside his father's house, then gestured to the colorful fabric kite in Melissa's hand. "I guess I can tell where you guys are going after this."

"Yep," Skye answered. "I've been begging and begging to fly our kite and today Mom said yes. We're going down to the beach by your house because the wind is always just right."

"Looks like a great kite."

It was shaped like a jellyfish, purple with rainbow-colored tentacles. "You should see how high it goes. Sometimes it goes up and up until I can barely even see it."

"Sounds amazing."

He and his mom used to fly kites on the beach often

after school. It had been one of their favorite pastimes. After the cancer made her too weak, she used to sit at the window here and watch him down on the beach below their house. Some nights he would fly a kite past dusk, hesitant to come in when he knew she enjoyed the sight of it flying and dipping so much.

"You can come with us," Skye suggested. "We always have a hard time getting it up in the air. I can never run fast enough to have the wind take it. Maybe you could help us."

He darted a look at Melissa but couldn't tell by her veiled expression what she thought about her daughter's spontaneous invitation.

"It's been a long time since I've flown a kite. I'm not sure I remember how."

"We can show you," Skye said.

"I'm sure Dr. Sanderson has other things to do right now," Melissa said.

"Like what?" Skye asked.

"Skye. It's rude to expect him to drop everything and come with us."

He ought to let the girl down gently and tell her he had other plans. But suddenly he wanted to fly a kite more than he had wanted to do anything else in a long time…except, perhaps, to kiss her mother.

"Thank you for inviting me," he said instead. "I would very much enjoy helping you fly this beautiful kite."

It definitely wasn't a good idea to spend more time with Melissa or with her daughter, not when he was having a hard time resisting both of them, but he told himself he could handle it. He only had to keep things in perspective, remind himself he was leaving in a few weeks.

He couldn't tell how Melissa felt about the prospect of him coming along, but her daughter made her delight clear. She beamed at him, the gap in her front teeth more pronounced. "Yay! Can Max come with us?"

"Sure. I don't see why not."

"I'll hold his leash, if you want."

"Thanks," he said, trying to keep the dryness out of his tone. "That's very nice of you."

He picked up his sunglasses from the hall table where he'd left them and walked outside into a lovely Oregon afternoon. The rain of the evening before was nowhere in evidence, though he knew the forecast called for possible heavy waves and wind later in the week.

"Let me take that," he said to Melissa, reaching for the colorful kite she carried.

"It's a kite. It's not exactly heavy."

"If it were heavy, it wouldn't fly," Skye pointed out with irrefutable logic.

"It's big and bulky, though. I don't mind."

She held it out for him. "Here you go. Knock yourself out."

He reached for it and though he didn't plan to and, in fact, actively tried to avoid it, his hands brushed hers.

Heat seemed to race along his nerve endings and his stomach muscles clenched.

So much for keeping control around her. If he could have that kind of reaction from a little accidental slide of skin on skin, he was in big trouble.

As they took the closest beach access, a narrow trail

between two houses, Skye hurried ahead of them with Max, leaving Eli to walk alone with Melissa.

"You really didn't have to come with us," she said after a moment. "Skye is right, we're not the greatest at getting the kite up in the air, but trying is half the fun."

Her cheeks were pink, but he couldn't tell if that was from embarrassment or from the breeze.

"I meant what I said. I'm looking forward to it. What better way to spend a windy April afternoon?"

When they reached the beach, she gave him a sidelong look.

"All morning, I've been thinking about how awkward it would be to face you again," she admitted, confirming his suspicion about the source of that rosy glow. "I'm kind of glad we got that out of the way now, instead of tomorrow morning in the office when you're seeing a patient."

Her words were a blunt reminder that she worked for his father. He had a strong suspicion that wasn't accidental, as if she needed both of them to remember their respective roles.

"You have nothing to feel awkward or embarrassed about," he assured her.

She snorted. "Sure. I only drank too much, which I never do, fell asleep in your car and then practically dragged you into my house and insisted on feeding you." She glanced at her daughter and then back at him. "And it's my fault we kissed again, when we both made it clear the first time that it shouldn't happen again."

Was she sorry it had happened? He couldn't tell from her response. He wasn't sure he regretted it. He should, he knew, but her kiss had been as warm and nurturing as the rest of her.

He wanted to kiss her again. Right now, right here. Instead, he gripped the kite more tightly and continued walking beside her while the April breeze that smelled of sand and sea danced around them. "It was a strange night. We're going to chalk it all up to that, right?"

She opened her mouth as if to argue, but her daughter interrupted before she could.

"What about here?" Skye asked. "Is this a good place to fly a kite?"

He managed to drag his gaze away from Melissa's mouth to focus on their surroundings, the beach a short distance from his father's house. "This looks like an excellent spot. No trees, no wires, no skyscrapers."

"I agree. It's a great place," Melissa said. She set her backpack on the sand and reached inside, pulling out a rolled sand mat. After spreading it out, she plopped down, then calmly pulled a book out of the backpack.

"I do believe this is a great spot for me to sit back and relax with a book while you guys run around and get all sweaty trying to get that big kite up in the air. I'll watch our stuff."

Eli snorted. "You're going to read a book while I help your daughter fly her kite. Why do I get the feeling I've just been played?"

She shrugged nonchalantly. "Nobody is playing anybody. If you remember correctly, I had no idea you would be here. We were only supposed to be dropping Max off at your place before coming down to fly the kite. I didn't plan things this way, but since you're here, I would be crazy to waste a chance to sit on the sand and enjoy this warm afternoon."

He laughed, completely delighted with her. Every time he was with her, he fell harder.

She stared at him, her features still and watchful, with an expression he couldn't read behind her sunglasses.

I wish you would do that more often. I like it so much.

He remembered her slightly tipsy words the night before in his dad's SUV after he had laughed then, and his insides felt achy with need. That encounter seemed a hundred miles away right now on this sunny beach with the waves washing against the sand and the seagulls crying out overhead.

After a moment, he turned to Skye. "Your mom wants to read her book and I can't argue it's a good plan. I guess it's up to us to fly this kite, then."

"We can do it," Skye said again. She jutted her chin into the air, looking like a mini pugilist version of her mother. "I know we can."

"You got it. Let's do this."

The afternoon turned into one of the most enjoyable he had spent in a long time.

He tried to steel his heart against Skye, using as a shield an image of a little dark-eyed orphan with a shy smile, but he quickly realized it was pointless.

He couldn't resist her any more than he'd been able to resist her mother.

Skye was completely adorable. She chattered endlessly about everything under the sun. She told him about the haystacks, how they had been formed by wind and water eons ago. She waved energetically at the people on recumbent bicycles who rode past them with some frequency on the hard-packed sand close to the water, telling him about the time she and her mother had rented them once when they first moved back to town and it had been really fun. She talked about her father and his new wife and the baby on the way and how it was a boy and she couldn't wait to hold him.

She was smart and funny and as openhearted as her mother.

Max ran around in excitement as they worked to get the kite up. Once it was soaring and dipping above them on the currents, the dog seemed to lose interest and plopped down beside Melissa, who reached absently to pet him while turning the page of her book with her other hand.

Whenever he looked over at her, his chest seemed to ache all over again. The sunlight gleamed in her hair and she looked fresh and sweet and beautiful.

It was a perfect moment here, beside the water he loved. A girl laughing with glee, her mother soft and relaxed on the sand, the wind catching the colorful kite and tugging it ever higher.

The restlessness inside him seemed to settle for now, and he wanted the moment to go on and on.

He and Skye flew the kite for over an hour, taking turns holding it and letting it dip and dance on the currents.

He thought Melissa might have fallen asleep, but he couldn't tell for sure with her sunglasses.

Sometime later, she finally rose with her elegant grace and came over to where he and Skye were holding the kite. "You guys have done a great job."

"It's higher than we've ever got it!" Skye exclaimed. "Eli is the *best* at flying a kite. He said he used to do it with his mom when he was a kid and flying a kite always makes him think of her."

Melissa sent him a swift look, and Eli pointedly busied himself with the kite.

"We should probably go, kiddo. We still have to fix dinner and get you to bed."

"Oh. Do we have to?"

"I'm afraid so. You had a big weekend with your dad. You don't want to be too tired for school tomorrow, right? It's your big field trip."

"Oh, yeah!" To Eli, she said, "We're going to the lighthouse in Astoria and my teacher said we could maybe even fly paper airplanes off the top of it. We're going to write our names on them and see whose goes the farthest. I bet it will be mine."

He remembered flying paper airplanes off that lighthouse when he was in elementary school and still remembered the triumph of his particular design beating everyone else in his class. "Sounds like fun. You'll have to let me know if you're the winner."

"I will."

Together, they started the process of winding the string from the kite back onto the reel. The kite fought them on the currents until he was able to pull it back down to earth.

"What do you say to Eli?" her mother prompted once they had the colorful kite back on the sand.

"Thanks a ton for helping me, Eli."

Skye beamed at him. Before he realized what she intended, she threw her arms around his waist and gave him a tight hug.

Emotions came out of nowhere and clogged his throat, much to his embarrassment, his mind on another girl who would never have the chance to fly kites on a beautiful April afternoon.

"It was my pleasure. Truly."

"I hope we can do it again sometime."

He didn't know how to answer. He would be gone again soon. Even if his father wasn't yet up to full strength, Eli would have to go and let a substitute doctor take his place. "Maybe."

"And you said I could play pool at your dad's house. Can we do that tonight?"

"No," Melissa said firmly. "Maybe another time."

He regretted that he likely wouldn't have the chance to follow through on his offer to let her come over and practice before he left town. Maybe his father could take on billiards lessons while he was recovering from his knee surgery. He would suggest it to Wendell the next day when he went to his father's rehabilitation center.

"I'll walk you back," he said after Melissa had gathered up her things.

"You don't have to do that."

"Somebody needs to haul this guy back for you."

She didn't argue, but he could tell she didn't need or want his help.

He couldn't tell her he would find any excuse to spend more time with her, already dreading the moment he would have to say goodbye.

As she walked along beside him, with Skye again racing ahead of them holding tight to Max's leash, Melissa came to the grave realization that she didn't need to worry any more that she might do something stupid like fall in love with Eli.

She already had.

Watching him fly a kite with Skye, seeing his patience and his kindness and the sheer fun he seemed to have with her daughter, had made that truth abundantly clear.

How could any woman hope to resist him? He was sexy and sweet and wonderful.

What a complete disaster. He was going to leave again. What was she supposed to do then?

When they reached Brambleberry House, he opened the sea gate for her. She was relieved when she spotted Fiona, who immediately rushed across the lawn to greet Max, tail wagging.

"Looks like your neighbor is back."

She waved to Rosa, who was sitting on the swing looking out at the water.

Rosa waved back, and Melissa didn't need to see her expression to guess she was wearing a speculative look seeing her with Eli again.

Rosa could speculate all she wanted. They were only together temporarily. He would be leaving soon and she would be alone again.

"Thanks for letting me fly the kite with you," he said to Skye. "I had a great time."

"Thanks again for helping me. Me and my mom never would've been able to get it up that high."

"I don't know. You seem like a pro."

"Thanks." She beamed at him. "Now that you showed me what to do, I bet the next time I can get it as high as you did this time."

"I don't doubt it for a minute."

"You can come watch and tell me if I'm doing it right," she declared.

"Maybe."

He wouldn't be here. He would be off saving the

world, leaving them here to figure out how to fly kites and play billiards without him. Melissa frowned but didn't want to ruin her daughter's happiness by pointing out that depressing truth.

"I guess I'll see you at the office tomorrow," she said instead.

"Right. I guess so."

With other friends, she might have hugged them or even given a kiss on the cheek before sending them on their way. With all these emotions churning through her, she didn't dare do anything but give Eli an awkward little wave.

He looked as if he wanted to say something else, but he finally nodded and waved, gripped Max's leash and headed back down the beach.

She did her best not to watch after him, though it took every ounce of self-control she had.

"I am so ready to have this baby, if only to be done with stirrups and paper gowns."

Melissa smiled at Julia Garrett, currently settled onto the exam table in said paper gown. "It looks so lovely on you. Are you sure you don't want a few more children?"

Julia made a face. "No. This is it. Our house is bursting at the seams and Will says he can't build on again and I can't bear to move. So we have to be done."

"At least until Maddie and Simon go off to college next year. Then you'll have plenty of room for more babies."

She gave a rough laugh. "I hope you hear how ridiculous that sounds. We'll never be empty nesters at this rate."

This was Julia's fifth child. She and her husband, Will, had her teenage twin boy and girl from her previous marriage as well as an eight-year-old and a four-year-old. Melissa could only imagine the chaos at their house, but Julia always seemed calm and composed. Oh, how she envied her and wished some of that serenity would rub off on her.

Julia had once lived in Brambleberry House with her twins, when she was a single widow with twins, before she married Will. She had a soft spot for the house and the gardens and the stunning beauty of the place.

When Melissa came back to town, the two of them had bonded over that right after they met, a bond that had deepened and strengthened into real friendship in the months since.

"This is the last one, for sure."

She touched her abdomen protectively and Melissa felt a sharp little ache in her own womb.

She had wanted more children but hadn't been willing to bring more children into the uncertainty of a shaky marriage.

The little twinge of regret annoyed her. She had an amazing daughter. She refused to waste the wonderful life she had, wishing she had made different choices.

"Dr. Sanderson should be here soon."

"When you say that, I keep picturing sweet Dr. Sanderson, then remember you're talking about someone else entirely. How is it, working for Wendell's son? He's quite gorgeous, isn't he?"

Oh, yes. Entirely *too* gorgeous. She had to brace herself against her instinctive reaction to him every time she came into the office. It had been three weeks since he came back to town, two since the day he had come with her and Skye to fly kites, and she was more tangled up than ever.

"Just like his father, Eli is an excellent doctor," she said. "I promise you'll be in great hands."

"Oh, I know. He was great when I came in for my checkup last week and the week before. Wendell has nothing but praise for him. Will remembers him, though Eli is a few years younger. Will said he was freaky smart in school."

Julia hadn't grown up in Cannon Beach but had spent summers here during her childhood. Will had been her first love, which Melissa found utterly charming.

"He was," she answered, wondering how they'd gotten on the subject of Eli. She had been doing her best *not* to think about him…which was particularly tough when they worked together each day. The only way she had survived the last few weeks was by staying busy with her classes and Skye and trying not to think about him leaving.

"How soon before his dad is back?"

"We're still not sure. His own doctors want him to take it easy, but you know Wendell. He is determined to come in next week for at least a few hours a day. Who knows, he might be back before you have the baby. When are you due again?"

"Three more weeks."

"Your chances are good, then."

She was aware with every passing day that Eli's time in Cannon Beach was drawing to a close. The prospect of him leaving filled her with a curious mix of dread and relief. She dreaded knowing he would be gone and she would be left to worry about him possibly being in harm's way. But she couldn't deny there would be a certain relief that she wouldn't have to pretend any more that she wasn't crazy in love with the man.

She had done her best to keep things polite and professional between them. She helped him in exams, she did triage assessment, she answered phone calls and forwarded prescriptions to him. And every time she was with him, she was aware of her feelings growing stronger by the moment.

He was an excellent doctor, compassionate and kind, as well as a devoted, loving son. She was head over heels and already aching at the idea that he wouldn't be in her life every day.

She pushed away the worry to focus on their patient. "Do you want Eli to wait a few minutes before doing your checkup, until Will can get here?"

"Better not. He wasn't sure if he would make it back to town in time. He's on a job up in Seaside, doing a bathroom remodel for a lady."

Her husband was a master carpenter who had done some amazing work at Brambleberry House and other places around town.

"I'll let Eli know you're ready, then."

When she opened the door, she found him pulling the chart out of the polished wood holder beside the door, which, she remembered now, Will Garrett had built right around the time she started working for Wendell Sanderson.

"Julia is ready when you are."

"Thanks." He gave her the same kind of careful smile they had both become experts at over the last few weeks. She had a feeling he felt as awkward and uncertain around her as she did around him.

He entered the exam room and she followed behind as he shook Julia's hand with a warm, comforting smile that made Melissa's ovaries tingle. Darn them.

"How are you feeling? Things are probably getting tight in there."

"Any tighter and I'm afraid I'm going to bust through the seams."

"Let's just take a look at things."

He listened to the baby's heartbeat first, then did a quick exam with brisk professionalism.

"Looks like you're only dilated to a one, so I think it's safe to say we still have a few weeks to go."

Melissa adjusted the sheet over her and then helped her sit up.

"The twins were a week early," Julia said, "but Tess was born the day before her due date and her brother was born the day after his."

Eli said. "You're the expert after five of these. I'm sure you can tell me a thousand ways every pregnancy is different, but it's good to know the pattern."

"No offense, Dr. Sanderson, but I was telling Melissa I would love it if your dad was back in action by the time I deliver. You've been great, but he delivered Will as well as my younger two kids and he's become kind of part of the family."

"None taken," Eli assured her. "I wish I had an answer for you. He's coming in for a few hours a day next week, though his surgeon and physical therapist want him to take it easy. Maybe he'll be back just in time to deliver your little girl."

"I hope so. He's home, right?"

"Yes. He came home a few weeks ago."

The day after they had flown kites and walked with

Max along the beach, in fact, after rebounding quickly from the temporary setback of his tumble. Melissa had been by to see him twice on her lunch hour and once with Skye after school. All three times she had managed to miss Eli.

"How is he doing?" Julia asked.

"Bored out of his mind," Eli said with a smile. "My dad is the kind of guy who likes to be on the go. I knew the toughest part of his recovery would be the monotony of being sidelined. But his knees are already stronger than they've been in years, so the surgery was a good thing, for him and for his patients here in Cannon Beach."

He wrapped up the appointment a few moments later with another handshake and a warm smile.

After he left, Julia shook her head at Melissa. "I love Dr. Sanderson Sr., I'm not going to lie, but that son of his. Yum. Honestly, even though I'm extremely pregnant and extremely happily married, I don't know how you keep from constantly melting into a pile of hormones with that slow smile of his."

Melissa couldn't tell her friend she did exactly that. "He's my boss," she reminded Julia. "I have to keep my hormones—and everything else—to myself where he's concerned."

"Good luck with that," Julia said with a laugh.

Melissa forced a smile. She needed far more than luck where Eli was concerned.

Eli wasn't sure what had happened, but somehow over the last few weeks, since the Sunday afternoon when he had gone with her and Skye to fly the girl's kite, Melissa had withdrawn from him, treating him with a polite reserve that was far different from the friendship that had been growing between them.

She wasn't rude. In fact, she was respectful and professional, but as distant as if he were just some scrub who had stepped in to help out at his dad's practice in Wendell's absence.

He was glad, he told himself. He had crossed too many lines he shouldn't have with her.

Still, he missed her easy smiles and her funny sense of humor and the warmth that seemed to envelop him around her.

"You all know my dad wants to come in next week," he said to her, Carmen and Tiffany as the three women prepared to leave for the day on Friday.

"I hope he doesn't overdo," Carmen said with her characteristic frown. "My sister had knee replacement surgery and had to have the whole thing done all over again six months later."

"We'll all have to make sure he takes it easy. It's going to have to be a team effort. But the truth is, he's going crazy at home after three weeks away and thinks his patients need him. He won't be up for much patient care, but he should be fine handling consultations or refilling prescriptions, if he could do that from his desk. We'll all have to watch out for him."

"We can make sure he behaves," Tiffany said. "I'm glad he's coming in. I was hoping he'd be back before I leave."

The CNA had put in her notice the week before and had been talking nonstop about her plans to move to Los Angeles, where they already had a manager and a few gigs lined up.

"It will be good to have him back," Melissa said. "I've missed him."

"I'll add a few appointments into his schedule," Carmen said. "Nothing too drastic. Just consultations, like you said."

"He wants to jump back into things with both of his artificial knees, but I worry about him overdoing."

"Sounds good, especially since you're going to be leaving us soon," Carmen said.

Against his will, he glanced at Melissa. Had she stiffened at that?

"Yes. I'll be here until the end of next week, and then I have to report to duty again. I've already talked to the medical temp agency in Portland about sending a replacement until my dad is back up to speed."

"We'll miss you," Carmen said gruffly.

"Especially the female patients," Tiffany said with a teasing grin.

Eli could feel his face flush and he forced himself not to look at Melissa, who hadn't said a word.

"If that's everything, can I go?" Tiffany asked. "We're playing down in Manzanita tonight, at least until the power goes out from the big storm on the way."

"They're not canceling your gig?" Melissa finally asked.

Tiffany shook her head. "Not that I've heard. The storm's not supposed to be here until nine or so. We'll play until we can't play anymore."

"That's the spirit," Carmen said.

"Could be nobody else will show up, then we can all go home. So can I take off?"

"Yes. That's all," Eli said. "I just wanted to talk for

a moment about the plan next week for my dad's return. Good luck with your show."

She flashed him a grin as she grabbed her backpack and hurried out the door, humming some of the lyrics he recognized from the night he and Melissa had gone to see her.

"I'm off, too," Carmen said. "I have to head to the grocery store. Every time the wind blows around here, the grocery stores run out of milk."

She hurried off after Tiffany. For the first time in longer than he could remember, he and Melissa were alone.

She jumped up from her desk and grabbed her sweater and her purse. "I need to go, too," Melissa said.

No, he wasn't imagining things. She was doing her utmost to avoid his company. He knew it was for the best so they didn't cross any more lines, but he missed her with a fierce ache.

"Big weekend plans?"

She made a face. "Cody's coming to pick Skye up again tonight. He wants to have her the whole weekend until Sunday this time, so I need to help her pack. He wants to get out of town before the storm hits. I tried to convince him it wasn't a good weekend for his visitation, but he insisted since he's going to be busy next weekend. Also, his sister is in town and she hasn't seen Skye in about a year."

"Go take care of what you need to at home. Don't worry about things here. I'll lock up."

"Thank you."

She gave him a stiff nod, gathered her purse from under her desk and hurried for the door.

That was the most personal conversation they had

shared in days. He felt an ache, missing the warm, funny woman he had come to know since returning to Cannon Beach.

It was better this way, that she had put up these walls between them, but he felt an ache.

How had she reacted when he'd said he would only be there another week? He hadn't been able to read her. Had she been relieved? Or would she miss him as deeply as he knew he would miss her?

He rubbed at that ache in his chest. Somehow Melissa had worked her way inside his own careful walls. She was there, lodged against his heart, and he didn't know how he was going to push her out again.

Chapter 10

The storm hit about four hours after Cody left for Portland with Skye in his impractical sports car.

Melissa sat in the window seat in the sunroom she loved, watching the waves grow higher as the sky darkened with rolling clouds.

Storms always made her blood hum. One good thing about formerly being married to a professional surfer—they had always lived next to an ocean. Whether it was Mexico or Hawaii or Australia, no matter what coastal area she and Cody and Skye had been living, she had always loved watching storms hit land, as long as she could observe the drama from somewhere safe.

She wasn't as crazy about being in the middle of them. She had been, a few times. Once she had been working at a hospital in Maui in the midst of a Category 3 hurricane and had worked for thirty-six hours straight when her coworkers couldn't make it to the hospital because of the storm.

Skye loved storms. She would have loved this one. Her daughter would have found it a great adventure to cuddle together and tell stories by candlelight. She missed her with a deep ache, which she knew was perfectly ridiculous. Somehow Melissa had to get used to these weekends without her child. She wanted her daughter to have a relationship with her father, and Skye and Cody couldn't truly have that through only occasional phone calls and video chats.

Melissa had lost her father when she was fourteen and still felt the emptiness of that. She didn't want Skye to grow up being resentful or angry that Cody wasn't in her life. Somehow she had to come to terms with being without her and fill the void with friends and hobbies.

The power went out two hours later, as she expected. Through the window, she could see only darkness, which told her Brambleberry House wasn't the only structure hit. It appeared power was out up and down the coast.

Fortunately, her e-reader was fully charged and would last for hours, and she had already gathered all the emergency supplies she might need during a storm.

She wasn't looking forward to a long night alone in the dark, but she tried to make her situation as comfortable as possible, lighting candles she had gathered earlier and carrying pillows and blankets to the window seat.

If the winds increased in intensity, she would probably feel safer away from the windows and the possibility of shattering glass from flying tree limbs or other debris, but for now she didn't feel in harm's way.

She was just settling in with her book when she heard a knock at the door.

"It's Rosa," she heard from outside. "And Fiona."

Melissa hurried to the door and found her friend standing in the entry holding two lit candles, her Irish setter at her side.

"This is some kind of storm, no?"

"It's crazy out there."

"Did I see our Skye go off with her father earlier tonight? Did they make it all right?"

She nodded, warmed by Rosa's use of the possessive pronoun when it came to her daughter. She loved having friends who cared. This was the reason she had come back to Cannon Beach, to forge this kind of powerful connection.

"He texted me that they were safely back in Portland and it wasn't even raining there."

"That's a relief." Rosa looked inside the apartment, where Melissa had lit a couple of emergency candles to push away the darkness. "I came down to check on you and make sure you had some kind of flashlight or candle, but it looks like you are all set."

This wasn't her first spring storm along the coast. Sometimes the big ones could wipe out power in the region for days.

"I should be fine. Thank you for worrying about me. Have you checked on Sonia?"

Rosa nodded, looking worried. "I know she doesn't like storms much."

Though it was nothing the other woman had told her, Melissa had the same impression during the most recent storm. Sonia became even more brusque than normal, her words clipped, and Melissa thought she glimpsed fear layering beneath it.

"I checked on her first. She assured me she is fine, that she has plenty of LED candles. She had four or five going, with extra batteries if necessary, so they can go all night, if it comes to that."

"I hope it doesn't." Again, she wondered about Sonia and the mysterious past that left her afraid of the dark.

"Since Skye is not here, do you want me to leave Fiona with you for the company? I asked Sonia and she said she would be fine."

Poor Rosa, having to watch over everyone in Brambleberry House. It wasn't her job, but somehow they all had become her responsibility anyway.

She patted Fiona, wishing she could say yes. She never would have guessed she would find so much solace in canine companionship. She and Skye really needed to get serious about going to the shelter and picking out a rescue.

"That's so sweet of you, but I think I'm okay. Much better than last time Skye was with her dad."

Rosa gave her a sympathetic look. "I'm sorry. Being a mother is hard business, no? It never seems to become easier."

That seemed an odd statement, filled with more knowledge than she might have expected from a woman who didn't have any children, at least as far as Melissa knew. Maybe it was just Rosa's unique word choices, where English was her second language.

She couldn't deny the truth in what her friend said, though. "It's so hard," she agreed.

"If you want some chocolate and the sympathy, you

know where to find me. I can maybe find a bottle of wine somewhere, also. We don't need light for that."

She managed a smile, tempted for a moment by the picture Rosa painted. Wine and chocolate and sympathy might just be the perfect prescription during a storm.

On the other hand, she wouldn't be good company for anyone.

This time, she knew her dark mood was only partially about the pang she felt at being separated from her child. The rest was about Eli and this wild morass of emotions she didn't know what to do about.

He would be there another week, he had said that afternoon. She had nearly gasped aloud at his words as the shock of them had ripped through her like a sharp blade. She was still trying to process the idea that she only had one more week with him.

"Thanks," she managed, "but I think I'll watch the storm for little longer, then go to bed."

"No problem. If you change your mind, you know where to find me."

She smiled. "Thanks. Good night."

After Rosa left, she sat in the window seat for a while longer, feeling more alone than she had in a long, long time.

She awoke to absolute darkness and the strange, disorienting awareness that she didn't know where she was.

She blinked, aware of cold and wind and the faint hint of roses hanging on the air.

Was that what had awakened her? She blinked again as the sunroom of her apartment at Brambleberry

House slowly came into focus. She was still curled up on the window seat, a blanket casually tossed over her. Her back ached from the odd position and her foot tingled, asleep.

She must have drifted off while watching the storm. She wasn't sure how she could have slept in the midst of the weather's intensity. Wind whined outside, fiercely hurling raindrops at the window.

Her phone suddenly rang and she had the feeling it wasn't the first time. It wasn't an alarm, but someone calling.

Skye!

Still trying to push away the tangled remnants of sleep, she scrambled for her phone and found it glowing under the throw blanket she must have tugged over her in the night.

"Hello?" She hardly recognized her own raspy voice.

"Melissa? Is that you?"

"I… Yes."

Not Skye, and not Cody. Some of her anxiety eased and she pulled the blanket tighter around her shoulders against the chill of the night and the storm.

"It's Julia Garrett. I'm so sorry to bother you, but I tried to call the clinic's emergency number and the phone lines must be down. I didn't have Eli's cell number and thought you might."

Her friend's words seemed to push away the last vestiges of sleep, and Melissa came fully awake. A hundred grim scenarios flashed through her head. It must be something serious for Julia to reach out at 1:00 a.m. in the middle of a storm.

"Are you all right? Is it one of the kids?"

"In a manner of speaking." Was that amusement she heard in Julia's voice? It hardly seemed appropriate, given the circumstances.

"I'm in labor."

Shock washed over her. "In labor. Now? Are you sure? Your cervix was only dilated to a one, eight hours ago when you left the office!"

"I've done this enough times, I'm pretty positive. I've had contractions all evening. I thought they were only Braxton Hicks, but in the past hour they've become much more regular."

"How far apart?"

"I'm down to about three minutes now."

Some of her wild panic subsided and she relaxed a little. "Okay. That's good. There's still time to make it to the hospital in Seaside."

"We thought so, too, but there's a problem. That's why I'm calling you. We were packing up the car and Will heard on the radio that the road is closed. The storm has knocked several big trees and power lines down between here and there."

Her voice cracked on the last word, and she started to breath heavily and regularly into the phone, obviously in the middle of a contraction. Melissa was already looking for her shoes by the door.

"That one was less than three minutes."

A new voice spoke into the phone. Julia must have handed the phone to her husband. Will was usually one of the most calm, measured people Melissa knew, but now he spoke briskly, his voice edged with the beginnings of panic. "I'm not sure what to do. Should I call for medevac?"

She wasn't at all prepared to make this sort of decision for the couple. "Let me call Eli and Wendell and see what they suggest. You told me you had a completely natural childbirth with your two youngest, with no complications. Eli may want to just have you meet us at the office."

"The only problem," Will said, "is that one of the downed power lines I heard about is apparently blocking the road between our place and Doc Sanderson's office. The only way I could figure out to get there is to walk, which I don't feel good about in this wind and storm, or to head down the beach on the four-wheeler."

"We're not doing either of those things," she heard Julia declare.

"Stay put," she said, shoving on her raincoat and her boots. "I'm on my way. I'll be there in five minutes. I'll get in touch with Eli and see if we can come up with a plan. If I can't get through, I'll stop and bang on his windows until he wakes up. Meanwhile, breathe, both of you. And don't let her have that baby yet."

"I'll do my best, but you know Jules. She can be pretty stubborn," Will said.

"I heard that," Melissa heard Julia say in the background.

Despite her own efforts to grab a flashlight and rush out the door, Melissa had to fight a smile. Will and Julia were a darling couple, overflowing with love for each other and their children. She adored both of them.

"Hang tight. I'll be there in a few minutes."

"Be careful," Will said. "It's still pretty nasty out there. I don't like the idea of you going out in it, either."

"I won't let a little rain stop me," she assured him. "See you soon."

She hung up the phone as a particularly strong gust of wind rattled the windows of the old house.

She wasn't eager to go out into the teeth of the storm, but she also wasn't about to let her friend down. Not when Julia needed her.

He was having a delicious dream.

He and Melissa were walking through one of the dense ancient forests around Cannon Beach, her hand tucked in his. She carried a blanket in rich jewel tones and wore a sundress the same green as her eyes. Dappled light shot through the trees, catching in her hair.

She pulled her hand from his and raced ahead a little, turning around to look at him with that laughing, teasing smile that always stole his breath. He caught up with her and she wrapped her arms around his waist, pulling him close, where he was safe and warm and loved.

It was magic here, with a peace he hadn't known in months. He wanted to stay forever.

His phone jerked him awake and for an instant he was back in his residency, surviving on energy bars and rare, haphazard chunks of sleep.

He fumbled for it. "Hello?

"Eli. It's Melissa."

The discord of hearing the woman who had just been holding him in his dreams jarred him. Unlike the relaxed, warm woman he'd been dreaming about, her voice was strained and she pitched her voice above howling wind.

That same storm howled outside his father's house. He had been sitting in his dad's old recliner awake most of the night but must have eventually drifted off. He had a feeling he hadn't been sleeping long.

Eli sat up, his surroundings coming sharply back into focus. Melissa was calling and she needed him.

"What is it? What's wrong? Are you hurt?"

"I'm not hurt. I'm fine. But Julia Garrett is in labor and apparently the storm has blocked the road between here and Seaside, as well as between her house and the clinic."

"She was barely dilated this afternoon!"

"Tell that to her baby. Apparently it's on its own schedule. Now she's having contractions that are less than three minutes apart. I'm heading to their place now."

"In this storm?" Fear for her washed over him like a twenty-foot-high swell. Anything could happen to her. She could get hit by flying debris, stumble into a downed power line, fall and injure herself in the deep, powerless darkness.

He couldn't lose her!

"I'm fine. She needs help. Can you meet me there?"

He was already throwing on his shoes. "I only need five minutes. Be careful!"

"I know. Same to you."

She hung up before he could argue with her and tell her to go back inside Brambleberry House, where she would be safe.

"What's happening?"

In the light of a lantern, Wendell stood in the doorway, holding on to the walker he detested but still needed for stability. His father's hair was messy, and in his flannel pajamas he looked his age.

"I'm sorry I woke you. Julia Garrett's in labor, and

apparently power lines are down between here and the hospital in Seaside."

"You didn't wake me. I can never sleep through storms like this. I've been in here fretting, wondering how long it would be before someone called, needing help. I didn't expect it to be Julia. She's three weeks from her due date."

He wasn't surprised that his father knew exactly when Julia was due, despite the fact that Wendell had been dealing with his own health issues and subsequent recovery for weeks.

"It was actually Melissa. Julia called her first and she was letting me know what was going on. Melissa is on her way over there and I'm going to meet her."

"She shouldn't be out in the storm, but you and I both know we can't stop her, especially since Julia is a friend of hers."

"We just saw Julia in the office yesterday. She was barely dilated, but of course babies have their own opinions about when they're going to make an appearance."

"Oh, yes. They love showing up when it's least convenient for anyone. You can take my emergency kit if you need it. I already pulled it out earlier in the evening and set it by the door. It should have everything you need."

He had his own emergency kit he kept stocked with supplies in a backpack, but he was touched his father had survived enough storms around Cannon Beach to make sure Eli, as his designated representative, was ready for anything.

"Thanks. I'll keep you posted."

"Take care of Julia. I know you will. You're an amazing doctor."

He wasn't as convinced, but his father's vote of confidence warmed him through. "I'll try."

"And take care of Melissa, too. She shouldn't be out in this storm."

"Exactly what I told her," he said. He didn't have time to tell his father how very much he yearned to take care of Melissa forever, to walk through all the storms of life together.

He grabbed his father's case and his own backpack, and headed out into the wind and lashing rain.

Melissa somehow beat him to the Garretts' house, but he suspected she hadn't been there long. Her hair was drenched, despite the raincoat she was taking off, and she looked cold.

He wanted to kiss the raindrops off her cheeks and hold her close to warm her up but knew both of them needed to focus on the crisis at hand.

"Thank you both for coming out in this crazy weather," Will Garrett said as he let Eli inside. "I'm sorry we had to call you in the middle of the night, but when we heard the roads were closed, we weren't sure what else to do."

"You did the right thing," Eli assured him.

"Trust Julia to make things more exciting," he said ruefully. "She's never content with the ordinary."

"You'll have a great story to tell this little one," Melissa said, her voice calm. She had so many strengths, but that was one he appreciated most: the calm that seemed to radiate from her.

"How do you have lights?" she asked.

"We have a whole-house generator. I put it in a few

years ago. Believe me, I've never been so grateful for anything in my life," Will said gruffly.

When Eli pushed the door open, Melissa close behind him, they found Julia Garrett, dressed in a pale blue nightgown, sitting on the edge of the bed. A pretty teenage girl who had to be one of her twins sat next to her.

"Hey, Julia. Hi, Maddie." Melissa greeted both of them with more of that calm.

Julia managed a smile in response though her features were taut and strained. "This isn't quite the way I planned this."

"What is it with babies, deciding to make their appearances in the middle of the night in the worst possible weather?"

"Inconsiderate little stinks, aren't they?"

She smiled at them and then caught her breath, pressing both hands over her abdomen.

"That one was barely a minute since the last one," Maddie said, eyes huge and frightened in her pretty face.

"We're okay," Julia said, reaching out a hand to give her daughter's arm a reassuring squeeze. "The cavalry is here now. You and Will won't have to deliver your baby sister."

"Whew," the girl said, vast relief on her face.

Eli considered his options quickly. "How do you feel about a home birth? I don't think we have time to call the air ambulance and have them here in time for the delivery, and I'm not sure they can fly in this wind anyway. We can have them on standby in case there any complications."

"Women have been giving birth at home forever,"

Julia said. "As long as she's safe, I don't care how she gets here."

He had plenty of colleagues who would have disagreed and would have insisted a hospital was the only safe place for a woman to give birth, but Eli's experience in war zones and refugee camps had told him that women could be incredibly resourceful. Under the circumstances, this was the safest possible place for Julia to have her baby, not in a helicopter or an ambulance trying to make its way through the storm.

Even if they had called for a chopper, it turned out that Julia's labor progressed so quickly it was clear it wouldn't have arrived in time. He and Melissa barely had time to arrange her on the bed, put a nervous Will at ease and send Maddie for clean towels and to boil water to sterilize any tools he needed to use.

Ten minutes later, he watched a head emerge.

Sweat poured down Julia's face and she gripped her husband's hand tightly. "I have to push."

"That's good," Eli said. "I need you to do just that. Now is the perfect time to push. You've got this."

A moment later, he delivered a chunky, red-faced baby, who took a shuddering breath, then began to wail.

"Love that sound," Melissa said, wiping off the baby's face with an awestruck expression. "Welcome to the world, little Garrett girl."

"Miriam Renee," Will said, his voice raw with emotions. "We want to call her Miri."

Eli caught his breath. It was a coincidence, he knew, but hearing the name out of the blue like that still made him feel as if he'd been run over by a tank.

For a moment he was frozen, picturing a sweet girl, bloodied and torn, her smile cut down forever by hatred and violence. A strangled cry choked him and he couldn't breathe or think. He had to get out of here before the memories consumed him and he fell apart. In a panic, his muscles tensed and he was about to rise, to escape, when he felt the gentle pressure of fingers on his shoulder.

Melissa.

His gaze met hers, and he saw a knowledge and compassion there that made him swallow back the emotions. She knew. She knew and somehow she steadied him. He had no idea how she managed it. He only knew that the warm touch of her hand on him seemed to clear away the panic and the grief and shock until he felt much more in control.

He drew in a shuddering breath and cleared his throat. "Miri is a beautiful name for a beautiful little girl."

"She's gorgeous," Will said gruffly. "Like her mother."

He kissed Julia's sweat-dampened forehead, running a tender hand down her hair. After Eli helped Will cut the cord with the sterilized scissors he had in his kit, Melissa took the baby and placed the naked, wriggling girl on Julia's chest. She instinctively rooted around, and Julia laughed a little before helping her latch on. Will stood next to them, his somewhat harsh features relaxed into an expression of love and amazement and a vast joy.

"Good job, Mama," Eli said.

His voice sounded ragged but he didn't care. He had delivered babies before, into the hundreds, but he couldn't remember when a birth had impacted him so deeply.

He was emotional about Miri but about so much more. He wanted this, what Will and Julia had created here. A family.

He had seen so much ugliness over the last five years of near-constant deployments. Pain and bloodshed and violence. Families torn apart, villages decimated, lives shattered.

All of it stemmed from hatred, from power struggles and greed and ideological differences.

He was so tired of it.

Maybe it was time he focused instead on love.

He had been doing important work overseas, helping people in terrible situations who had few options and little hope. He couldn't deny that what he had been doing *mattered*.

Justine had been doing important work, and some part of him would always feel a responsibility to try harder and be better because of her example and the tragic way she had died.

But this was important, too, these small but significant moments. Helping to bring new life into the world. Caring for neighbors and friends. Continuing his father's legacy in this community, where Wendell was so loved.

"Are you all right?" Melissa asked a short time later, after the baby was bundled and the ambulance had been called. Both mom and baby were fine, but as soon as the road was cleared, Eli wanted them to be checked out at the hospital, where little Miri could have a full assessment and Julia could receive care while she recovered.

He wanted to tell her some of the many thoughts

racing through his head, but now didn't seem the proper time.

"I'm fine. It's always amazing, seeing new life come into the world and remembering what a miracle it is, every time. I heard it said once that a baby is God's opinion that the world should go on. I think I needed that reminder."

Her features softened and she touched his arm again. The tenderness of the gesture made those emotions well up.

He was so deeply in love with her. How had he ever been crazy enough to think he could go on without her?

"I didn't know about the name. They were still trying to decide, the last I talked to Julia about it. If I had known, I would have warned you."

"It's a lovely name," he said. "I hope she's as sweet as the other little girl I once knew who carried it."

Before she could answer, Eli's phone rang. When he saw his father on the caller ID, he quickly answered it.

"Hey, son," Wendell said. "How are things going there? How's Julia?"

"Good. Both the mama and baby girl are doing fine."

"Oh, that's wonderful to hear. I knew you could do it."

His father's confidence in him warmed him. "Right now we're waiting for the road to open so we can get them to the hospital in Seaside. The crews are saying about another half hour."

"Great news. Listen, I just got a call from Elisa Darby. A branch came through her teenage boy's bedroom window about a half hour ago."

"Oh, no!"

"He's fine, just shaken up, but might need a couple of stitches. It's not a big deal, not big enough to try getting to the ER in Seaside in this storm, but she called to see if someone could come by, check things out and maybe stitch him up. You up for another house call?"

He assessed the situation with the Garretts. Will and Julia had things under control. Right now, their teenage daughter was holding the bundled baby and her siblings were waiting in line for their turn.

"I can do that. Text me the address. I'll wrap up with Julia and head there within the next fifteen or twenty minutes."

"If other people call, want me to start making a list? I can be your dispatcher."

"Sure."

He hung up from his father to find Julia watching carefully. "What's happened?"

"I've got a teenage boy with an injury from broken glass after a branch came through a window."

"I was worried about that very thing happening to me earlier. I fell asleep in the window seat while I was watching the storm and woke up thinking it probably wasn't a good idea."

"It wasn't. You should probably not do that again." He wanted to be here to hold her during the next storm. The two of them could keep each other warm and watch the clouds roll over the ocean together.

"Where did it happen?" she asked.

"The house of Elisa Darby. Do you know her?"

"Yes. She doesn't live far from here.

"Apparently, her son might need a few stitches."

"You'll need help."

To give someone stitches? Probably not. He'd been

doing that since his first day of med school, but he couldn't deny the two of them made a good team. She seemed to know exactly what supplies he needed without being asked, and he definitely needed her amazing skill at calming any situation.

"I don't want to take you away if you think you're still needed here."

Will glanced over, obviously listening to the conversation. "We're fine. The ambulance should be here soon. You've done great work and I can't thank you enough for our little Miri here, but it sounds like somebody else needs you now."

"If you're sure."

Melissa seemed reluctant to leave, but she gathered up their supplies, gave Julia a kiss on the cheek and hugged Will. Then she kissed the baby's forehead before following Eli out into the pearly light of predawn.

The wind had finally slowed, though the rain continued. The sun was still an hour or so from coming up above the mountains to the east, but there was enough light for them to see some of the damage left behind by the storm.

On this street alone, nearly every house had at least one tree branch down, and he could see a metal shed collapsed at the Garretts' neighbors. This was only one small sample of what the storm could do. He had a feeling the rest of the region had been hit just as hard.

He met Melissa's gaze. "I have a feeling it's going to be a busy day."

Chapter 11

Eli's words turned out to be prophetic. By the time they finished at the Darbys' house, Wendell had called them to report three more people had phoned him looking for emergency medical care. They all had mild cuts and bruises, except for one man who sustained minor burns trying to start a malfunctioning generator. Eli patched him up as best he could but ordered him to the hospital as soon as he could make it there.

They made house calls at first, but as they started to receive reports that the roads were slowly being cleared throughout the morning, he and Melissa were finally able to retreat to the clinic, sending out word to the real dispatchers and the paramedics that they would stay open to take some of the more mild emergencies where a trip to the hospital wasn't necessarily warranted.

She loved seeing Eli in action during a crisis. Over the last three weeks during routine office visits, she had observed that he was truly a wonderful doctor, one who spent as much time as each patient needed, dispensing advice and compassion.

Observing him during an emergency situation was something completely different. He was focused, concise, with an uncanny ability to take care of whatever situation walked through the door with skill and care.

No wonder he was so passionate about his military career. Eli was a man who truly thrived under pressure.

She couldn't expect someone with a gift like that to be content as a family physician in a small practice.

The realization depressed her, though she was not sure why. Maybe she had been holding out some slim hope that Eli might be able to find a place to belong here on the beautiful Oregon Coast where he had been raised, exactly as *she* had over the last seven months.

Around noon, she closed the outside doors after their last patient, a tearful eight-year-old girl who had stepped on a nail while helping her family clean up debris. When the family drove away, no cars were left in the parking lot. She locked the doors and turned the Open sign to Closed.

At last report, the dispatchers assured them all the roads were clear now along the coast and people in need could make it to the emergency room or the urgent-care clinics in Seaside or Astoria, if necessary.

"Good work," Eli said when she walked back. "You've been amazing today. An army medic trained in battlefield emergency care couldn't have done better."

His admiring words and expression left her flustered and not sure how to respond. "You were the one doing all the care. I've only been providing support."

"That's completely not true and you know it. Every time I needed something, you were right there with it before I had to ask, and you are amazing at calming down every panicked mother or crying child."

"We make a good team." For another week, anyway. The thought made her chest ache.

"Do you have any idea of how necessary you are to my father's practice? Why do you think I've tried so hard to..." He bit off his words, leaving her intensely curious about what he intended to say.

"Why you've tried so hard to what?" She had to ask.

His smile appeared forced. "Uh, make sure you know exactly how much you're appreciated."

She had a feeling that wasn't what he'd almost said at all, but he didn't appear inclined to add anything more.

"I was going to say the same to you," she said. "It's not every day you deliver a baby, sew thirty-six stitches in five different patients and give eight tetanus shots, all before noon."

He smiled. "All in all, a good morning. I'm glad we could help."

"If you hadn't been here, I'm not sure what people in Cannon Beach would have done."

"My dad is not the only doctor in town. Someone else would have stepped up."

Wendell might not be the only doctor, but he was one of the most beloved.

Eli was well on his way to matching his father's popularity. Everyone in town loved Eli, after he had been here only three weeks to fill in for his father.

Especially her.

She pushed the thought aside. Not now. She couldn't think about her impending heartache. He was leaving in a week, and somehow she was going to have to figure out how to go on without that slow, gorgeous smile in her life.

She had to say at least a little of what was on her mind. It seemed vitally important that she let him know what she had been thinking all morning as she watched him work.

"You're an amazing doctor, Eli. You make a great family physician in the proud tradition of your father, but today, working together in an emergency situation with you, showed me you're doing exactly what you need to be doing for the army. You obviously thrive in stressful situations. You care passionately about what you're doing and you're good at it—exactly the sort of person who can make a much-needed difference in the world."

He looked touched, his eyes warm, and he opened his mouth to answer, but his cell phone rang before he could say anything. He gave the phone a frustrated look that shifted to one of concern when he saw the caller ID.

"I need to get that. Looks like it's the Seaside hospital, probably the attending physician at the women's center, calling about Julia and Miri."

"While you talk to the Attending, I'll go straighten up the exam rooms we used today so they're ready for Monday."

She was just finishing up when Eli appeared in the doorway, again looking dark and lean and so gorgeous it made her catch her breath.

"Mom and baby are doing well," he reported. "I figured you'd want to know."

"Yes. I was going to call her later. I appreciate the update."

"Everyone is healthy. The attending physician suggests keeping them overnight, but it sounds like Julia is eager to be home with their other children. I'll go check things out, and if all appears okay she might be released by tonight."

"She'll be happy about that."

He leaned against the door frame and scratched his cheek. "Better yet, I'll pick up my dad and take him with me to do the honors. He'll want to see the baby and check on Julia himself."

Her heart melted at his thoughtfulness, both on his father's behalf and on Julia's, and she fell in love with him all over again.

"You are a good man, Eli Sanderson."

He made a face. "Why? Because I'm going to take my dad with me to the hospital to check on a patient?"

"Because you know how important it is for him to make sure she's all right and also how much it will set Julia's mind at ease to have him there."

"It's not a big deal."

"It is to me, just as it will be for Julia and your dad."

She smiled at him, and he gazed at her for a long moment, then growled something she couldn't hear and lowered his mouth to hers.

The fierce kiss came out of the blue and was the last thing she expected him to do, yet somehow was exactly what she needed.

His mouth was hard and intense on hers, searching and demanding at the same time. She answered him kiss for kiss, taste for taste. Heat raced through her and she wrapped her arms around him, but the hunger contained something else, something deeper.

This was goodbye.

He was leaving in a week, and this likely would be the last chance she would have to hold him like this before he left. She tightened her arms, trying to burn the taste and the feel and the smell of him into her mind. When he was gone, back doing the work he loved, and she was alone here in Cannon Beach, at least she would have these slices of memories to comfort her.

She tried to pour everything in her heart into the kiss. All her love and admiration and sadness, wrapped together and delivered on a breathless sigh. She had no idea how long they stayed locked together there in the doorway. She only knew the emotions in the kiss would leave her forever changed.

She would have stayed forever, but she was aware, always aware, that someone else needed him, too.

After long, heady moments, she finally pulled her mouth away and stepped back, her breathing ragged and her face flaming. Could he sense in her kiss all the love she couldn't say?

She looked away, hoping desperately that she hadn't revealed entirely too much by that kiss.

"Melissa."

His voice sounded raw, breathless. She could feel his searching gaze on her and forced herself to offer back a bland smile. "You should probably go check out Julia and Miri. The Garretts will be waiting for you."

"I… Yes."

She didn't want him to offer any explanations or apologies or, worse, ask any questions. Any conversation between them and she was afraid she would burst into tears she couldn't explain.

"I'll see you later. Drive carefully."

With that, she turned around and hurried out of the room, wishing with all her heart that things could be different between them.

Though she was tired down to her bones, Melissa spent the afternoon working with Sonia to clean up the battered gardens at Brambleberry House. Rosa was busy doing the same at the gift store in town, which had suffered some water damage from a roof leak.

The gardens looked sad, with broken limbs, crushed flowers, scattered leaves.

She felt a little like the landscaping around the house—damaged, scarred. She had to hope she could be like a few of the shrubs around the house, which had been bent by the storm but were already beginning to straighten again.

"I don't think we can save this one." Sonia sat before one of the brambleberry bushes, her lovely, perfect features creased with a grief that seemed out of proportion to a little storm damage.

"Are you sure we can't salvage some of the canes?"

"They won't be the same. I'm not sure they'll be able to produce much fruit at all."

She seemed devastated by the loss. Maybe she had an extreme fondness for that particular brambleberry bush, or maybe her grief was for something else entirely.

Melissa tried to choose her words carefully. "You know, my dad used to say that not everything that's broken is worthless. It might not ever be what it was, but that doesn't mean it can't be something else. Maybe something even better."

She wasn't sure if she had helped or made things worse. Sonia gave her a long look, nodded slowly, then went back to work.

"That's all we can do tonight," Sonia said sometime later. "It's going to be dark soon. You look very tired. You need to rest."

Her exhaustion had deepened, and she thought she might fall asleep right here in the cool, storm-battered garden.

"I'll just stay with Fiona for a moment, then we'll come inside."

Sonia gave her a long look and she could see the concern on her friend's features. She didn't pry, though. One of the best things about Sonia was her ability to let other people keep their own secrets, too. After a moment, the other woman twisted her mouth into what other people might consider a smile and headed into the house.

Melissa sat for a few moments more, heart aching. She needed to go inside but couldn't seem to find the energy to do it.

She wanted her daughter here. A Skye hug always went a long way toward healing her soul from life's inevitable disappointments. Her daughter would be home the next day. They would have plenty of time for hugs then.

She was just about to head into the house when Fiona suddenly turned around and raced for the edge of the garden.

What on earth?

"Fiona," she called. "Come on, girl. Home."

The dog ignored her, headed with single-minded purpose in the other direction. There was probably some poor mole who had been foolish enough to set up shop in the gardens the Irish setter considered her own.

Fiona didn't stop when she reached the beach access gate. To Melissa's astonishment, she nudged open the latch and raced through, leaving her little choice but to chase after the dog.

She was too tired for this, but Fiona didn't seem to care about that.

Exasperated, Melissa followed the dog onto the beach. "Come on, Fi. Here girl," she called, then her voice faltered.

Fiona wasn't alone. She stood on the sand not far from the house, nose to nose with another dog. A little black schnauzer, whose leash was currently held by the one man she didn't feel strong enough to face again right now.

Her heart seemed to stutter, and she wanted to slip back through the gate and hurry into the house.

After that emotional kiss earlier when she had bared everything in her heart, she didn't want to face him right now...or ever again, if she could arrange it.

But he was here and she had no choice. She forced herself to move toward him. "Sorry. She got out somehow. Come on, Fiona. Inside."

The dog showed no sign of obeying her, and Melissa sighed, taking another step toward him and the two dogs.

"Julia and Will send their love and gratitude," he said when she was an arm's length away.

Despite her discomfort, she couldn't help a smile

at that. "How is Julia? I wanted to go visit but thought I would give her a day or two to be settled at home."

"She's good. Glowing."

That made her smile again. "And baby Miri?"

"Beautiful. I held her for a good fifteen minutes while the infant unit nurses were giving me their report and she slept the whole time. She obviously likes me."

Why wouldn't she? The man was irresistible. Her heart ached when she pictured him in a hospital nursery, holding a tiny baby who shared the same name as someone dear to him, someone he had lost.

She was suddenly deeply grateful she would have the chance to watch this Miri grow up. She would be here to see her learn to walk, to ride a bike, to go on dates. Melissa, at least, wasn't going anywhere.

"Maybe Julia can keep in touch with you after you're back on active duty and send you pictures of her."

He was quiet, his hands on Max's leash. "That would be great, except I'm not going back on active duty."

She stared at him in the gathering twilight. "You're…what?"

He returned her shocked look with an impassive one she couldn't read. "I called my commanding officer on my way back from the hospital and told her I wouldn't be signing up for another tour."

"But…but why? I thought you loved what you do in the military. You were doing important work. Necessary work."

"I am. I was. But today when we were delivering Miri, I realized something."

He gazed toward the ocean and the dramatic rock formations offshore, his features in shadow.

"There is more than one way to make a difference in

the world," he said slowly. "Sometimes that involves focusing on helping out those in critical situations. That's a good and honorable thing to do, and I will always be grateful I had the experiences and learned the lessons I did."

He glanced back at her, blue eyes glittering in the fading light. "I'm glad I had the chance to serve. I'm a better doctor and a better person for it. But I have no obligation to do it forever. Even Justine was never planning to serve for the rest of her life. She was making plans for after she left Doctors Without Borders. She was going to adopt Miri and take her back to France with her."

"Yes. That's what you said."

"If she could make plans for a different future someday, why can't I?"

"What kind of future?" Her heart now seemed to be racing in double time as she tried to absorb this shocking information.

"I want to be home. I want to help my neighbors and be around when my dad needs me and watch Miri and any other babies I deliver grow up and have babies of their own."

"You're leaving the army." She couldn't seem to process it even after his explanation.

He shrugged. "I'm leaving active duty. I'll stay in the reserves. If my country needs me, I may end up being called up in emergencies. I'm more than willing to do that on a temporary basis, but I want something else. I want to go into practice with my dad. Sanderson and Sanderson. Has a nice ring, don't you think?"

Oh, that would make Wendell happy beyond words. "Your dad will be thrilled."

"He will. With me here to share the burden, who knows? He might even slow down and little and start to enjoy life outside of medicine."

She wasn't sure that would happen, but she hoped so for his father's sake.

As she processed the news, the magnitude of what he was telling her began to soak through her shock. He was staying in Cannon Beach. Staying at the clinic where she worked. That would only mean one thing.

She would have no choice.

"That's great. I'm happy for you. You'll be gr-great."

Tears began to burn behind her eyes, and she had to hope he couldn't see them in the dusky light.

Unfortunately, she forgot how sharp-eyed the man could be. His gaze narrowed and he watched her with an intensity she couldn't escape.

"What's wrong? I was hoping for a...different reaction."

"I'm happy for you. I really am. This is exactly what your father would have wanted."

"So why do you look like I just started clear-cutting the Brambleberry House gardens?"

She wanted to come up with something clever that would explain the tears she was afraid he had seen, but she was too tired to tell him anything but the truth.

"I love working at your dad's practice," she said softly. "But if you're coming home for good, I'm afraid I'll have to quit."

His mouth sagged. "Quit? Why the hell would you do that?"

She had to tell him, especially now that she'd started. The words caught in her throat, but she forced them out.

"I can't work for you, Eli. I can't. Not when I…" She faltered, losing her nerve.

He looked thunderstruck, as if she'd just thrown a handful of sand in his eyes. "When you what?"

She closed her eyes, mortified to her soul that she'd said anything at all. She should have just let the dust settle for a week or so and then quietly tendered her resignation.

"Are you really going to make me say it? Fine. I'll say it, then. I can't work for you when I have…have feelings for you."

This was the most difficult conversation she'd ever had. She wanted to find a hole and let Fiona and Max bury her in it like a leftover soup bone.

"These last two weeks have been torture," she finally admitted, "trying to keep things on a professional level when my heart wants so much more. I'm sorry. I can't do it. I'm not strong enough. I'll have to go somewhere else to work. I'm sure I can find another job somewhere else along the coast. I only hope your dad will be able to give me a good reference."

He didn't say anything for a full minute, his expression filled with shock and something else, something she couldn't identify.

"Say something," she finally couldn't help but say.

When he continued to stare at her, she grabbed Fiona's collar and turned to head to the house, wanting only to escape.

"Melissa. Stop. Please!"

Fiona plopped her hindquarters in the sand, refusing to move other step, while a warm, rose-scented breeze seemed to eddy around them.

She couldn't face him. Humiliated and miserable,

she stood there outside the beach gate, not knowing what to do.

She thought she knew what love was. She had been married for five years, for heaven's sake. But everything she understood before seemed wholly insignificant compared to this vast ache of emotion coiling through her.

"Melissa."

He tugged her around to face him, and she finally slowly lifted her gaze to his. The emotions blazing there made her catch her breath. Her pulse in her ears seemed louder than the surf.

"I want to stay in Cannon Beach for dozens of reasons," he said, his voice low and intense. "And almost every single one of them is because of you."

She gazed at his strong, lean features, everything inside her tuned to this moment.

"I came back to town broken," he went on gruffly. "I didn't want to admit it to myself or anyone else, but something inside my head and heart shattered when Miri and Justine died. I wouldn't say it was post-traumatic stress disorder, but the whole world seemed empty, joyless. Wrong."

He smiled a little and reached for her hand. His skin was warm against hers, and she shivered at the contrast, wanting to lean into him but afraid to move.

"And then I came back to town and met up with the girl I had the biggest crush on when I was eighteen and she was just fifteen, and I started to heal."

"You did not have a crush on me."

He raised an eyebrow. "Do you remember that time we danced together at the prom? Your boyfriend tried to beat me up later, but I didn't care. I would have done it all over again. It was all worth it, for the few moments I got to hold you in my arms."

"Why didn't you say anything? Back then or now?"

"You were way out of my league back then. You still are. I know I'll never be good enough for you, but that doesn't seem to matter anymore. The only thing that matters is that I'm in love with you and want the chance to show you I can make you happy."

Joy exploded through her, fierce and bright and perfect. "You love me."

"I think I've loved you a little since we were in high school together. But when I came back to Cannon Beach and met you again—the strong, amazing, compassionate woman you've become—I fell in love all over again."

Warmth flowed over her, healing and blissful. He loved her. She would never get tired of those words.

She reached up on tiptoe and kissed him, and this time when his mouth met hers there were no reservations between them, no uneasiness or worry or doubts.

Only love.

He kissed her for a long time, until the sun had almost slipped into the ocean. She would never grow tired of his kisses, either.

"I love you, Elias Sanderson. I'm so in love with you, I've barely been able to function around you. I'm amazed I could do my job, I was so busy trying to hide my feelings about you."

"Whatever you did worked. I had no idea."

She wanted to laugh and dance barefoot in the sand and fly a hundred kites with hearts all over them. Joy soared through her, wild and fierce and perfect.

He wouldn't be returning to harm's way. He would

be here in Cannon Beach with her where they could walk the dogs at sunset and teach Skye how to play billiards and listen to music at The Haystacks on Saturday nights.

They could work together, helping the neighbors and friends they cared about.

Storms would come. Tree limbs would fall and brambleberry bushes would be broken and torn. But they would get through it all together.

He kissed her, and that future seemed sweet and full of incalculable promise.

"I'm not that young, perky cheerleader anymore," she eventually felt compelled to remind him when his hands started to wander.

"I know," he murmured against her mouth. "You're so much more than that now. A loving mother, a compassionate nurse, a loyal friend. And the woman who has my heart."

She could live with that.

She smiled and kissed him as a warm, rose-scented breeze danced around them like an embrace.

Epilogue

Humming one of her favorite Christmas songs, Rosa Galvez twisted another string of lights around one of the porch columns. She only had two more to go, then this part of her holiday decorating would be done.

She loved this time of year. Brambleberry House was at its most beautiful at Christmas. The old Victorian was made for the season. Wreaths hung on the front door and in every window and her neighbor Sonia had been busy for the past two weeks hanging lights around the garden. Well, busy supervising a crew of teenage neighbor boys, anyway, who were earning a little extra change while helping them decorate.

The house would be spectacular when they finished.

She twisted the last of the strand of lights around the column, grateful for her coat against the cool, damp afternoon.

Though it was barely December, a Christmas tree already gleamed in the window of the first-floor apartment and she could see Skye peeking out. The girl waved at Rosa and at Fiona, sprawled out on the porch watching her work, then disappeared from view, back inside where she was baking something with Melissa.

Rosa had to smile, though she felt a little pang in her heart. The house would seem so empty when Skye and her mother moved out, but at least she wouldn't have to worry about that for a few more months. Eli Sanderson and Melissa Fielding planned to marry here at Brambleberry House in April, when the flowers were first beginning to bloom in the gardens. It would be a lovely place to marry. She wanted to think Abigail would have been happy at the romantic turn of events.

Melissa and Eli were already looking at houses and seemed to have found a lovely Craftsman home close to Wendell Sanderson's house.

She was happy for her friend but, oh, she would miss her and Skye. So would Fiona. Who was going to take the Irish setter on runs along the shore? Certainly not Rosa.

She was hanging the last of the lights when a big late-model pickup truck she didn't recognize pulled into the driveway and a tall, serious-looking man climbed out. He stood for a moment, looking up at the house, then walked toward her.

For reasons she couldn't have explained, Rosa tensed.

She hardly ever had the panic attacks and meltdowns that had afflicted her so much after the dark period of her youth, before she had been rescued by Sheriff Daniel Galvez and his wife, Lauren, who later adopted her. Those terrible months seemed a lifetime ago. She was a different person now, one who had worked hard to find happiness.

Every once in a while, she felt as if all the progress she had achieved over the last fifteen years was for nothing—that somewhere deep inside, she would always be a frightened girl, tangled in a situation out of her control.

"May I help you?" she asked as the man approached the porch.

"I hope so."

Up close, he seemed even more grim than he had appeared when he climbed out of his vehicle. No trace of a smile appeared on his features, only tight control.

"I'm looking for a woman. I'm pretty sure she lives here. Her name is Elizabeth Hamilton."

The name meant nothing to Rosa, who knew all the past tenants going back to the original owner. Still, she felt a stirring of unease.

"I know no one by this name," she said. She was nervous, which was probably the reason that her Spanish accent became more pronounced. "I believe you have the wrong house."

"It's not the wrong house," he said flatly. "I know she's here."

"And I know she is not," Rosa retorted. Like her accent, her unease was becoming more pronounced, as well. This man made her nervous, though she couldn't have said why.

She wondered, for one fleeting moment, whether she should pull her phone out and call 911. It was a crazy reaction, she knew. The man wasn't threatening anyone. He was only looking for a woman who did not live there. She could only imagine trying to explain why she had called the police for such a reason to the frustrating but gorgeous new police chief. Wyatt Townsend would look at her with even more suspicion than he usually did.

"Now, I must ask you to leave."

She saw frustration cross features that she would ordinarily call handsome. Right now, they only looked dangerous.

"Sorry, ma'am, but I've come too far to leave now."

There was a bit of a Western twang to his voice, one that seemed similar to those she heard throughout her teenage years living in Utah.

"The woman you are seeking, this Elizabeth Hamilton, she does not live here."

He let out a sigh and looked down at the piece of paper. "What about Sonia Davis. Is she here?"

Now her nervousness bloomed into full-on fear. What could he possibly want with their Sonia?

Her neighbor was home. Rosa had seen her come in earlier and make her painstaking way up to her second-floor apartment, looking more weary and sore than usual.

She wanted to tell him no. She wanted to tell him to go away and not come back. Some instinct warned Rosa that this man was a threat to her secretive, vulnerable neighbor, who had already been through so very much.

She opened her mouth to lie but closed it again. What if Sonia was expecting him? What if she wanted to see this handsome man in cowboy boots and a worn ranch jacket, who drove a pickup truck that had Idaho license plates and the words Hamilton Construction on the side.

"She lives upstairs." She couldn't see any point in lying. He obviously knew Sonia lived here. "If you would like, I can see if she is home. What name should I tell her? And is there a message you would you like me to give her?"

He glanced up, almost as if he could see through the porch ceiling to the floor above. Now the tight expression showed a crack of emotion, something stark and raw. She thought she saw longing, frustration, pain, before his features became closed again.

"Sure. My name is Luke Hamilton. And you can tell this Sonia—whose real name, by the way, is Elizabeth Sinclair Hamilton—that her husband has come to take her home."

* * * * *

USA TODAY bestselling author **Lee Tobin McClain** watched *Doctor Zhivago* way too young and developed a lifelong passion for angsty romance. When she's not writing, she's probably FaceTiming with her college-aged daughter, mediating battles between her goofy goldendoodle and her rescue cat, or teaching aspiring writers in Seton Hill University's MFA program. She is probably not cleaning her house. For more about Lee, visit her website at leetobinmcclain.com.

Books by Lee Tobin McClain

Love Inspired

Rescue Haven

The Secret Christmas Child
Child on His Doorstep

Redemption Ranch

The Soldier's Redemption
The Twins' Family Christmas
The Nanny's Secret Baby

Rescue River

Engaged to the Single Mom
His Secret Child
Small-Town Nanny
The Soldier and the Single Mom
The Soldier's Secret Child
A Family for Easter

Visit the Author Profile page
at Harlequin.com for more titles.

ENGAGED TO
THE SINGLE MOM

Lee Tobin McClain

I owe much appreciation to my Wednesday-morning critique group—Sally Alexander, Jonathan Auxier, Kathy Ayres, Colleen McKenna and Jackie Robb— for being patient through genre shifts while gently insisting on excellence. Thanks also to my colleagues at Seton Hill University, especially Michael Arnzen, Nicole Peeler and Albert Wendland, whose support and encouragement keep me happily writing. Ben Wernsman helped me brainstorm story ideas, and Carrie Turansky read an early draft of the proposal and critiqued it most helpfully. I'm grateful to be working with my agent, Karen Solem, and my editor, Shana Asaro—dog lovers both—who saw the potential of the story and helped me make it better. Most of all, thanks belong to my daughter, Grace, for being patient with her creative mom's absentmindedness and for offering inspiration, recreation and eye-rolling, teenage-style love every step of the way.

And we know that all things work together for good
to them that love God, to them who are the called
according to *His* purpose.
—*Romans* 8:28

Chapter 1

"You can let me off here." Angelica Camden practically shouted the words over the roar of her grandfather's mufflerless truck. The hot July air, blowing in through the pickup's open windows, did nothing to dispel the sweat that dampened her neck and face.

She rubbed her hands down the legs of the full-length jeans she preferred to wear despite the heat, took a deep breath and blew it out yoga-style between pursed lips. She could do this. Had to do it.

Gramps raised bushy white eyebrows as he braked at the top of a long driveway. "I'm taking you right up to that arrogant something-or-other's door. You're a lady and should be treated as one."

No chance of that. Angelica's stomach churned at the thought of the man she was about to face. She'd fight lions for her kid, had done the equivalent plenty of times, but this particular lion terrified her, brought back feelings of longing and shame and sadness that made her feel about two inches tall.

This particular lion had every right to eat her alive. Her heart fluttered hard against her ribs, and when she took a deep breath, trying to calm herself, the truck's exhaust fumes made her feel light-headed.

I can't do this, Lord.

Immediately the verse from this morning's devotional, read hastily while she'd stirred oatmeal on Gramps's old gas stove, swam before her eyes: *I can do all things through Him who gives me strength.*

She believed it. She'd recited it to herself many times in the past couple of difficult years. She could do all things through Christ.

But this, Lord? Are you sure?

She knew Gramps would gladly go on the warpath for her, but using an eighty-year-old man to fight her battles wasn't an option. The problem was hers. She'd brought it on herself, mostly, and she was the one who had to solve it. "I'd rather do it my own way, Gramps. Please."

Ignoring her—of course—he started to turn into the driveway.

She yanked the handle, shoved the truck door open and put a booted foot on the running board, ready to jump.

"Hey, careful!" Gramps screeched to a stop just in front of a wooden sign: A Dog's Last Chance: No-Cage Canine Rescue. Troy Hinton, DVM, Proprietor. "DVM, eh? Well, he's still a—"

"Shhh." She swung back around to face him, hands

braced on the door guards, and nodded sideways toward the focus of her entire life.

Gramps grunted and, thankfully, lapsed into silence.

"Mama, can I go in with you?" Xavier shot her a pleading look—one he'd perfected and used at will, the rascal—from the truck's backseat. "I want to see the dogs."

If she played this right, he'd be able to do more than just see the dogs during a short visit. He'd fulfill a dream, and right now Angelica's life pretty much revolved around helping Xavier fulfill his dreams.

"It's a job interview, honey. You go for a little drive with Gramps." At his disappointed expression, she reached back to pat his too-skinny leg. "Maybe you can see the dogs later, if I get the job."

"You'll get it, Mama."

His brilliant smile and total confidence warmed her heart at the same time that tension attacked her stomach. She shot a glance at Gramps and clung harder to the truck, which suddenly felt like security in a storm.

He must have read her expression, because his gnarled hands gripped the steering wheel hard. "You don't have to do this. We can try to get by for another couple of weeks at the Towers."

Seeing the concern in his eyes took Angelica out of herself and her fears. Gramps wasn't as healthy as he used to be, and he didn't need any extra stress on account of her. Two weeks at the Senior Towers was the maximum visit from relatives with kids, and even though she'd tried to keep Xavier quiet and neat, he'd bumped into a resident who used a walker, spilled red punch in the hallway and generally made too much noise. In other words, he was a kid. And the Senior Towers was no place to raise a kid.

They'd already outstayed their welcome, and she knew Gramps was concerned about it. She leaned back in to rub his shoulder. "I know what I'm doing. I'll be fine."

"You're sure?"

She nodded. "Don't worry about me."

But once the truck pulled away, bearing with it the only two males in North America she trusted, Angelica's strength failed her. She put a hand on one of the wooden fence posts and closed her eyes, shooting up a desperate prayer for courage.

As the truck sounds faded, the Ohio farmland came to life around her. A tiny creek rippled its way along the driveway. Two fence posts down, a red-winged blackbird landed, trilling the *oka-oka-LEE* she hadn't heard in years. She inhaled the pungent scent of new-mown hay.

This was where she'd come from. Surely the Lord had a reason for bringing her home.

Taking another deep breath, she straightened her spine. She was of farm stock. She could do this. She reached into her pocket, clutched the key chain holding a cross and a photo of her son in better days, and headed toward the faint sound of barking dogs. Toward the home of the man who had every reason to hate her.

As the sound of the pickup faded, Troy Hinton used his arms to lift himself halfway out of the porch rocker. In front of him, his cast-clad leg rested on a wicker table, stiff and useless.

"A real man plays ball, even if he's hurt. Get back

up and into the game, son." His dad's words echoed in his head, even though his logical side knew he couldn't risk worsening his compound fracture just so he could stride down the porch steps and impress the raven-haired beauty slowly approaching his home.

Not that he had any chance of impressing Angelica Camden. Nor any interest in doing so. She was one mistake he wouldn't make again.

His dog, Bull, scrabbled against the floorboards beside him, trying to stand despite his arthritic hips. Troy sank back down and put a hand on the dog's back. "It's okay, boy. Relax."

He watched Angelica's slow, reluctant walk toward his house. Why she'd applied to be his assistant, he didn't know. And why he'd agreed to talk to her was an even bigger puzzle.

She'd avoided him for the past seven years, ever since she'd jilted him with a handwritten letter and disappeared not only from his life, but from the state. A surge of the old bitterness rose in him, and he clenched his fists. Humiliation. Embarrassment. And worse, a broken heart and shattered faith that had never fully recovered.

She'd arrived in her grandfather's truck, but the old man had no use for him or any of his family, so why had he brought her out here for her interview? And why wasn't he standing guard with a shotgun? In fact, given the old man's reputation for thrift, he'd probably use the very same shotgun with which he'd ordered Troy off his hardscrabble farm seven years ago.

Troy had come looking for explanations about why Angelica had left town. Where she was. What her letter had meant. How she was surviving; whether she was okay.

The old man had raved at him, gone back into the past feud between their families over the miserable acre of land he called a farm. That acre had rapidly gone to seed, as had Angelica's grandfather, and a short while later he'd moved into the Senior Towers.

In a way, the old man had been abandoned, too, by the granddaughter he'd helped to raise. Fair warning. No matter how sweet she seemed, no matter what promises she made, she was a runner. Disloyal. Not to be counted on.

As Angelica approached, Troy studied her. She was way thinner than the curvy little thing she'd been at twenty-one. Her black hair, once shiny and flowing down her back in waves, was now captured in a careless bun. She wore baggy jeans and a loose, dusty-red T-shirt.

But with her full lips and almond-shaped eyes and coppery bronze skin, she still glowed like an exotic flower in the middle of a plain midwestern cornfield. And doggone it if his heart didn't leap out of his chest to see her.

"Down, boy," Troy ordered Bull—or maybe himself—as he pushed up into a standing position and hopped over to get his crutches.

His movements must have caught the attention of Lou Ann Miller, and now she hobbled out the front screen door.

She pointed a spatula at him. "You get back in that chair."

"You get back in that kitchen." He narrowed his eyes

at the woman who'd practically raised him. "This is something I have to do alone. And standing up."

"If you fall down those steps, you'll have to hire yet another helper, and you've barely got the charm to keep me." She put her hands on bony hips. "I expect you to treat that girl decent. What I hear, she's been through a lot."

Curiosity tugged at him. People in town were too kind to tell him the latest gossip about Angelica. They danced around the subject, sparing his ego and his feelings.

What had Angelica been through? How had it affected her?

The idea that she'd suffered or been hurt plucked at the chords of his heart, remnants of a time he'd have moved mountains to protect her and care for her. She'd had such a hard time growing up, and it had made him feel ten feet tall that she'd chosen him to help her escape her rough past.

Women weren't the only ones who liked stories of knights in shining armor. Lots of men wanted to be heroes as well, and Angelica was the kind of woman who could bring out the heroic side of a guy.

At least for a while. He swallowed down his questions and the bad taste in his mouth and forced a lightness he didn't feel into his tone. "Who says I won't treat her well? She's the only person who's applied for the job. I'd better." Looking at his cast, he could only shake his head. What an idiot he'd been to try to fix the barn roof by himself, all because he didn't want to ask anyone for help.

"I'll leave you alone, but I'll know if you raise your

voice," Lou Ann warned, pointing the spatula at him again.

He hopped to the door and held it for her. Partly to urge her inside, and partly to catch her if she stumbled. She was seventy-five if she was a day, and despite her high energy and general bossiness, he felt protective.

Not that he'd be much help if she fell, with this broken leg.

She rolled her eyes and walked inside, shaking her head.

When he turned back, Angelica was about ten feet away from the front porch. She'd stopped and was watching him. Eyes huge, wide, wary. From here, he could see the dark circles under them.

Unwanted concern nudged at him. She looked as though she hadn't slept, hadn't been eating right. Her clothes were worn, suggesting poverty. And the flirty sparkle in her eyes, the one that had kept all the farm boys buying gallons of lemonade from her concession stand at the county fair…that was completely gone.

She looked defeated. At the end of her rope.

What had happened to her?

Their mutual sizing-up stare-fest lasted way too long, and then he beckoned her forward. "Come on up. I'm afraid I can't greet you properly with this bum leg."

She trotted up the stairs, belying his impression that she was beaten down. "Was that Lou Ann Miller?"

"It was." He felt an illogical urge to step closer to her, which he ascribed to the fact that he didn't get out much and didn't meet many women. "She runs my life."

"Miss Lou Ann!" Angelica called through the screen

door, seemingly determined to ignore Troy. "Haven't seen you in ages!"

Lou Ann, who must have been directly inside, hurried back out.

Angelica's face broke into a smile as she pulled the older woman into a gentle hug. "It's so nice to see you! How's Caleb?"

Troy drummed his fingers on the handle of his crutch. Caleb was Lou Ann's grandson, who'd been in Angelica's grade in school, and whom Angelica had dated before the two of them had gotten together. He was just one of the many members of Angelica's fan club back then, and Troy, with his young-guy pride and testosterone, had been crazy jealous of all of them.

Maybe with good reason.

"He's fine, fine. Got two young boys." Lou Ann held Angelica's shoulders and studied her. "You're way too thin. I'll bring out some cookies." She glared at Troy. "They're not for you, so don't you go eating all of them."

And then she was gone and it was just the two of them.

Angelica studied the man she'd been so madly in love with seven years ago.

He was as handsome as ever, despite the cast on his leg and the two-day ragged beard on his chin. His shoulders were still impossibly broad, but now there were tiny wrinkles beside his eyes, and his short haircut didn't conceal the fact that his hairline was a little higher than it used to be. The hand he held out to her was huge.

Angelica's stomach knotted, but she forced herself to reach out and put her hand into his.

The hard-calloused palm engulfed hers and she yanked her hand back, feeling trapped. She squatted down to pet the grizzled bulldog at Troy's side. "Who's this?"

"That's Bull."

She blinked. Was he calling her on her skittishness?

That impression increased as he cocked his head to one side. "You're not afraid of me, are you?"

"No!" She gulped air. "I'm not afraid of you. Like I said when we texted, I'm here to apply for the job you advertised in the *Tribune*."

He gestured toward one of the rockers. "Have a seat. Let's talk about that. I'm curious about why you're interested."

Of course he was. And she'd spent much of last night sleepless, wondering how much she'd have to tell him to get the job she desperately needed, the job that would make things as good as they could be, at least for a while.

Once she sat down, he made his way back to his own rocker and sat, grimacing as he propped his leg on the low table in front of him.

She didn't like the rush of sympathy she felt. "What happened?"

"Fell off a roof. My own stupid fault."

That was new in him, the willingness to admit his own culpability. She wondered how far it went.

"That's why I need an assistant with the dogs," he explained. "Lou Ann helps me around the house, but she's not strong enough to take care of the kennels. I can't get everything done, and we've got a lot of dogs right now, so this is kind of urgent."

His words were perfectly cordial, but questions and undercurrents rustled beneath them.

Angelica forced herself to stay in the present, in sales mode. "You saw my résumé online, right? I worked as a vet assistant back in Boston. And I've done hospital, um, volunteer work, and you know I grew up in the country. I'm strong, a lot stronger than I look."

He nodded. "I've no doubt you could do the work if you wanted to," he said, "but why would you want to?"

"Let's just say I need a job."

He studied her, his blue eyes troubled. "You haven't shown your face in town for seven years. Even when you visit your grandfather, you hide out at the Senior Towers. If I'm giving you access to my dogs and my computer files and my whole business, especially if you're able to live here on the grounds, I need to know a little more about what you've been up to."

He hadn't mentioned his main reason for mistrusting her, and she appreciated that. She pulled her mind out of the past and focused on the living arrangement, one of the main reasons this job was perfect for her. "I'm very interested in living in. Your ad said that's part of the job?"

"That's right, in the old bunkhouse." He gestured toward a trim white building off to the east. "I figured the offer of housing might sweeten the deal, given that this is just a temporary job."

"Is it big enough for two?"

"Ye-es," He leaned back in the rocker and studied her, his eyes hooded. "Why? Are you married? I thought your name was still Camden."

"I'm not married." She swallowed. "But I do have a son."

His eyebrows lifted. "How old is your son?"

"Is that important?" She really, really didn't want to tell him.

"Yes, it's important," he said with a slight sigh. "I can't have a baby or toddler here. It wouldn't be safe, not with some of the dogs I care for."

She drew in a breath. Now or never. "My son's six, almost seven." She reached a hand out to the bulldog, who'd settled between them, rubbed it along his wrinkled head, let him sloppily lick her fingers.

"Six! Then…"

She forced herself to look at Troy steadily while he did the math. Saw his eyes harden as he realized her son must have been conceived right around the time she'd left town.

Heat rose in her cheeks as the familiar feeling of shame twisted her insides. But she couldn't let herself go there. "Xavier is a well-behaved kid." At least most of the time. "He loves animals and he's gentle with them."

Troy was still frowning.

He was going to refuse her, angry about the way she'd left him, and then what would she do? How would she achieve the goal she'd set for herself, to fulfill as many of Xavier's wishes as she could? This was such a perfect arrangement.

"I really need this job, Troy." She hated to beg, but for Xavier, she'd do it.

He looked away, out at the fields, and she did, too. Sun on late-summer corn tassels, puffy clouds in a blue sky. Xavier would love it so.

"If you ever felt anything for me…" Her throat tightened and she had to force out the words. "If any of your memories about me are good, please give me the job."

He turned back toward her, eyes narrowing. "Why do you need it so badly?"

She clenched her hands in her lap. "Because my son wants to be close to Gramps. And because he loves animals."

"Most people don't organize their careers around their kids' hankerings."

She drew in a breath. "Well, I do."

His expression softened a little. "This job…it might not be what you want. It's just until my leg heals. The doc says it could be three, four months before I'm fully back on my feet. Once that happens, I won't need an assistant anymore."

She swallowed and squeezed her hands together. *Lord, I know I'm supposed to let You lead, but this seems so right. Not for me, but for Xavier, and that's what matters. It is of You, isn't it?*

No answer from above, but the roar of a truck engine pierced the country quiet.

Oh no. Gramps was back too soon. He'd never gotten along with Troy, never trusted him on account of his conflicts with Troy's dad. But she didn't want the two men's animosity to get in the way of what both she and her son wanted and needed.

The truck stopped again at the end of the driveway. Gramps got out, walked around to the passenger door.

She surged from her chair. "No, don't!" she called, but the old man didn't hear her. She started down the porch steps

Troy called her back. "It's okay, they can come up.

Regardless of what we decide about the job, maybe your son would like to see the dogs, look around the place."

"There's nothing he'd like better," she said, "but I don't want to get his hopes up if this isn't going to work out."

Troy's forehead wrinkled as he stared out toward the truck, watching as Gramps helped Xavier climb out.

Angelica rarely saw her son from this distance, and now, watching Gramps steady him, her hand rose to her throat. He looked as thin as a scarecrow. His baseball cap couldn't conceal the fact that he had almost no hair.

Her eyes stung and her breathing quickened as if she were hyperventilating. She pinched the skin on the back of her hand, hard, and pressed her lips together.

Gramps held Xavier's arm as they made slow progress down the driveway. The older supporting the younger, opposite of how it should be.

Troy cleared his throat. "Like I said, the job won't be long-term. I…it looks like you and your son have some…issues. You might want to find something more permanent."

His kind tone made her want to curl up and cry for a couple of weeks, but she couldn't go there. She clenched her fists. "I know the job is short-term." Swallowing the lump that rose in her throat, she added, "That's okay with us. We take things a day at a time."

"Why's that?" His gaze remained on the pair making their slow way up the driveway.

He was going to make her say it. She took a shuddering breath and forced out the words. "Because the doctors aren't sure how long his remission will last."

* * *

Troy stared at Xavier, forgetting to breathe. Remission? "Remission from what?"

Angelica cleared her throat. "Leukemia. He has…a kind that's hard to beat."

Every parent's nightmare. Instinctively he reached out to pat her shoulder, the way he'd done so many times with pet owners worried about seriously ill pets.

She flinched and sidled away.

Fine! Anger flared up at the rejection and he gripped the porch railing and tamped it down. Her response was crystal clear. She didn't want any physical contact between them.

But no matter his own feelings, no matter what Angelica had done to him, the past was the past. This pain, the pain of a mother who might lose her child, was in the present, and Angelica's worn-down appearance suddenly made sense.

And no matter whose kid Xavier was…no matter who she'd cheated on him with…the boy was an innocent, and the thought of a child seriously, maybe terminally, ill made Troy's heart hurt.

Again he suppressed his emotions as his medical instincts went into overdrive. "What kind of doctors has he seen? Have you gotten good treatments, second opinions?"

She took a step back and crossed her arms over her chest. "I can't begin to tell you how many doctors and opinions."

"But are they the best ones? Have you tried the Cleveland—"

"Troy!" She blew out a jagged breath. "Look, I don't need medical interference right now. I need a job."

"But—"

"Don't you think I've done everything in my power to help him?" She turned away and walked down the steps toward her son. Her back was stiff, her shoulders rigid.

He lifted a hand to stop her and then let it fall. *Way to go, Hinton. Great social skills.*

He'd find out more, would try to do something to help. Obviously Angelica hadn't done well financially since she left him and left town. Xavier's father must have bolted. And without financial resources, getting good medical care wasn't easy.

"Mom! Did you get the job?"

Angelica shot Troy a quick glance. "It's still being decided."

The boy's face fell. Then he nodded and bit his lip. "It's okay, Mama. But can we at least see the dogs?"

"Absolutely," Troy answered before Angelica could deny the boy. Then he hobbled down the porch stairs and sank onto the bottom one, putting him on a level with the six-year-old. "I'm Troy," he said, and reached out to shake the boy's hand.

The boy smiled—wow, what a smile—and reached out to grasp Troy's hand, looking up at his mother for reassurance.

She nodded at him. "You know what to say."

Frowning with thought, the boy shook his head.

"Pleased to…" Angelica prompted.

The smile broke out again like sunshine. "Oh yeah. Pleased to meet you, sir. I'm Xavier." He dropped Troy's hand and waved an arm upward, grinning. "And this is my grandpa. My *great*-grandpa."

"I've already had the pleasure." Troy looked up and met the old man's hostile eyes.

Camden glared down at him, not speaking.

Oh man. Out of the gazillion reasons not to hire Angelica, here was a major one. Obviously her grandfather was an important part of her life, one of her only living relatives. If she and Xavier came to live here, Troy would see a lot of Homer Camden, something they'd managed to avoid for the years Angelica was out of town.

Of course, he'd been working like crazy himself. Setting up his private practice, opening the rescue, paying off debt from vet school, which was astronomical even though his family had helped.

Troy pushed himself to his feet and got his crutches underneath him. "Dogs are out this way, if you'd like to see them." He nodded toward the barn.

"Yes!" Xavier pumped his arm. "I asked God to get me a bunch of dogs."

"Zavey Davey..." Angelica's voice was uneasy. "Remember, I don't have the job yet. And God doesn't always—"

"I know." Xavier sighed, his smile fading a little. "He doesn't always answer prayers the way we want Him to."

Ouch. Kids were supposed to be all about Jesus Loves Me and complete confidence in God's—and their parents'—ability to fix anything. But from the looks of things, young Xavier had already run up against some of life's hard truths.

"Come on, Gramps." When the old man didn't move, Xavier tugged at his arm. "You promised you'd be nice. Please?"

The old man's face reddened. After a slight pause that gave Troy and Angelica the chance to glance at each other, he turned in the direction Troy had indicated and started walking, slowly, with Xavier.

Angelica touched Troy's arm, more like hit him, actually. "Don't let him go back there if you don't want to give me the job," she growled.

Even angry, her voice brushed at his nerve endings like rich, soft velvet. Her rough touch plucked at some wildness in him he'd never given way to.

Troy looked off over the cornfields, thinking, trying to get control of himself. He didn't trust Angelica, but that sweet-eyed kid...how could he disappoint a sick kid?

Homer Camden and the boy were making tracks toward the barn, and Troy started after them. He didn't want them to reach the dogs before he'd had a chance to lay some ground rules about safety. He turned to make sure Angelica was following.

She wasn't. "Well?" Her arms were crossed, eyes narrowed, head cocked to one side.

"You expect me to make an instant decision?"

"Since my kid's feelings are on the line...yeah. Yeah, I do."

Their eyes locked. Some kind of stormy electrical current ran between them.

This was bad. Working with her would be difficult enough, since feelings he thought he'd resolved years ago were resurfacing. He'd thought he was over her dumping him, but the knowledge that she'd conceived a child with someone else after seeming so sincere about their decision to wait until marriage... His neck felt as tight as granite. Yeah. It was going to take a while to process that.

Having her live here on the grounds with that very child, someone else's child, the product of her unfaithfulness…he clenched his jaw against all the things he wanted to say to her.

Fools vent their anger, but the wise hold it back. It was a proverb he'd recently taught the boys in his Kennel Kids group, little dreaming how soon and how badly he'd need it himself.

"Mom! Come on! I wanna see the dogs!" Xavier was tugging at his grandfather's arm, jumping around like a kid who wasn't at all sick, but Troy knew that was deceptive. Even terminally ill animals went through energetic periods.

Could he deprive Xavier of being with dogs and of having a decent home to live in? Even if having Angelica here on the farm was going to be difficult?

When he met her eyes again, he saw that hers shone with unshed tears.

"Okay," he said around a sigh. "You're hired."

Her face broke into a sunshiny smile that reminded him of the girl she'd been. "Thank you, Troy," she said softly. She walked toward him, and for a minute he thought she was going to hug him, as she'd been so quick to do in the past.

But she walked right by him to catch up with her son and grandfather. She bent over, embraced Xavier from behind and spoke into his ear.

The boy let out a cheer. "Way to go, Mama! Come on!"

They hurried ahead, leaving Troy to hop along on his crutches, matching Angelica's grandfather's slower pace.

"Guess you hired her," the old man said.

"I did."

"Now you listen here." Camden stopped walking, narrowed his eyes, and pointed a finger at Troy. "If you do anything to hurt that girl, you'll have me to contend with."

Troy took a deep breath and let it out slowly. He was doing this family a favor, but he couldn't expect gratitude, not with the history that stood between them. "I have no plans to hurt her. Hoping she'll be a help to me until I'm back on my feet." He glanced down. "Foot."

"Humph." Camden turned and started making his way toward the barn again. "Heard you fell off a roof. Fool thing to do."

Troy gritted his teeth and swung into step beside Camden. "According to my brother and dad, you've done a few fool things in your day." This was a man who'd repeatedly refused a massive financial package that would have turned his family's lives around, all in favor of keeping his single-acre farm that stood in the middle of the Hinton holdings.

Not that Troy blamed the old man, particularly. Troy's father was an arrogant, unstable man with plenty of enemies. Including Troy himself, most of the time.

Even after Homer Camden's health had declined, forcing him to move into the Senior Towers, he clung stubbornly to the land. Rumor had it that his house had fallen into disrepair and the surrounding fields were nothing but weeds.

Not wanting to say something he'd regret, Troy motored ahead on his crutches until he reached Xavier and Angelica, who'd stopped at the gate.

"If you wait there," he said to them, "I'll let the

dogs out into the runs." The breeze kicked up just as he passed Angelica, and the strawberry scent of her hair took him back seven years, to a time when that smell and her gentle, affectionate kisses had made him light-headed on a regular basis.

"Wait. Mr. Hinton." Xavier was breathing hard. "Thank you…for giving Mama…the job." He smiled up at Troy.

Troy's throat constricted. "Thank you for talking her into doing it," he managed to say, and then swung toward the barn.

He was going to do everything in his power to make that boy well.

Inside, joyful barks and slobbery kisses grounded him. His dogs ranged in age and size but tended toward the large, dark-coated bully breeds. The dogs no one else wanted to take a risk with: pit bulls, aggressive Dobermans and Rotties, large mutts. They were mixed in with older, sicker dogs whose owners couldn't or wouldn't pay the vet bills to treat them.

He moved among them, grateful that he'd found his calling in life.

Yes, he was lonely. Yes, he regretted not having a family around him, people to love. But he had his work, and it would always be there. Unlike people, dogs were loyal and trustworthy. They wouldn't let you down.

He opened the kennel doors to let them run free.

When he got back outside, he heard the end of Homer Camden's speech. "There's a job might open up at the café," he was saying, "And Jeannette Harold-son needs a caregiver."

For some reason that went beyond his own need for a temporary assistant, Troy didn't want the old man to talk her out of working for him. "Look, I know you've got a beef with the Hintons. But it's my dad and my brother who manage the land holdings. My sister's not involved, and I just run my rescue."

"That's as may be, but blood runs true. Angie's got other choices, and I don't see why—"

"That's why, Grandpa." Angelica pointed to Xavier. He'd knelt down beside the fence, letting the dogs lick him through it. On his face was an expression of the purest ecstasy Troy had ever seen.

All three adults looked at each other. They were three people at odds. But in that moment, in complete silence, a pact arose between them: whatever it takes, we'll put this child first and help him be happy.

Chapter 2

Angelica watched her son reach thin, bluish fingers in to touch the dogs. Listened to Troy lecture them all about the rules for safety: don't enter the pens without a trained person there, don't let the dogs out, don't feed one dog in the presence of others. Her half-broken heart sang with gratitude.

Thanks to God, and Troy, Xavier would have his heartfelt wish. He'd have dogs—multiple dogs—to spend his days with. He'd have a place to call home. He'd have everything she could provide for him to make his time on this earth happy.

And if Xavier was happy, she could handle anything: Troy's intensity, the questions in his eyes, the leap in her own heart that came from being near this too-handsome man who had never been far from her thoughts in all these years.

"Do you want to see the inside of the barn?" Troy asked Xavier.

"Sure!" He sounded livelier than he had in weeks.

Troy led the way, his shoulders working the crutches. He was such a big man; he'd probably had to get the extra-tall size.

Gramps patted her back, stopping her. "I don't like it," he said, "but I understand what you're doing."

She draped an arm around his shoulders. "Thanks. That means a lot."

"Think I'll wait in the truck, though," he said. "Being around a Hinton sticks in my craw."

"Okay, sure." Truthfully, she was glad to see Gramps go. She doubted that he and Troy could be civil much longer.

She held Xavier's hand as they walked into the barn and over to the dog pens. The place was pretty clean, considering. Troy must have been wearing himself out to keep it that way.

As Xavier and Troy played with the dogs, she looked around, trying to get a clue into the man. She wandered over to a desk in the corner, obviously a place where he did the kennel business, or some of it.

And there, among a jumble of nails and paper clips, was a leather-studded bracelet she hadn't seen in seven years. She sucked in a breath as her heart dove down, down, down.

She closed her eyes hard, trying to shut out the memories, but a slide show of them raced through her mind. First date, whirlwind courtship and the most romantic marriage proposal a girl from her background could have imagined. For a few months, she'd felt like a princess in a fairy tale.

Back then, as an engaged couple, they'd helped with the youth group and had gotten the kids True Love Waits bracelets—leather and studs for the guys, more delicate chains for the girls. There had been a couple of extra ones, and one night when the waiting had been difficult, she and Troy had decided to each wear one as a reminder.

Carefully, she picked up the leather band. Her eyes filled with tears as she remembered stroking it on his arm, sometimes jokingly tugging at it when their kisses had gotten too passionate. Back in those innocent, happy days.

She'd ripped hers off and thrown it away on the most awful night of her life. The night she'd turned twenty-one and stupidly gone out with a bunch of friends to celebrate. The night she'd had too much to drink, realized it and accepted the offer of an older acquaintance to walk her home.

The night her purity and innocence and dreams of waiting for marriage had been torn forcibly away.

The next day, when Troy had noticed her bracelet was missing, she'd lied to him, telling him it must have fallen off.

But he'd continued to wear his, joking that he probably needed the reminder more than she did.

"Hey." He came up behind her now. When he noticed what she was holding, his eyebrows shot up and he took a step back.

She dropped it as if it were made of hot metal. "I'm sorry. That's not my business. I just happened to see it and…got carried away with the memories."

He nodded, pressed his lips together. Turned away.

That set face had to be judging her, didn't it? Feeling disgust at her lack of purity.

She'd been right to leave him. He could never have accepted her after what happened, although knowing him, he'd have tried to pretend. He'd have felt obligated to marry her anyway.

"Mom! Come see!" Xavier cried.

"Xavier!" He'd gone into a section of the barn Troy had warned them was off-limits. "I'm sorry," she said to Troy, and hurried over to her son. "You have to follow the rules! You could get hurt!"

"But look, Mama!" He knelt in front of a small heap of puppies, mostly gray and white, all squirming around a mother who lay on her side. Her head was lifted, her teeth bared.

"Careful of a mama dog," Troy said behind her. "Pull him back a foot or two, will you, Angelica? These little guys are only two weeks old, and the mom's still pretty protective."

She did, hating the crestfallen expression on Xavier's face. This ideal situation might have its own risks.

And then Troy reached down, patted the mother dog and carefully lifted a tiny, squirming puppy into Xavier's lap.

Xavier froze, then put his face down to nuzzle the puppy's pink-and-white snout. It nudged and licked him back, and then two more puppies crawled into his lap, tumbling over each other. Yips and squeals came from the mass of warm puppy bodies.

"Mom," Xavier said reverently. "This is *so* cool."

Angelica's heart did a funny little twist. She reached out and squeezed Troy's arm before she could stop herself.

"Do we really get to live here? Can we sleep in the barn with the puppies?"

Troy laughed. "No, son. You'll stay in a bunkhouse. Kind of like an Old West cowboy. Want to see?"

"Sure!" His eyes were on Troy with something like hero worship, and worry pricked at Angelica's chest. Was Xavier going to get too attached to Troy?

Then again, if it would make him happy… Angelica swallowed hard and shut out thoughts of the future. "Let's go!" she said with a voice that was only slightly shaky.

When they reached the bunkhouse and walked inside, Angelica felt her face break out into a smile. "It's wonderful, Troy! When did you do all this work on it?" She remembered the place as an old, run-down outbuilding, but now modern paneling and new windows made it bright with sunshine on wood. It needed curtains, maybe blue-and-white gingham. The rough-hewn pine furniture was sparse, but with a few throw pillows and afghans, the place would be downright homey.

A home. She'd wanted one forever, and even more after she'd become a mom.

Troy's watchful eyes snapped her out of her happy fantasies. "You like it?"

"It's fantastic." She realized he'd never answered her question about when he'd done the work.

"You're easy to please." His voice was gruff.

She smiled and squatted down beside Xavier. "We both are. Pretty near perfect, isn't it, Zavey Davey?"

"Yes. Sure, Mama."

Her ear was so attuned to his needs that she heard the slight hesitation in his voice. "What's wrong?" she asked, keeping her voice low to make the conversation private, just between her and her son. "Isn't this everything you've always wanted?"

"Yes. Except…" He wrinkled his freckled nose as though he was trying to decide something.

"What? What is it, honey?"

He pressed his lips together and then lost the battle with himself, shrugged and grinned winningly at her. "It's the last thing on my list, Mama."

The last thing. Her heart twisted tight. "What? What do you need?"

He leaned over and whispered into her ear, "A dad."

When Angelica emerged from the bunkhouse the next Saturday, every nerve in Troy's body snapped to attention. Was this the same woman who'd been working like a ranch hand this week, wearing jeans and T-shirts and boots, learning the ropes in the kennel?

It was the first time he'd seen her in a top that wasn't as loose as a sack. And was that makeup on her eyes, making them look even bigger?

"What?" she asked as she walked up beside him. She seemed taller. He looked down and saw that she was wearing sandals with a little heel, too.

Angelica had always been cute and appealing. But now she was model-thin, and with her hair braided back, her cheekbones stood out in a heart-shaped face set off by long silver earrings. A pale pink shirt edged with lace made her copper-colored skin glow. With depth and wisdom in her brown eyes, and a wry smile turning up the edges of her mouth, she was a knockout.

And one he needed to steer clear of. Beauty didn't

equate to morality or good values, and one whirl with this little enchantress had just about done him in.

Though to be fair, he didn't know the rest of her story. And he shouldn't judge. "Nothing. You look nice."

"Do you have the keys?"

"What?"

"Keys." She held out her hand.

He had to stop staring. The keys. He pulled them out of his pocket and handed them over.

She wasn't here for him. She was here because she needed something, and when she got it, she'd leave. He knew that from experience.

"Bye, Mama!" Xavier's voice was thin, reedy, but for all that, cheerful.

When he turned, he saw Xavier and Lou Ann standing on the porch, waving.

"You be good for Miss Lou Ann." Angelica shook her finger at Xavier, giving him a mock-stern look.

"I will, Mama."

Lou Ann put an arm around the boy. "We'll have fun. He's going to help me do some baking."

"Thank you!" Angelica shot a beaming smile toward the porch, and Troy's heart melted a little more.

With him, though, she was all business. "Let's get going. If we're to get there by nine, we don't have time to stand around."

She walked toward the truck, and he couldn't help noticing how well her jeans fit her slender frame.

Then she opened the passenger door and held it for him.

He gritted his teeth. Out of all the indignities of being injured, this had to be the worst. He liked to drive, liked to be in control, liked to open the door for a lady. Not have the door held for him. That was a man's proper role, pounded into him from childhood. No weakness; no vulnerability. Men should be in charge.

While his years in college and vet school, surrounded by capable and brilliant professional women, had knocked some feminist sense into his head, his alpha-male instincts were as strong as ever.

"You need help getting in?" she asked.

Grrrr. "I have a broken leg. I'm not paralyzed." He swung himself into the truck, grunting with the awkward effort.

"Sor-ry." She shrugged and walked back around to the driver's side.

When they headed down the driveway, he said, "Take a right up there at the stop sign."

She did, rolling down her window at the same time. Hot, dusty July air blew tendrils of her hair loose, but she put her head back and breathed it in deeply, a tiny smile curving her full lips.

He liked that she'd stayed a farm girl, not all prissy and citified. Maybe liked it a little too much. "Slow down, this is a blind curve. Then go left after that barn."

"Troy." She shifted gears with complete competence. "I grew up here, remember? I know how to get to town."

Of course she did. She was a capable assistant…and no more. He needed to focus on his weekly vet clinic and how he was going to manage it on crutches. Forget about Angelica.

Easier said than done.

* * *

Angelica turned down the lane that led into town, trying to pay attention to the country air blowing through the truck's open windows rather than on the man beside her. He'd been staring at her nonstop since she came outside today. She already felt self-conscious, all dolled up, and Troy's attitude made it worse. She wasn't sure if he was judging her or...something else, but his gaze made her feel overheated, uncomfortable.

Or maybe the problem was that she'd dressed up on purpose, with the notion of finding a dad—or a temporary stand-in for one—to fulfill Xavier's wish. The thought of putting herself out there for men to approach made her feel slightly ill; dating was the last thing she wanted to do. And it wasn't likely that anyone would want damaged goods like her, not likely she'd attract interest, but she had to try. She'd promised herself to make her son's days happy, since she couldn't be sure how many he had left, and she was going to do her best.

Once they reached the residential area that surrounded Rescue River's downtown, Angelica's stomach knotted. Everyone in town knew about what she'd done to Troy, their beloved high school quarterback and brilliant veterinarian and all-around good guy. No doubt her own reputation was in the gutter.

There was the town's famous sign, dating back to Civil War years when the tiny farm community had been home to several safe houses on the Underground Railroad:

Rescue River, Ohio.

All Are Welcome, All Are Safe.

Funny, she didn't feel so safe now. She cruised past the bank and the feed store, and then thoughts of herself vanished when she saw the line of people snaking around the building that housed Troy's veterinary practice. "Wow. Looks like your clinic is a success."

"Lots of people struggling these days."

"It's free?"

He nodded, pointed. "Park right in front. They always save me a place."

She noticed a few familiar faces turning toward their truck. Someone ran to take a lawn chair out of the single remaining parking spot and she pulled in, stopped and went around to see if Troy needed help getting out. But he'd already hopped down, so she grabbed his crutches out of the back and took them to him.

"Here." She handed him the crutches, and his large, calloused hand brushed hers.

Something fluttered inside her chest. She yanked her hand back, dropping a crutch in the process.

"Hey, that you, Angie? Little Angie?"

She turned to see a tall, skinny man, his thin hair pulled back in a ponytail, his face stubbly. She cocked her head to one side. "Derek? Derek Moseley?"

"It *is* you!" He flung an easy arm around her and she shrugged away, and then suddenly Troy was there, stepping between them. "Whoa, my friend," he said. "Easy on my assistant."

"I'm fine!" She took another sidestep away.

Derek lifted his hands like stop signs. "Just saying hi to my old buddy's little sister, Doc." He turned to Angelica. "Girl, I ain't seen you in ages. How's your brother?"

She shook her head. "I don't see him much myself. He's overseas, doing mission work."

"Carlo? A missionary?"

"Well, something like that." In reality, her brother, Carlo, was halfway between a missionary and a mercenary, taking the word of God to people in remote areas where he was as likely to be met with a machete as a welcome.

"Carlo's a great guy. Tell him I said hello."

"I will." That evaluation was spot-on—her brother was a great guy. Carlo was the one who'd gone to Gramps and told him he had to take her in when their parents' behavior had gone way out of control. He'd been sixteen; she'd been nine. He'd gone out on his own then, had his dark and dangerous times, but now he'd found Jesus and reformed. He wrote often, sent money even though she told him not to, probably more than he could afford. But she didn't see him enough and she wished he'd come home. Especially now, with Xavier's health so bad.

A shuffling sound broke into her consciousness. She looked around for Troy and saw him working his way toward the clinic on his crutches, large medical bag clutched awkwardly at his side.

She hurried to him. "Here, let me carry that."

"I can get it."

Stepping in front of him, she took hold of the bag. "Probably, but not very well. This is what you're paying me for."

He held on to the bag a second longer and then let it go. "Fine."

As they walked toward the clinic, people greeted Troy, thanked him for being there, asked about his leg. The line seemed endless. Most people held dogs on leads, but a few had cat carriers. One man sat on a bench beside an open-topped cardboard box holding a chicken.

How would Troy ever take care of all these people? "The clinic's only until noon, right? Do you have help?"

"A vet tech, whenever he gets here. And I stay until I've seen everyone. We work hard. You up for this?"

She was and they did work hard; he wasn't lying. The morning flew by with pet after pet. She held leashes for Pomeranians and pit bulls, got scratched by a frightened tomcat with a ripped ear and comforted a twenty-something girl who cried when her two fluffy fur-ball puppies, one black and one white, had to get shots. She wrote down the particulars of rescue situations people told Troy about. Dogs needed rabies shots and ear medicine, X-rays and spaying. If it was something he couldn't do right at the moment, he made a plan to do it later in the week.

She asked once, "Can you even do surgery, with your leg?"

"My leg doesn't hurt as much as that guy's hurting," he said, scratching the droopy ears of a basset-beagle mix with a swollen stomach. The owner was pretty sure he'd swallowed a baby's Binky. "Feed him canned pumpkin to help things along," he told the owner. "If he doesn't pass it within three days, or if he's in more pain, call me."

A fiftysomething lady came in with a small, scruffy white dog wrapped in a towel. "Afraid he's got to be put to sleep, Doc." Her voice broke as she lifted the skinny animal to the metal exam table.

Angelica moved closer and patted the woman's back, feeling completely ineffectual. She wanted to help, but sometimes there wasn't anything you could do.

"Let's not jump to that conclusion." Troy picked up the whimpering little creature, ignoring its feeble effort to bite at him. He felt carefully around the dog's abdomen and examined its eyes and ears. "I'm guessing pancreatitis," he said finally, "but we'll need to do some blood work to be sure."

"What's that mean, Doc?" the woman asked. "I don't have much extra money…and I don't want him to suffer." She buried her face in her hands.

Angelica's throat ached. She could identify. She found a box of tissues and brought it over.

"Hey." Troy put a hand on the woman's shoulder. "Let's give treatment a try. If you can't afford the medicine, we'll work something out."

"Is he even likely to live?"

"Fifty-fifty," Troy admitted. "But I'm not a quitter. We can bring the dog to the farm if you don't have time to do the treatments. Aren't you a night waitress out at the truck stop?"

She nodded. "That's the other thing. I can't stick around home to care for him. I gotta work to pay my rent."

"Let me take him to the farm, then," Troy said. "It's worth it. He may have years of running around left. Don't you want me to try?"

"You'd really do that for him?" Hope lit the woman's face as she carefully picked up the little dog and cradled him to her chest. When she looked up, her eyes shone. "You don't know how much this means to me, Doc. He's been with me through two divorces and losing my day job and a bout with cancer. I want to be able to give back to him. I'll donate all my tips when I get them."

"Give what you can. That's all I ask." He told Angelica what to do next and took the dog away.

A man in jeans and a scrub top strode into the clinic then, and Angelica studied him as he greeted Troy. He must be the vet tech they'd been waiting for.

"Buck," Troy said. "How goes it?"

Buck. So that was why he looked so familiar—he was an old classmate, one of the nicer boys. "Hey," she greeted him. "Remember me?"

"Is that you, Angie?" A smile lit his eyes. "Haven't seen you in forever. How's your grandpa?"

They chatted for a few minutes while Troy entered data into a computer, preparing for the next appointment. Buck kept smiling and stepped a little closer, and Angelica recognized what was happening: he *like* liked her, as her girlfriends back in Boston would say. She took a step away.

And then it dawned on her: Buck would be a perfect guy to help fulfill Xavier's dream. Oh, not to marry, she couldn't go that far, but if she could find a nice, harmless man to hang out with some in the evenings, watch some family shows with, play board games with…that didn't sound half-bad. Xavier would be thrilled.

Come on, flirt with the man. You used to be good at it.

But she barely remembered how to talk to a man that way. And anyway, it felt like lying. How could she pretend to have an interest in a nice guy like Buck just to make her son happy? Maybe this wasn't such a good plan after all.

When Troy came back, ready for the next patient,

Buck cocked his head to one side. "Are you two together? I remember you used to—"

"No!" they both said at the same time.

"Whoa, okay! I just thought you were engaged, back in the day."

Angelica felt her face heat. "I'm just his assistant while he gets back on his feet," she explained as the next patient came in.

"Glad to hear you've come to your senses about him," Buck joked.

Troy's lips tightened and he turned away, limping over to greet a couple with a cat carrier who'd just walked in.

"You back in town for a while?" Buck looked at Angelica with sharpened interest.

"Yes. For a…a little while."

"Long enough to have dinner with an old friend?"

He was asking her out. To dinner, and really, what would be the harm? This was what she wanted.

"Sure," she said. "I'll have dinner with you."

"Saturday night? Where are you staying?" He touched her shoulder to usher her over to the side of the exam area, and she forced herself not to pull away.

They agreed on a time and exchanged phones to punch in numbers.

When she looked up, Troy was watching them, eyes narrowed, jaw set.

She shook her hair back. There was no reason for him to feel possessive. What had been between them was long gone.

So why did she feel so guilty?

Chapter 3

By the time they'd gotten back to the farm, it was suppertime and Troy's blood was boiling as hot as the pot of pasta on the stove.

Did Angelica have to make her date plans right in front of him? And with Buck Armstrong?

But it wasn't his business, and he had no reason to care. He just needed some time to himself.

Which apparently he wasn't going to get, because the minute they set down their things, Xavier was pulling at his hand. "Mr. Troy, Mr. Troy, we're all going to have dinner together!"

Great. He smiled down at the boy. How was he going to get out of this?

"Xavier, honey." Angelica knelt down beside her son. "We'll have dinner at the bunkhouse. We can't impose."

She tugged the ponytail holder out of her hair, and the shiny locks flowed down her back. Her hand kneaded Xavier's shoulder. She was all loving mother.

And all woman.

"But, Mama! Wait till you see what Miss Lou Ann and me cooked!"

Lou Ann rubbed Xavier's bald head. "I'm sorry, Angelica. I told him we could probably all eat together. We picked zucchini and tomatoes from the garden and cooked up some of that ratatouille."

"And we made a meat loaf, and I got to mix it up with my hands!"

The boy sounded so happy. Troy's throat tightened as he thought about how Angelica must feel, cherishing every moment with him and wondering at the same time whether he'd ever make meat loaf again, whether this was the last chance for this particular activity.

Angelica glanced up at him, eyebrows raised. "Maybe we'll get together another time. Mr. Troy's been working all day and he's tired. Let's let him rest."

What was he supposed to do now, squash down all of this joy? And he had to admit that the thought of having company for dinner in the farmhouse kitchen didn't sound half-bad, except that the pretty woman opposite him was hankering after another man.

At the thought of Angelica dating Buck Armstrong, something dark twisted his insides. With everything he knew about Buck, he should warn her off, and yet it would serve her right to go out with him and find out what he was really like.

"Can we stay, Mr. Troy?"

He looked at the boy's hopeful eyes. "Of course."

His words sounded so grudging that he added, "Sounds like a good meal you fixed."

"It is good, and wait till you see dessert!"

By the time Xavier helped Lou Ann serve dessert—sliced pound cake, topped with berries and whipped cream—he looked beat. But his smile was joyous. "I had so much fun this afternoon, Mama!"

Troy praised the food, which was really good, thanks he was sure to Lou Ann's guidance. But his stomach was turning, wouldn't let him really enjoy it.

Angelica looked beautiful at the other end of the table, her black hair tumbling down past her shoulders and her cheeks pink as apples. And now, with Xavier so happy, she didn't seem as worried as usual; the little line that tended to live between her eyebrows was gone, and her smile flashed frequently as Xavier described all that he and Lou Ann had done that day.

Troy had always wanted this. He wanted a warm, beautiful woman and cute, enthusiastic children at his table, wanted to be the man of the family. And this sweet, feisty pair seemed to fit right into his home and his heart. But he had to keep reminding himself that this wasn't his and it wouldn't last.

Looking at Xavier, he couldn't believe the child had been so sick and might relapse at any moment. Yeah, he was drooping, getting tired, but he was so full of life that it made no sense that God might take him away.

Any more than it made sense that God would put him and his siblings in a loveless family, let alone give Angelica all the heartaches she'd endured growing up, but that was God for you—making sense wasn't what He was about. That was why Troy had stopped trusting Him, starting taking most things into his own hands.

He believed, sure; he just didn't trust. And he sure didn't want to join the men's Bible study his friend Dion was always bugging him about.

"This little one needs to get to bed," Lou Ann said. "Troy, I know you can't carry much with those crutches, but why don't you at least help her with the doors and such?"

"Oh, you don't have to—" Angelica stood, looking suddenly uncomfortable. "We've already taken too much of your time. We can make it."

But Troy moved to intercept her protest. "Come on, pal. Let's get you out to bed."

Angelica started gathering Xavier's pills and toys and snacks together, stuffing them into a Spider-Man backpack. Before she could bend to pick Xavier up, Troy leaned on one crutch, steadied himself with a hip against the table and picked up the boy himself. He was amazingly light. He nestled right against Troy's chest and Troy felt his heart break a little. He glanced over at Angelica and saw that she had tears in her eyes. "Ready?" he asked. Then, gently, he put her son in her arms, taking the boy's backpack to carry himself.

She bit her lip, turned and headed off, and he grabbed his crutches and followed her. They walked out to the bunkhouse together and Troy helped Angelica lay Xavier in his bed, noticing the homey touches Angelica had put around—a teddy bear, a poster of a baseball player, a hand-knitted afghan in shades of blue and brown. It was a boy's room, and it should be filling up with trophies from Little League games. They said every kid got a trophy these days, and wasn't that awful? But not Xavier. This kid hadn't had the opportunity to play baseball.

Not yet.

Angelica knelt beside the bed. "Let's thank God for today."

"Thank You, God, for letting me cook dinner. And for Lou Ann. And the dogs."

Angelica was holding Xavier's hand. "Thank You for giving us food and love and each other."

"Bless all the people who don't have so much," they said together.

"And, God, please get me a daddy before…" Xavier trailed off, turned over.

Whoa. Troy's throat tightened.

"Night, sweetie, sleep tight." Angelica's voice sounded choked.

"Don't let the bedbugs… Love you, Mama." The words were fading off and the boy was asleep.

They both stood looking down at him, Troy on one side of the bed and Angelica on the other.

"Did he say he wants a…dad?" Troy ventured finally.

Angelica nodded.

"Does his dad ever spend time with him?"

She looked up at him. "No. Never."

"Does he even know him?"

Her lips tightened. "I… Look, Troy, I don't want to talk about that."

"Sure." But he'd like to strangle the guy who'd loved and left her, and not just because he remembered how difficult it had been to keep his hands off Angelica back when they were engaged. He took a deep breath and loosened his tightly clasped fists. She'd gotten pregnant with Xavier right around the time she left town, so was Xavier's dad—the jerk—from here or from elsewhere? She hadn't married him, apparently, but... "If the guy knew Xavier, knew what he was like and what he's facing, surely he'd be willing—"

"No."

"No?"

"Just...no, okay?" She stood and stalked out to the living room, and Troy wondered whether he'd ever stop putting his plaster-covered foot in his mouth around her.

The next Saturday, Angelica touched up her hair with a curling wand and applied blush and mascara. And tried not to throw up.

She didn't want to go out on a date. But there was no other way to get Xavier off her case.

In fact, he was beside her now, hugging her leg. "You never had a date before, Mama."

She laughed. "Yes, I did. Back in the day. Before you."

"Did you go on dates with my dad?"

All Xavier knew was that his father had died. He hadn't ever asked whether Angelica and his father had been married, and Angelica hoped he didn't go there any time soon. For now, she would stick as close to the truth as possible. "No, not with him, but with a few other guys." She tried to deflect his attention. "Just like I'm doing now. Do I look all right?"

"You're beautiful, Mama."

She hugged him. "Thanks, Zavey Davey. You're kinda cute yourself."

"Do I get to meet him? Because I want to see, you know, if he's the right kind of guy for us."

"My little protector. You can meet him sometime,

but not now. Miss Lou Ann is going to come over and play with you. And I think I hear her now."

Sure enough, there was a knock on the bunkhouse door. Xavier ran over to get it while Angelica fussed with herself a little more. She'd much rather just stay home with Xavier tonight. What if Buck tried something? She knew him to be a nice guy, but still…

"Well, how's my little friend for the evening?" Lou Ann asked, pinching Xavier's cheek. "You set up for a Candy Land marathon, or are we building a fort out of sheets and chairs?"

"You'll build a fort with me?" Xavier's eyes turned worshipful. "Mom always says it's too messy."

"It's only too messy if we don't clean up later. And we will, right?"

"Right. I'll get the extra sheets."

As soon as he was out of the room, Lou Ann turned to Angelica. "You look pretty," she said. "Somebody's already cranky, and when he sees you looking like that…" She smacked her lips. "Sparks are gonna fly."

That was the last thing she needed. Her face heated and she changed the subject. "Xavier can stay up until eight-thirty. He gets his meds and a snack half an hour before bed." She showed Lou Ann the pills and the basket of approved snacks.

"That's easy. Don't worry about us." Lou Ann leaned back and looked out the window. "I think your friend just pulled in."

"I wanna see him!" Xavier rushed toward the window, dropping the stack of sheets he'd been carrying.

"Well," Lou Ann said, "that's just fine, because I want to claim the best spot in the fort."

Xavier spun back to Lou Ann. "I'm king of the fort!"

"You'd better get over here and help me, then."

Thank you, Angelica mouthed to Lou Ann, and slipped out the door.

Buck emerged from his black pickup, looking good from his long jean-clad legs to his slightly shaggy brown curls. Any girl would feel fortunate to be dating such a cute guy, Angelica told herself, trying to lighten the lead weight in her stomach.

He's a nice guy. And it's for Xavier. "Hi there!"

"Well, don't you look pretty!" He walked toward her, loose limbed.

To her right, the front door of the main house opened. Troy. He came out on the porch and stood, arms crossed. For all the world as if he were her father.

She narrowed her eyes at him, trying to ignore his rougher style of handsome, the way his broad shoulders, leaning on his crutches, strained the seams of his shirt. She was through with Troy Hinton, and he was most certainly through with her, wouldn't want anything to do with her if he knew the truth.

She deliberately returned her attention to Buck. He reached her and opened his arms.

Really? Was a big hug normal on a first date? It had been so long…and she'd been so young… She took a deep breath and allowed him to hug her, at the same time wrinkling her nose. Something was wrong…

"Baby, it's great to see you. Man, feels good to hug a woman." Buck's words were slurred. And yes, that smell was alcohol, covered with a whole lot of peppermint.

She tried to pull back, but he didn't let go.

Panic rose in her. She stepped hard onto his foot. "Let go," she said, loud, right in his ear.

From the corner of her eye, the sight of Troy made her feel secure.

"Sorry!" Buck stepped back. "I didn't mean...I was just glad...oh man, you look so good." He moved as though he was going to hug her again.

She sidestepped. "Buck. How much have you had to drink?"

"What?" He put an arm around her and started guiding her toward his truck. "I had a drink before I came over. One drink. Don't get uptight."

Could that be true? Without a doubt, she was uptight around men. But this felt wrong in a different way. "Wait a minute. I...I think we should talk a little bit before we go."

"Sure!" He shifted direction, guiding her toward a bench and plopping down too hard, knocking into her so that she sat down hard, too.

She drew in a breath and let it out in a sigh. He was drunk, all right. It wasn't just her being paranoid. But now, how did she get rid of him?

"I really like you, Angelica," he said, putting an arm around her. He pulled her closer.

She scooted away. "Look, Buck, I can't...I don't think I can go out with you. You've had too much to drink."

"One drink!" He sounded irritated.

Angelica stood and backed away. Couldn't something, just once, be easy? "Sorry, friend, but I can't get in the truck with you. And you shouldn't be driving, either."

There was a sound of booted feet, and then Troy was beside her. "She's right, Buck."

"What you doing here, Hinton?"

"I live here, as you very well know."

"Well, I'm taking this little lady out for a meal, once—"

"You're not going anywhere except home. As soon as your sister gets here to pick you up."

"Oh man, you didn't call Lacey!" Buck staggered to his feet, his hand going to his pocket. He pulled out truck keys. "This has been a bust."

Angelica glanced at Troy, willing him to let her handle it. She had plenty of experience with drunk people, starting with her own parents. "Can I see the car keys a minute?"

He held them out, hope lighting up his face. "You gonna come after all? I'll let you drive."

She took the keys. "I'm not going, and sorry, but you're not fit to drive yourself, either."

He lunged to get them back and Troy stuck out a crutch to trip him. "You're not welcome on this property until you're sober."

Angelica kept backing off while, in the distance, a Jeep made clouds on the dusty road. That must be Buck's sister.

So she could go home now. Back inside. Face Xavier and tell him the date was off.

Except she couldn't, because tears were filling her eyes and blurring her vision. She blinked hard and backed up as far as the porch steps while Troy greeted the woman who'd squealed up in the Jeep.

The woman pushed past Troy, poked a finger in Buck's chest and proceeded to chew him out. Then she and Troy helped him into the passenger seat. They stood beside the Jeep for a minute, talking.

When Angelica turned away, she realized that

Xavier could see her here if he looked out the window. Hopefully he was too deep into fort-building to notice, but she wasn't ready to see him and she couldn't take the risk. She headed out to the kennels at a jog. Grabbed one of the pit bulls she'd been working with, a black-and-white beauty named Sheena, attached a leash to her and started walking down the field road as unwanted, annoying tears came faster and faster.

She sank to her knees beside a wooden fence post, willing the tears to stop, hugging the dog that licked her cheek with canine concern.

"Get yourself together, girlie. Nobody said life's a tea party."

Gramps' words, harsh but kindly meant, had guided her through the storms of adolescence and often echoed in her mind.

Today, for some reason, they didn't help. She squeezed her eyes shut and tried to pray, but the tears kept coming.

After long moments, one of the verses she'd memorized during Xavier's treatment came into her mind.

Fear not, for I am with you; be not dismayed, for I am your God; I will strengthen you, I will help you, I will uphold you with My righteous right hand.

Slowly, peace, or at least resignation, started to return. But every time she thought about Xavier and how disappointed he'd be, the tears overflowed again.

A hand gripped her shoulder, making her start violently. "You that upset about Buck?" Troy asked.

She shook her head, fighting for control. It wasn't about Buck, not really. He was a small disappointment in the midst of a lot of big ones, but it was enough to push her over the edge. She couldn't handle the possibility of losing Xavier, the only good thing in her life, and yet she had to handle it. And she had to stay strong and positive for him.

It was pretty much her mantra. She breathed in, breathed out. *Stay strong*, she told herself. *Stay strong*.

A couple of minutes later she was able to accept Troy's outstretched hand and climb to her feet. He took the dog leash from her and handed her an ancient-looking, soft bandanna. "It's not pretty, but it's clean."

She nodded and wiped her eyes and nose and came back into herself enough to be embarrassed at how she must look. She wasn't one of those pretty, leak-a-few-tears criers; she knew her eyes must be red and puffy, and she honked when she blew her nose. "Sorry," she said to him.

"For what?"

She shook her head, and by unspoken agreement they started walking. "Sorry to break down."

"You're entitled."

The sun was setting now, sending pink streaks across the sky, and a slight breeze cooled the air. Crickets harmonized with bullfrogs in a gentle rise and fall. Angelica breathed in air so pungent with hay and summer flowers that she could almost taste it, and slowly the familiar landscape brought her calm.

"You know," Troy ventured after a few minutes, "Buck Armstrong's not really worth all that emotion. Not these days. If I'd known you were this into dating him, I might have warned you he has a drinking problem."

She laughed, and that made her cry a little more, and she wiped her eyes. "It's not really about Buck."

He didn't say anything for a minute. Then he gave

her shoulder a gentle squeeze. "You've got a lot on your plate."

"I've got a plan, is what I've got," she said, "and I was hoping Buck could be a part of it." Briefly, she explained her intention of finding a stand-in dad for Xavier.

Troy shook his head. "That's not going to work."

"What do you mean?"

"He's a smart kid. He'll know. You can't just pretend you're dating someone so that he'll think he's getting a dad."

"I can if I want to." They came to a crossroads and she glanced around. "I'm not ready to go back home and admit defeat yet, and I don't want him looking out the window and seeing me cry."

"Come the back way, by the kennel."

Sheena, the dog she'd brought with her, jumped at a squirrel, and Troy let her off the lead to chase it. She romped happily, ears flopping.

"So you think getting a dad will make Xavier happy? Even if it's a fake dad?"

"It's not fake! Or, well, it is, but for a good reason." She reached into her pocket and pulled out the picture she always carried, Xavier in happier times. "Look at that face! For all I know, he'll never be really healthy again." She cleared her throat. "If I can make his life happy, I'm going to do it."

He studied the picture. "He played Little League?"

She swallowed hard around the lump in her throat. "T-ball. He'd just started when he was diagnosed. He had one season."

"He started young."

She nodded. "They let him start a few weeks before

his birthday, even though officially they aren't supposed to start until they turn four."

"Because he was sick?"

She shook her head. "Because he was so good. He loved it." Tears rushed to her eyes again and she put her hands to her face.

"Hey." He took the sloppy bandanna from her hand, wiped her eyes and nose as if she were a child, and pulled her to his chest. And for just a minute, after a reflexive flinch, Angelica let herself enjoy the feeling. His chest was broad and strong, and she heard the slow beating of his heart. She aligned her breath with his and it steadied her, calmed her.

In just a minute, she'd back away. Because this was dangerous and it wasn't going anywhere. Troy wouldn't want a woman like Angelica, not really, so letting an attraction build between them was a huge mistake.

Troy patted Angelica's back and breathed in the strawberry scent of her hair, trying to remind himself why he needed to be careful.

He wanted to help Angelica and Xavier in the worst way. His heart was all in with this little family. But that heart was broken, wounded, not whole.

He felt her stiffen in his arms, as though she was just realizing how close he was. For the thousandth time since he'd reencountered her, he wondered about her skittishness around men. Or was it just around him? No, he'd seen her tense up when Armstrong had hugged her, too.

Carefully, he held her upper arms and stepped away. Her face was blotched and wet, but she still looked beautiful. Her Western-style shirt was unbuttoned down to a modest V, sleeves rolled up to reveal tanned forearms. Her jeans clung to her slim figure. Intricate silver earrings hung from her ears, sparkling against her wavy black hair.

"Come on," he said gruffly, "let's go in the house. We'll get you something to drink."

"Okay." She looked up at him, her eyes vulnerable, and he wanted nothing more than to protect her.

Don't go there, fool.

They walked back along the country road as the last bit of sun set in a golden haze. A few dogs barked out their farewell to the day. At the kennel, they put Sheena back inside, and then he led Angelica up to the house.

He loved his farm, his dogs, his life. He had so much. But what right did he have to be happy when Angelica's problems were so big?

How could he help her?

An idea slammed into him, almost an audible voice. *You could marry her.*

Immediately he squelched the notion. Ridiculous. No way. He wouldn't go down that path. Not again, not after what she'd done to him.

And even outside of the way she'd dumped him, he'd never seen a good marriage. He didn't know how to be married; didn't know how to relate to people that way; didn't know how to keep a woman happy or make it last. He didn't want to be like his dad, the person who failed his wife. He didn't want to let Xavier down.

But the point was, he thought as he held the door for her, Xavier might not have the time to be let down. Xavier needed and wanted a dad now, and Troy already knew the boy liked him.

As they walked into the kitchen, he remembered

proposing to Angelica the last time. Then he'd been all about wanting to impress her, to sweep her away. He'd hired Samantha Weston, who usually used her small plane for crop dusting, to sky-write his proposal at sunset during an all-town Memorial Day picnic. Angelica had laughed, and cried, and joyously accepted. Her friends had clustered around them, and he'd presented her with a diamond way too big for a new vet with school loans to pay off.

He still had that ring, come to think of it. He'd stuffed it in his sock drawer when she mailed it back to him, and he'd never looked at it again.

It was upstairs right now. He could go and get it. Help her handle this massive challenge life had given her. And Xavier... Boy, did he want to help that kid!

Angelica perched on a kitchen stool and rested her chin in her hands. "I guess the idea of Buck as a pretend husband does seem kinda crazy, when I think about it," she admitted. "Anyway, enough about me. How long has Buck had a drinking problem?"

"Since he lost his wife and child," Troy said. "Not only that, but he served a couple of tours in Afghanistan. Which is why I cut the guy a break and let him work at my weekend clinic. I've offered him a full-time job, too, but only if he'll stay sober for six months first. So far, he hasn't been able to do that."

"That's so sad." She bit her lip. "I hope he's going to be okay tonight. I felt bad, but there was no way I was getting into a truck with him."

"And no way he could be Xavier's pseudodad."

"No."

He cracked open a Pepsi and handed it to her. "Here. Sugar and caffeine. It'll make you feel better."

"Always. Thanks." She swung her feet. "Remember buying me a Coke at the drugstore, that very first time we went out?"

He nodded. "And I remember how you sat there drinking it and explaining to me your dating rules. No kissing until the third date. No parking. No staying out past eleven."

"I know, and it wasn't even Gramps making those rules, it was me. I was so scared of getting myself into the same bad situations that landed my folks in trouble. Plus, my brother told me I should be careful about you. Since you were an older man and all." She smiled up at him through her lashes.

His heart rate shot through the ceiling. "Your brother was protective," he said, trying to keep his voice—and his thoughts—on something other than how pretty she was. One question still nagged at him: if she'd had all those rules, then how had she ended up unmarried and pregnant?

"Xavier really misses my brother. Carlo lived near us in Boston for a while, and he's the one who got Xavier involved in T-ball. He did the whole male influence thing, until he got the call to go overseas." She flashed Troy a smile. "If I keep thinking about Carlo I'll get sad again. Save me, Bull!" She slid off the stool and sat cross-legged on the floor. The old bulldog climbed into her lap, and she leaned down and let him lick her face.

"Whoa, Bull, be a gentleman! She'll pass out from your breath!" But he couldn't help enjoying Angelica's affectionate attitude toward his dog. A lot of women didn't want a smelly old dog anywhere around their stockings and fancy dresses, but Angelica was a blue-jeans girl from way back.

He sank down beside her, petting Bull. "So, what are you going to do now? About your plan, I mean?"

She shook her head. "I don't know. I guess I'll have to disappoint him. I mean, I'm not the most outgoing person when it comes to dating, and I don't want to mislead any guys about where it's all headed." She forced a smile. "Know any eligible bachelors I could snare?"

"Me," he heard himself saying. "You could marry me."

Chapter 4

As he watched the color drain from Angelica's face, Troy's chest tightened and he wished he could take back his words. What had he just said? What had he been thinking?

Cynical doubts kicked at the crazy adrenaline rush coursing through his body. Why would he want to propose to Angelica again when she'd dumped him without explanation before? He'd already done what he could to help her and her son. He'd given her a job and provided a place to live, but this was way beyond the call of duty.

He opened his mouth to say so, but she held up a hand.

"Look, it's amazingly kind of you to offer that, especially after…after everything. You've already done so much for us. But I could never expect anything like that. And I couldn't marry someone without…"

He crossed his arms over his chest. "Without loving him?"

"I was going to say…" She lowered her head and let out a sigh. "Never mind."

Suddenly warm, he stood, grabbed a crutch and limped across the room. He flicked on the air-conditioning and fiddled with the thermostat on the wall.

She'd brought up all the very same objections he'd had himself. She'd given him a way to back out.

So why did he feel so let down?

She scrambled to her feet, watching him as if he were a wild animal she had to protect herself from. All comfort, all closeness between them was gone. "Um, I should go." Her hand on the screen door handle, she stilled. "Uh-oh."

"What's wrong?" He came up behind her and looked over her shoulder out the door as the scent of her hair tickled his nose.

In the outdoor floodlight he saw Xavier was running toward the house, his face furrowed. Teary hiccups became more audible as he got closer. Behind him, Lou Ann followed at a dangerously fast pace, huffing and puffing and calling the boy.

Angelica opened the screen door just as Xavier got to the top of the porch steps. She knelt, and Xavier ran into her arms, causing her to reel backward.

Troy balanced on his crutch and reached out to steady the pair. "Whoa there, partner, slow down!"

"Is it true?" Xavier demanded. "What Miss Lou Ann said?"

At that moment the lady in question arrived at the top of the front porch steps. "Xavier!" She paused for breath. "You come…when I call you. I'm sorry," she added, turning to Angelica. "I said something I shouldn't have. It upset him."

"She said it wasn't going to work out for that man to be my daddy, and I might not get a daddy!"

"Come on in, baby." Angelica scooped her son into her arms and struggled to her feet, shrugging off Troy's attempt to help her. She carried Xavier inside. "Is it okay if we talk a minute in here?"

"Sure."

And then he watched her focus entirely on her son. She sat down on the couch and pulled the boy, all angular arms and long legs, in her lap. "So tell me more about those tears, mister."

"I want a daddy!" he sulked. "I thought you were gonna get me one."

She rubbed his hairless head. "I know how much you want a dad. You want to be like other kids."

"I want somebody to play T-ball with me and take me fishing." Behind the words, Troy heard a poignant yearning for all Xavier wanted and might not get, all he'd missed during the long months of treatment.

"I know," Angelica said, rocking a little. "I know, honey."

"So why did you send that man away?"

She shot a glance at Troy. "He wasn't feeling well."

"So he might come back when he's better?"

Slowly, Angelica shook her head. "No, honey. Turns out he's not right for us."

Tears welled in the boy's eyes again, but she pulled his head against her chest. "Shh. I know it's hard, but we have to let God do His work. He takes care of us, remember?"

"Sometimes He does a bad job!"

Angelica chuckled, a low vibration that brushed along Troy's nerve endings. "He never does a bad job, sweetie. Sometimes you and I can't understand His ways, but He's always taking care of us. We can relax because of that."

Her voice sounded totally confident, totally sure, and Troy wished for some of that certainty for himself.

She was such a good mother. She knew exactly how to reach her son, even when he was upset. She could listen, handle his bratty moments and get him to laugh. She was meant to mother this boy, and most of the resentment Troy felt about her pregnancy fell away. Whatever had happened, whatever mistakes she'd made, she'd paid for them. And as she said, God was always taking care of things. He'd given one sick young boy the perfect mother.

Who, when she met his eyes over the child's head and gave him a little smile, looked like the perfect wife, as well.

A week later, Angelica was chopping vegetables for stew and marveling at how quickly they'd settled into a routine. Lou Ann took an online class every Tuesday and Thursday, so those days, Angelica started dinner for all of them while Xavier rested.

As she chopped the last carrot, though, Xavier burst into the kitchen. "Can I go outside and see Mr. Troy and the dogs?"

Thrilled to see this sign of improved energy, she nonetheless narrowed her eyes at him. "What are you doing off the couch? You're supposed to rest from two to four every afternoon. Doctor's orders."

"I don't want to rest anymore. Besides, it's almost four."

"Is it really?" She looked at the clock. "Three-thirty isn't four, buster." But it was close. Where had the time gone? Troy had been wonderful about letting her set up a flexible schedule around Xavier, but she needed to get back out to the kennels at four. She bit the inside of her cheek.

"I want to go outside." Xavier's lower lip pushed out.

"That's not going to work, honey. After you rest, you need to stay in here with Miss Lou Ann so I can work."

"But I wanna go outside!" Xavier yelled.

Angelica dried her hands on a dishcloth and shot up a prayer for patience. Then she knelt in front of Xavier. "Inside voice and respect, please."

"Sorry." He didn't sound it, but she stood up anyway. With a sick kid, you had to choose your battles.

"I see someone's feeling better." Troy limped into the kitchen, wearing jeans and a collared shirt. His shoulder muscles flexed as he hopped nimbly over on his crutches.

He looks good! was her first thought, and it made her cheeks heat up. "I didn't know you were here today. Thought you had vet patients in town."

"I come home early on Thursdays. Snagged a ride with our receptionist." He was looking at her steadily, eyebrows raised a little, as if he could read her mind. How embarrassing!

Xavier tugged at his leg. "Can I come outside with you, Mr. Troy? Please?"

"It's okay with me, buddy." Troy reached down to pat Xavier's shoulder. "But what does your mom say? She's the boss."

"I can't let him follow you around and bother you."

"I think you and Xavier were at the doctor's last week, so you wouldn't know that Thursdays are special. I do some other stuff."

"Stuff I can do with you?" Xavier was staring up at Troy, eyes wide and pleading.

Angelica bit back a smile. Her son, the master manipulator. "Honey, we have to respect—"

"Actually," Troy interrupted, "this might be a really good activity for Xavier. If you're willing."

"What is it?" She covered the stew pot and lowered the gas heat.

"Dog training. Takes a lot of patience." He winked at her. "Some kid training, too. Let him come with me, and then you come out, too, in a little while. I may need some help."

"Please, Mom?"

She threw up her hands. "I give up. Go ahead."

She watched out the window as Xavier and Troy walked off together. Troy was getting more and more agile with his crutches, and she suspected he'd be off them soon. His head was inclined to hear what Xavier was saying, and as for her son, he was chattering away so joyously that she was glad she'd let him go with Troy.

She wanted him to be happy, and right now, somehow, that happiness was all tied up in Troy. Troy and the dogs. Pray God it would last.

"They look more like father and son than most father and sons," Lou Ann said, walking into the room with an armload of books and paperwork. "That's good for Troy. He didn't have a great relationship with his own dad. Still doesn't, for that matter."

"I remember, but I never knew why." Angelica reached down to scratch Bull's head. "Go back to your bed, buddy. I'm done cooking, and Daddy says no table scraps for you."

"That doesn't keep him from begging, though." Lou Ann put her laptop and books on the built-in desk in the corner of the kitchen. "Clyde Hinton is a hard man, especially with his boys. His older son fought back, and that's why the two of them can work together now. Troy, though, wasn't having any of it. He shut the door on his dad a long time ago. They hardly ever see each other."

"Interesting." During their engagement, she and Troy hadn't visited much with his father, and the little time they'd spent at Troy's family home was stiff and uncomfortable.

Settling into a chair at the kitchen table, Lou Ann put her feet up on one of the other chairs and stretched. "Where's Xavier going, anyway? I'm ready to play some *Extreme Flight Simulator* with him. Clear my brain from all that psychology."

"Troy's taking him out to the kennels." Angelica turned to the woman who was rapidly becoming a good friend. "I'm so impressed you're working on your degree online."

"Never had the chance before," Lou Ann said, "and it's a kick. I always did like school, just never had time to really pursue it. And Troy insists on paying for it. Says it's the least he can do since I agreed to come back to work for him."

"Wow, I didn't know that."

"There's a lot of things you don't know about that

man," Lou Ann said. "He's not one to toot his own horn."

Angelica tucked that away for consideration. "He's sure being good to Xavier. Though he doesn't know what he's getting into, taking him out to the kennels. He'll have to watch him like a hawk, and he won't get any of his own work done."

"It's Thursday, isn't it?" Lou Ann glanced up at the calendar on the wall. "Thursdays, he has the rascals over. Maybe he's going to get Xavier involved with them."

"The rascals, huh?" Just what Xavier needed. "Who are they?"

One side of Lou Ann's mouth quirked up. "They're some kids I wouldn't work with to save my life, but somehow Troy has them helping at the kennel, training dogs and cleaning cages. He's a rescuer, always has been."

"Dangerous kids?" Angelica paused in the act of handing Lou Ann a cup of coffee.

"No, not dangerous. Just full of beans. Relax!" Lou Ann reached for the coffee, took a sip and put it down on the table. "Thanks, hon. There are some real poor folks in this county. Kids who live on hardscrabble farms, hill people just up from down South, migrants who've set up their trailers at the edge of some field."

"Sounds like the way I grew up," Angelica said wryly.

"That's right." Lou Ann looked thoughtful for a minute. "Anyway, when Troy was…well, when he went through a rough spot a while back, Pastor Ricky approached him about setting up a program for those kids. Troy went along, because a lot of them hadn't a notion of the right way to take care of a dog. It's grown, and now he's got ten or twelve coming every week to help out."

"That's amazing, with everything else he does."

"He'd help anyone in the world. What doesn't come so easy to him is taking help himself."

"I'm going to go out." Angelica rinsed the cutting board and stood it in the drainer. "Just as soon as I get those bathrooms clean."

"You go ahead now," Lou Ann said. "I can tell you're a little worried about your boy. I think you'll like what you see."

"Thanks." Impulsively, she gave the older woman a hug.

Five minutes later, Angelica was leaning on the fence outside the kennel, watching Xavier run and play with dogs and boys of all sizes, shapes and colors. He looked so happy that it took Angelica's breath away. She didn't know she was crying until Troy came up beside her and ran a light finger under each eye.

She jerked back, not comfortable with the soft, tender touch.

"You okay?"

She drew in a breath and let it out in a happy sigh. "I'm fine. And I'm so grateful to you for letting Xavier have some normal kid moments."

Troy frowned. "He doesn't get to do stuff like this often?"

She shook her head. "He's been in treatment so much that he hasn't had the chance to play with other boys. Let alone a bunch of dogs."

"It's good for the kids. They need to get their energy out in an accepting environment. And I need someone

to play with the dogs. Easy there, Enrique!" he called
to a boy who was roughhousing with a small white
mutt a little too vigorously.

"Sorry, Señor Troy." The boy in question backed off
immediately, then knelt and petted the dog.

"Hey, that's the little dog from the clinic! The owner
thought he was going to die!"

Troy nodded, looking satisfied. "He's responding
to the medication. He should be able to go back home
within a week. I know Darlene will be glad. She calls
every couple of days."

She studied Troy's profile. He helped dogs who
needed it, owners who couldn't pay, kids who'd grown
up without advantages. And of course, he was helping
her and Xavier.

"Anyway, thanks for giving my son this opportunity."

When he looked down at her, arms propped on
the fence beside hers, she realized how close together
they were.

The thought she'd been squelching for the past week,
the topic she'd been dodging the couple of times Troy
had brought it up, burst into the front of her mind:
he'd asked her to marry him just a week ago. He was
a man of his word. She could have this. She could have
a home, a farm, a man who liked to help others. Most
of all, a father for Xavier.

But she'd struggled so long alone that being here,
in this perfect life, felt scary, almost wrong. She didn't
deserve it.

The other thing she'd been trying not to think about
made its way to the surface. She was tainted, dirty. In
his heart, Troy would want someone pure. He'd said it

enough times when they were engaged—how important it was to him that she'd never been with anyone, that she'd saved herself for marriage. *"I'm a jealous guy,"* he'd said. *"I want you all for my own."*

She tore her eyes away from him, cleared her throat and focused on Xavier, who was rolling on the grass while a couple of the pit bull puppies, already bigger and steadier than they'd been a week ago, licked his face.

She had to live in the moment and focus on all the benefits this lifestyle was bringing her son. And stay as far as possible away from this man who'd proposed marriage.

Troy was a good person, even a great one, but she wasn't a rescue dog. She needed to be with a man who loved her and could accept her mistakes and her past.

"Mom!" Xavier came over, panting, two high red spots on his cheeks. "This is so much fun. Did you see how I was throwing the Frisbee with the guys?"

When he said "the guys," his tone rang with amazed, self-conscious pride. He'd never been one of the guys, but it was high time he started. And Troy was helping make that happen. "I missed your Frisbee throwing, buddy," she said, "but I'll watch it the next time, okay?"

When she glanced up at Troy to thank him again, she found him staring down at her with a look in his dark eyes that was impossible to read. Impossible to look away from, too. She caught her breath, licked her lips.

As if from a great distance, she heard Xavier calling her name, felt him tugging at her hand. "Hey, Mom, I had a great idea," he was saying.

She shook her head a little, blinked and turned to look at her son. "What's the idea, honey?"

"Do you think Mr. Troy could be my dad?"

Chapter 5

Xavier's words were still echoing in Troy's mind the next day. He was riding shotgun—man, he hated that, but the doctor hadn't yet cleared him to drive—while his friend Dion Grant drove his van. They were taking a group from their church, including Angelica and Xavier, to weed the garden at the Senior Towers.

"Do you think Mr. Troy could be my dad?"

He listened to the group's chatter as they climbed out of the van and pulled garden tools from the back. *Could* he become Xavier's dad? Angelica's husband?

It seemed as if those questions hovered in the air every time he was around Angelica. She'd never responded to his proposal, and yesterday she'd brushed aside Xavier's words and scolded the child.

But was the thought so repugnant to her? Once, she'd wanted to marry him.

Sure, she'd left him, apparently for someone else, since she immediately became pregnant. Knowing her now, he didn't think she'd cheated on him while they were together; she wouldn't have had that in her.

But if she'd fallen in love with someone else and been too embarrassed to admit it…maybe when she'd gone to visit her aunt that summer…

The moment he emerged from the driver's seat, a small hand tugged at his. "Dad! Dad!"

"Xavier!" Angelica hurried up behind Xavier and put her hands on his shoulders. "Honey, you can't call Mr. Troy 'Dad.'" Her face was bright red, and she wouldn't meet Troy's eyes.

"It's okay." Troy patted her shoulder.

"No, it's really not." Angelica kept her voice low and nodded sideways toward the row of ladies sitting on the porch of the Senior Towers. "Let's just hope nobody heard. Come on, Zavey Davey," she said, "you have a playdate with your new friend Becka from church."

"A girl?" Xavier groaned.

"Yes, and she's a lot of fun. Her mom said you two were going to hunt for bugs in the park. She has a magnifying glass."

Xavier screwed up his face and looked thoughtful.

"And she's into soccer, so maybe you two can kick around a soccer ball."

"Okay. That's cool."

Troy watched as Angelica led her son toward a one-story house set between the Senior Towers and the town park. Her long hair was caught up in a high ponytail, and she wore old jeans and a T-shirt emblazoned with a Run for Shelter/Stop Domestic Violence logo. When had she gotten time to do a charity run, with all she had on her plate? And how did she manage to put zero time into her appearance and still look absolutely gorgeous?

"Breathe, buddy." His friend Dion gave him a light punch in the arm. "Didn't know she was your baby mama, but half the town will pretty soon."

"What? She's not my baby mama," Troy said automatically, and then met his friend's eyes. "Uh-oh. Who all heard what Xavier just said?"

"Miss Minnie Falcon, for one." Dion nodded toward the front porch of the Senior Towers.

Troy shrugged and lifted his hands, palms up. "Xavier's not my kid, but he wants me to be his dad. Guess he's decided to pretend it's so."

"You could do a lot worse than those two."

"Yeah. Except she dumped me once before, and she doesn't want anything but a professional relationship with me."

"You sure about that, my friend?"

He wasn't sure of anything and he felt too confused to discuss the subject. "Come on, we'd better start weeding or the ladies are going to outshine us."

He'd brought a low lawn chair so he could weed without bending his injured leg. Working the earth, just slightly damp from a recent rain, felt soothing to Troy, and he realized he'd been spending too much time indoors, doing paperwork and staying late at his office in town. The dirt was warm and pungent with an oniony scent. Nearby, he could hear the shouts of kids at the park and the occasional car or truck driving by.

Even after Angelica returned and started weeding across the gardens from him, he didn't sweat it. The jokes and chatter of the group, most of whom knew each other well from years of adult Sunday school class together, made for an easy feeling. He was glad they'd come.

"Hey, beautiful, when did you get back to town?"

The voice, from a passerby, sounded pleasant enough, but he turned to see who was calling a member of the group "beautiful" with the tiniest bit of snarkiness in his tone. It took a minute, but he recognized the guy from a few classes behind him in high school, dressed in a scrub shirt and jeans. Logan Filmore. Brother of a friend of his. Guy must be in some kind of medical field now.

And of course, he was speaking to Angelica.

Troy's eyes flashed to her and read her concern, even distaste.

He pushed to his feet, grabbed a crutch and limped across the garden to stand beside her. "How's it going?"

"Okay." She looked uneasily at Logan, who'd stopped in front of them.

The guy looked at Troy and seemed to read something in his eyes, because he took a step back. He gave Angelica a head-to-toes once-over, then waved and walked on, calling, "Nice to see you" over his shoulder.

Angelica squatted back down and Troy eased himself down beside her.

"Someone you know?"

She yanked a thistle out of the ground. "Sort of."

"Is there anything I can do?"

Another weed hit the heap in the center of the garden. "Stop talking about it?"

He lifted his hands, palms up. "Okay. Just trying to help."

For several minutes they pulled weeds in silence.

Troy was totally aware of her, though: the glow of her skin, the fine sheen of sweat on her face, the vigorous, almost angry way she tugged weeds.

Finally she turned her face partway toward him. "I'm sorry. I…I used to know him and I really dislike him. Thanks for coming over."

"Sure." A few more weeds hit the pile. "I like helping you, you know."

"Thanks."

"I like it a lot." He wanted to protect her from people like the guy who'd just passed by. He wanted to protect her full-time. Of course, he mainly wanted to marry her for Xavier's sake. That was all.

He reached across her to tug on a vine. Their hands brushed.

He was expecting her to jerk away, but she didn't; she just went a little still.

That gave him the hope he needed. "You still haven't answered my question," he said quietly.

"What question was that?"

"About whether you'd marry me."

She laughed a little. "Oh, that."

"Yes, that. Have you thought about it?"

She shut her eyes for a moment. "I've hardly thought of anything else."

"And?"

"And…I don't know."

"Fair enough," he said. "But is there anything I could do to help you decide?"

She gave him a narrow-eyed look and for a moment, he thought she was going to scold him. "Yes," she said finally. "You could tell me why you want to do it."

"That's easy. I want to do it because Xavier wants a dad. And because I like helping you."

Her mouth got a pinched look. If he hadn't known better, he'd have thought she felt hurt. "Those aren't... those aren't the reasons people get married."

"Are they bad reasons, though?"

She shook her head, staring at the ground. "They're not bad, no. They're fine. Kind. Good."

"Then what's standing in the way?"

She shrugged, looked away. There was a fine film of tears over her eyes. "Nothing. I don't know."

"Look," he said, touching her under the chin with one finger, lifting her face toward his. "Let's do it. Let's surprise Xavier." He didn't know what was making him force the issue.

Maybe something he saw in her eyes. Some part of her wanted to. And maybe it was for Xavier, or mostly so; but he had a funny feeling that she saw him as a man and was drawn to him.

"We'd be doing it for Xavier." She stared at him, her eyes huge.

"Yes, for Xavier. So, are you saying yes?"

"I think I am."

He nodded. "Then...let's seal it with a kiss." He leaned over and ever so gently brushed her lips with his.

It was meant to be just a friendly peck on the lips, but he lingered a couple of seconds, feeling the tingle of awareness he'd felt before but something else, too, something deeper.

She gasped and jerked away. "We'll...have to figure out...what kind of boundaries..." She trailed off, still staring at him. "You know."

She looked so appealing that he wanted to kiss her again, a real kiss. But the defenseless look on her face got to him and he pulled her into his arms, as slow and light and careful as if she were a wounded animal. "We'll figure it out," he whispered into her soft, dark hair.

"Mom! Can I? Can I?"

Angelica turned away from the church group and from Troy, standing just a little too close for comfort, to greet her son. It was late afternoon, and they were all saying their goodbyes in front of the weeded, re-mulched Senior Towers gardens.

Running ahead of Becka and her mom, Xavier looked so…normal. His striped shirt was mud-stained, his legs pumping sturdily beneath thrift-store gym shorts. Joy flooded her to see how healthy he looked. And what a relief to get out of the sticky, messy, impossibly emotional situation with Troy and back to what grounded her.

"Can you what, honey?" She knelt to catch Xavier as he ran into her arms, relishing the sweaty, little-boy smell of him.

"Can I play soccer with Becka? Her mom is the coach of the team!"

She hugged him close. "We'll see."

"You say that when you mean no!" Xavier pulled away. "Please, Mom?"

Becka and her mom arrived and Angelica stood up. "Thanks so much for watching him," she said.

"Well, I may have done something wrong." Becka's mom wore shorts and a T-shirt, her hair back in a no-nonsense ponytail under a baseball cap. "Becka and I were talking about soccer practice tonight, and when Xavier was interested, I told him he could join the team."

Angelica felt her eyebrows draw together. "Hmm. I'm not sure."

"Mom!"

"We'll have to see." Angelica bit her lip. She wanted him to be able to do it, to do everything a normal, healthy boy could do, but… "Soccer's pretty strenuous, isn't it?"

"At this age? No more so than normal play." Linda Mason gave her trademark grin. "The kids run around a lot, yeah. And I try to teach them some skills. But it's not competitive. It's just for fun."

"Practice is tonight, Mom!"

"Tonight?" Xavier hadn't had his usual afternoon rest. "I don't think so, sweetie. That's just too much."

A light touch warmed her shoulder. Troy. Her heart skittered as she looked back at him.

He raised an eyebrow, squeezed her shoulder once and then reached out to shake Linda's hand. "Hey, Linda. He'd need a sports physical anyway, wouldn't he?"

"Exactly." Linda nodded. "What we could do, if you don't think it's too much, is to have him come over to the park for a half-hour practice session I do with some of the kids, before the official practice. But you're right, Troy, he couldn't actually be on the team until getting a physical."

Angelica flashed Troy a grateful smile. She hadn't known that kids needed physicals for team sports, and it made the perfect delay tactic.

Xavier's face fell, and tears came to his eyes. "I just wanna play!"

"Then you have to get a physical, buddy!" Angelica gave him a one-armed hug. "All the kids have to get physicals. I'm sure Becka did, right?"

"Yeah, and I had to get a shot."

Xavier grimaced. "Yuck."

As the kids started comparing horror stories about doctors and needles, the three adults sat down on the bench outside the Senior Towers. "I'm really sorry," Linda said. "I didn't mean to get him all excited. But he seems like a great kid, and he had so much fun kicking around a ball with Becka. I'm sure he'd be good at soccer."

"We'll see what the doctor says," Troy said.

Angelica stared at him. "Excuse me?"

"Um, I'm going to go check on the kids." Linda looked from one to the other, frank curiosity in her eyes. "If that half-hour practice is okay, I'll walk them over to the park. Come on over and watch."

"Okay," Angelica said distractedly as Linda herded the kids toward the park. What did Troy mean, acting as if he had some say in Xavier's life? "Look, I'm sure you didn't mean it this way, but it sounded like you thought we'd all go to the doctor together."

"That's what I was thinking." Troy raised his eyebrows and met her eyes. "Is that a problem?"

"I don't want you to think you're the authority on Xavier after knowing him for, what, three weeks?"

"I can tell," Troy said mildly. "But after all, I'm going to be his father."

Angelica stared at him, momentarily speechless. Adrenaline flooded her body, and her breathing quickened.

She'd have to set some boundaries. She was so used to having full say about Xavier and what he did, how he lived—whether he could play soccer, for instance—and now Troy was wanting to get all high-handed.

In most matters, she'd be fine collaborating with Troy. But where Xavier was concerned, not so much.

"Some people say a two-parent family is good for this very reason." Troy sounded maddeningly calm. "A lot of moms are a little more protective. Dads help kids get out there and see the world."

"Look, you have no experience being a parent, and you don't know what Xavier's been through."

"Come on, let's walk. You want to see him play, don't you?"

"Um…yes! Of course!" Angelica stood, feeling a stiffness in her neck that bespoke a headache to come. "But we're not done talking about this."

How had Troy so smoothly taken control? She had to admit, looking up at him as he strode by her side, ushering her around a broken spot in the sidewalk, nodding to people he knew, that something about his confidence felt good. That it attracted her. She had to admit it, but… "Listen, this is making me a little uncomfortable," she said. "I'm used to having control of Xavier, and I'm not sure I'm willing to give that up."

He nodded. "I understand. I feel like I should have some say, but of course, you're his mom."

"And I make the decisions."

He slanted his eyes down at her. "Right. Okay. You make…the final decisions. Right."

She had to laugh. "Boy, that was pretty hard for you to say. Control much, do you?"

"You know me."

She did. She'd known him for a long time. But this new, older version, a little less driven, a little more humble… Wow. Despite all the craziness in her life, a core of excitement and hope was building inside her.

They approached the park together. Large oaks and maples provided shade against the late-afternoon sun, shining bright in a sky spotted with a few puffy white clouds. Kids shouted and ran around the old-fashioned swings and slide. Ragweed and earth scents mingled with the savory smell of someone's grilled burgers.

On the other side of town, a train on its late afternoon run made a forlorn whistle.

A family sprawled on a blanket together: Mom, Dad, a boy about Xavier's age and a toddler girl with curly red hair and an old-fashioned pink romper. The little girl put her arms around the boy and hugged him, and the father and mother exchanged a smile. Angelica's heart caught. That was what she'd always longed for: a loving man who could share in the raising of the children. A little sister for Xavier.

But that wasn't in the cards for her. What Troy was proposing was purely a marriage of convenience. She had to remember the limits, the reason he'd proposed at all: he wanted to help her, and especially to help Xavier. It wasn't romantic, it wasn't love. Nothing of the kind. Troy was a rescuer, and she and Xavier just so happened to be in need of some rescuing.

They walked over to the area where Linda was leading Xavier, Becka and three other kids through some soccer drills. "He seems to be doing okay," Troy said. "What do you think?"

Tugging her thoughts away from what couldn't be changed, she studied her son, noticing the high spots of color in his cheeks. "He's getting tired. But I'll let him stay for the half hour. I'll make sure he gets some extra rest tomorrow."

They sat down on the bleachers by the soccer field. Troy took her hand and squeezed it, and warmth and impossible hope flooded through her.

"We should talk about those other boundaries," Troy said.

"What...oh." When she saw the meaningful look in his eyes she knew exactly what he was talking about. The physical stuff.

"I'm attracted to you. You can probably tell."

Angelica looked down. She was attracted to him, too, or she thought she was. What else would her breathless, excited feeling be about? But she was too afraid to say so. Too afraid to tell him about all her issues. She pulled her hand away and pressed her lips together to keep herself from blurting out this shameful part of her past.

After a minute, he let out a sigh. "We don't have to hold hands or kiss or anything like that. I know you're doing this for Xavier, not for love. I want the same thing. I want to take care of you and Xavier, but I won't put pressure on you."

"Right." Her heart felt as if it were shrinking in her chest.

"Now, what about our...personal lives?" He looked at her sideways, raising an eyebrow.

Did he have any idea how handsome he was?
"What?"

"I mean your...social life."

What was he talking about?

"Other men, Angelica."

"Other...ooooh." She shook her head. "It's not an
issue. I don't date." In fact, she'd never really been in
love with anyone but Troy.

"You sure?" He looked skeptical.

"I'm sure!" She looked away. This was the best
someone like her could hope for.

Other families were arriving for the soccer game.
Mothers in pretty clothes with designer handbags, kids
with proper soccer garb. In her garden-stained jeans
and T-shirt, carrying her discount-store purse, Angelica wondered if she could ever fit in. If the other
families would look askance at Xavier for his murky
background, his lack of a father, his mismatched, thrift-
shop clothes.

Being with Troy was a chance to be a real part of
the community. She wouldn't impose on him to buy
her fancy things, but she'd happily accept decent cloth-
ing and soccer duds for Xavier. Would happily accept
Troy's good name in the town, too, paving the way for
her son to be accepted and have friends.

Troy was giving her a lot, and he was even saying he
wouldn't expect the physical side of marriage in return.

She should be grateful instead of wanting more.

Chapter 6

Two days later, on a rainy Monday, Angelica was cleaning out kennels when the door burst open and two women stalked in, slamming it behind them.

"Where is he?" one of them asked loudly over the dogs' barking.

She started to put down her shovel and then paused, wondering if she should keep it for self-defense. "Where's who?"

"The boy. Xavier."

Angelica's fingers tightened on the handle of the shovel. "Why do you want to see Xavier?"

As the dogs' barking subsided, one of the women stepped forward into the light, and Angelica recognized her. "Daisy! I haven't seen you in—"

Troy's sister, Daisy, held out one hand like a stop sign. "Don't try to be nice."

Angelica studied the woman she'd once called a friend. Just a couple of years older than Angelica, she wore purple harem pants and a gold shirt. Her hair flowed down her shoulders in red curls, and rings glittered on every finger. Short, adorably chubby and always full of life, she'd been Angelica's main ally in Troy's family back when she and Troy were engaged. Angelica had hoped they'd be friends again one day.

But Daisy pointed a finger at Angelica. "I want to see my nephew, and I want to see him now."

"Your nephew? Wait a minute. What's going on? What's got you mad?"

"What's got me mad is that I have a nephew who's six years old and I've never even met him. I may not ever be going to have children of my own, but I've always wanted to be an aunt. And now I hear I've been one for years and the boy's been kept from me!"

"Oh, Daisy." Things were starting to fall into place. "Xavier isn't your nephew."

The other woman, whom Angelica didn't recognize, stepped forward—tall and thin, with streaked hair and Asian features. "We heard it on good faith from Miss Minnie Falcon."

Of course. The day of weeding at the Senior Towers. News traveled fast. Angelica shook her head. "Come on, you guys. Sit down. Miss Minnie's got it wrong, but I can explain."

"You've got some explaining to do, all right." Daisy made her way over to Troy's office area and pulled out the desk chair, clearly at home here. "I was already mad at you for what you did to Troy, but this beats all. And I'm sorry, but you were engaged to Troy, and then you left, and now you have a kid. How can he not be my nephew?"

Angelica perched on a crate and gestured to the other woman to do the same.

The woman held out a hand to Angelica. "I'm Susan, Daisy's best friend," she said, "and I'm here to keep her from becoming violent."

"It's nothing to joke about!" Daisy glared at her friend.

Angelica leaned forward. "Daisy, I can tell you for sure that Troy isn't Xavier's father." She explained Xavier's desire for a father and how he'd wishfully called Troy Dad.

"But word was you and Troy were all over each other," Daisy said skeptically.

"All over each other." Angelica rubbed her chin. She was tempted to tell the ladies what was really going on, except she hated to do that without Troy. They hadn't had the chance to discuss what they'd tell the world about their so-called engagement; Xavier didn't even know, because once Xavier knew, everyone in town would know.

She needed time to prepare, but there wasn't any. "Listen," she said, "I'm gonna go get Troy."

"Don't you try to hide behind him. He's a sucker where you're concerned."

"Daisy," the other woman said in a low voice. "We shouldn't judge. Especially considering we came straight from Bible group."

"Even Jesus got righteously angry." Daisy sulked, but then she nodded at her friend. "You're right. I'm not giving you much of a chance, Angelica, am I? But the truth is, I always really liked you, and when you dumped Troy, you dumped me, too. And now to hear that you've actually had a baby… That pretty much beats all."

"Let me get Troy."

"No, I'll text him."

Before Angelica could stop her, Daisy was on her phone, and a couple of minutes of awkward small talk later, Troy walked in. "What's going on?"

Angelica's mind raced through the possible outcomes of this confrontation. They weren't great. If they didn't reveal their marriage of convenience now, it would make Daisy mad, and as Daisy went, so went the family. On the other hand, if they did explain that it wasn't a real marriage, that would get out, too. And that was exactly what she didn't want Xavier to find out.

Without thinking it through, she walked over to Troy and put an arm around him. "Honey," she said. "Can we spill the beans a tiny bit early and tell Daisy and Susan our news?"

When Angelica put her arm around him, Troy almost fell off his crutches. She was so resistant to getting physically close that her act of affection stunned him. It took another moment for him to realize what she'd said.

Really? She wanted to tell his sister, who knew everyone in town and loved to talk, about their pseudo-engagement?

Troy blinked in the dark kennel. Automatically, he hobbled over—his leg was bad today—toward one of the barking dogs in the front, a fellow named Crater for the ugly scar in the middle of his back, and opened the gate of his kennel. Crater leaped with joy and Troy knelt awkwardly to rub and pet him.

Then he looked back at Angelica.

She cocked her head to one side and raised her eyebrows. She must have had a reason for what she'd done; she wasn't one to playact for no reason. And if he was going to marry her, maybe even to make it a good marriage, he needed to show her his trust. "Are you sure about this?"

"I think we should tell them." She was communicating with her eyes, willing him to say something, and he only hoped he'd get it right.

"Okay," he said, pushing himself to his feet and limping over to drape an arm around Angelica's shoulders. "Guys…Angelica and I have decided to get married."

There were no happy hugs, no shouts of joy. Daisy's lips pressed together. "Are you sure that's a good idea?"

"Of course," he said. "We've…settled our differences." He tightened his arm around Angelica for emphasis and noticed that she was shaking. "Hey, it's okay. It's Daisy. She'll be happy for us!" He glared at his sister. "Won't you?"

"Are you kidding?" Daisy was nothing if not blunt. "I can't be happy to watch you setting yourself up for another fall."

He felt Angelica cringe.

"Daisy!" Susan put a hand on her hip. "Be nice."

Troy rubbed Angelica's shoulder a little, still feeling her tension. "Look, the past is water under the bridge. We've started over, and we'd appreciate it if you would be supportive." He frowned at Daisy. "For all of us, especially Xavier."

He watched as his opinionated sister struggled with herself. Finally she nodded. "All right," she said. "I'll do my best."

Angelica chimed in. "You said you'd always wanted to be an aunt. Well, now you'll be one. Xavier will be thrilled to have a bigger family. We've been pretty much…" She cleared her throat. "Pretty much on our own, since my aunt passed away."

For the millionth time, he wondered what had happened to make her leave him and leave town. And what had happened to Xavier's father.

Apparently he wasn't the only one. "One thing I've got to know," Daisy said. "Who's Xavier's father if it's not Troy?"

The question hung in the air. It was what Troy had wanted to ask but hadn't had the guts to. Trust Daisy to get the difficult topics out into the open.

Angelica didn't speak. She was staring at the ground as if the concrete floor held the answer to Daisy's question.

"Well?" Daisy prompted. "If we're all starting fresh, what better basis than honesty?"

Angelica looked up, shot a glance at Troy and then lifted her chin and met Daisy's eyes. "I'm not at liberty to share that information," she said. "It's Xavier's story, and when he's old enough, he'll decide who he wants to share it with. Until then, it's private."

"Does he even know?" Daisy blurted.

"No!" Angelica stood, crossed her arms and paced back and forth. "And I'd appreciate all of you avoiding the topic with him. He's not old enough to understand, and I don't want him to start questioning. Not yet."

Something ugly twisted in Troy's chest. He wanted

to know, if only so he could watch out for the guy, keep him away from her in the future, know his enemy. To have that unknown rival out there made the hairs on the back of his neck stand up.

"I guess that makes sense," Daisy said doubtfully. "Thank you for respecting my son's right to privacy."

As he accepted the forced hugs of his sister and pretended to be an excited, normal fiancé to Angelica, Troy had to wonder whether they were doing the right thing.

"I don't know, man." Troy's friend Dion, the police chief of Rescue River, sat across from him at the table of the Chatterbox Café later that afternoon. They were drinking coffee and Troy had confided the truth about the marriage of convenience, knowing Dion could keep a secret. "I just don't know. You say you're doing it for Xavier, but Father God has His plans for that boy. What if He takes him young, him being so sick with leukemia? You going to divorce Angelica then?"

"No!" Troy's coffee cup clattered into the saucer, liquid sloshing over the sides. "I wouldn't leave her, not in her time of need, not ever."

"Think she'll stay with you?"

Troy drew in a breath and let it out in a sigh. "I hope so, but I can't know for sure. She left me before."

"And she won't tell you who the daddy is?"

Troy shook his head. "Says it's between her and Xavier, and she doesn't want the whole town to know before he does. Says it's his story to tell."

Dion shook his head. "That's a nice theory. But a man and his wife shouldn't have secrets." He rubbed a hand over his nearly shaved head. "Secrets destroy a marriage. I'm living proof of that."

Troy nodded. Dion didn't talk much about his marriage, but Troy knew there had been rough patches. Then they'd straightened things out, and then Dion's wife had passed away. Dion had turned to God and he had a deeper faith than anyone else Troy knew, which was why he'd come to his friend with his own issue. "Do I try to force it out of her, though?" he asked. "Is it even my right to know?"

"All kinds of reasons to know about paternity," Dion pointed out. He paused while the waitress, a little too interested in their conversation, poured them some more coffee. "Thanks, Felicity," he said to her. "We won't be needing anything else."

After she left, Troy chuckled. "She's curious what we're talking about, and she's even more curious what you're doing Friday night."

Dion shook his head. "Got a date with the baseball game on TV, just like usual. Anyway, what if something happened to Angelica? You'd need to know Xavier's story. For his health, if nothing else, it's important to know who his daddy is."

"I guess."

"Something else. Everybody in town gonna think you're the daddy. Some already do. You okay with that?"

"What people say doesn't matter."

Dion looked out the window, a little smile on his face. "Maybe not," he said finally. "But you won't look like the good guy anymore. People might think you've been neglecting your duties."

"What the gossips say doesn't matter. Period."

"Okay." Dion studied him. "I believe you. Still, you gotta know."

"You've convinced me of that."

"Talk to her, man. But pray first. Because it's not easy to be calm about the guy who got your girl pregnant, but in this situation, calm is what you'll have to be."

Troy nodded thoughtfully. How was he going to bring this up? One thing Dion was sure right about—he needed every bit of help the good Lord could offer him. Only thing was, he hated asking for help of any kind. Even from God.

Chapter 7

Angelica was in the kitchen washing breakfast dishes when she heard the screeching of brakes out on the road.

"Zavey?"

No answer.

She grabbed a dish towel on her way out the door, drying her hands as she climbed the slight rise to where she could see the road.

Her heart seemed to stop. Xavier was on his knees beside the road, screaming.

She practically flew over the ground until she reached him and saw the situation.

In front of Xavier, a couple of feet from the edge of the road, Bull lay in the gravel, his sturdy body twisted at an odd angle. A car was pulled halfway into the ditch across the road, and in front of it, a middle-aged woman pressed her hand to her mouth.

Heart pounding, Angelica knelt by her son, patting his arms and legs, examining him. "Are you okay?"

Xavier gulped and nodded and pointed toward Bull. "I'm… It's my fault… I let him off his lead. I wanted him to play fetch." His voice rose to a wail. "I think he's dead."

"I'm sorry, I'm so sorry!" The driver came over and sank to her knees beside them, her voice shaking, tears streaking her face. "I didn't see the dog, he came running out so fast…"

And suddenly Troy was there, kneeling awkwardly beside Bull.

"Oh, honey." Angelica scooped Xavier up into her arms, reached out a hand to pat the stranger's shoulder and leaned toward Troy and Bull, her heart aching at the sight of the still, twisted dog. "Is…is he alive?"

Busy examining Bull, Troy didn't answer, so she set Xavier down and instructed him to stay out of Troy's way. She took information from the distraught driver and walked her back to her vehicle, promising to call and let her know how the dog was, making sure the woman was calm enough to drive and able to back her car out of the ditch.

And then she knelt beside Troy and Xavier, putting her arm around her son.

"I'm sorry I let him off his lead! It's my fault!" Xavier buried his face in her shoulder, weeping.

"Shh. It was an accident. You didn't know." She bit her lip and touched Troy's arm. "Is he breathing?"

Troy took one quick glance toward them and then went back to examining the dog. "Yes, but he's pretty badly injured. I'd like to do surgery right away. Here. No time to get to town." He scanned the area. "Can you grab me a big board out of the shed? There's a stack beside the door."

"Of course. Xavier, stay here." She ran to the shed and came back with a piece of plywood.

"Give me your hoodie," Troy was saying to Xavier. "I'm going to wrap Bull up in it. T-shirt, too, buddy."

Xavier shucked his hoodie and started pulling off his T-shirt, shivering in the chilly morning air.

Her son was so vulnerable to colds. "But, Troy, he shouldn't—"

"I can do it, Mom!" Xavier's trembly voice firmed up and he sniffed loudly and wiped his face on the T-shirt before handing it over to Troy.

"We need to keep Bull warm," Troy explained in a calm voice, slipping out of his own much larger T-shirt and kneeling to cover the old bulldog. "And," he said, lowering his voice so only Angelica could hear, "Xavier needs to help."

Gratitude spread through Angelica's chest. "Thank you." She knelt and helped him ease the dog onto the wide wooden plank she'd found.

Bull yelped once and his old eyes opened, then closed again. His breathing came in hard bursts.

Together, Angelica and Troy lifted the makeshift stretcher. Once, Troy lurched hard to one side, and it took both Xavier and Angelica to steady Bull. Angelica's heart twisted when she saw that a smear of blood had gotten on Xavier's hand. With his medical history, he was oversensitive to blood.

But he just wiped his hand on his jeans. "Where are your crutches, Mr. Troy?"

"Dumped 'em. Come on."

Worry pinged Angelica's heart. Troy had been to the

doctor just yesterday and had gotten another full cast and a warning that he was putting too much weight on his leg.

"Can you fix him?" Xavier asked as they walked toward the kennel building.

Troy glanced down at Xavier. "They say I'm good," he tried to joke, but his voice cracked. He was limping badly now.

Angelica gulped in a breath. "Who can I call to help?"

"Buck's my only trained surgical assistant, but I'm not having him on the property. I'll manage."

"I'll help as best I can." But how would she do that? she wondered; Lou Ann wasn't here and Xavier needed her. He couldn't watch the surgery.

They got Bull to the kennel and onto the small examining table Troy had for emergencies.

"You've gotta fix him, Mr. Troy! I love him!"

"I know, son." Troy turned to Xavier. "Watch him, and if he starts to move, hold him while I wash up and prep. Angelica, you help him."

"Okay. But I don't think Xavier should stick around."

By the time Troy had assembled his instruments and gotten back to the dog, he had to lean hard on the operating table, and Angelica saw his face twist with pain.

How would he stand, possibly for several hours, and do delicate surgery without help?

Angelica hurried Xavier outside and pulled out her phone. Buck had given her his number when they were going to go out, and hopefully… Good, she'd never deleted it. She hit the call button.

"Hey, Angie," he said, sounding sleepy.

"I've got an emergency," she said, not bothering to greet him. "Listen, are you sober?"

"Yeah. Just woke up."

"Can you come out to the farm and help Troy with a surgery? Bull is hurt."

"Be right there."

She went back in and helped Troy hold Bull still and administer something with a needle. As he ran careful hands over the dog's leg, his face was set, jaw clenched.

"Is he gonna be okay, Mr. Troy?" Xavier asked from the doorway.

Angelica and Troy met each other's eyes over the table.

"I don't know," Troy said, his voice husky. "I'm going to do my very best. You've been a big help."

The dog's laceration looked bad, but as Troy continued to examine it, his face relaxed a little. "I don't think any internal organs are affected, though we can't be sure about that. It's the leg I'm worried about. I'll try to pin it, but I'm not sure it'll work."

"You can fix him. Right?" Xavier's voice was hopeful.

Troy turned to her son. "It's hard to tell," he said. "He's an older guy, and I had to give him strong medicine to make him sleep. That's hard on him. And his leg might be the more serious injury. We just don't know, buddy."

The anesthetic had set in and Troy was just starting to clean the wound when a car sounded. "Can you see who that is?" Troy said without looking up.

She went out, opened the door and let Buck in. "He's just getting started," she said. "Let me walk back with you. He doesn't know you're here."

Buck, already dressed in scrubs, followed her in.

"Troy, I have Buck here to help you."

Troy's shoulders stiffened. "How'd you manage that?"

"I have his number from before."

No answer.

"Stone-cold sober, man, and ready to help." Buck pulled on some gloves. He glanced up at Troy's face. "Whoa, chill. I'm here by invitation. And truth is, you look like you could use the help. Sure you didn't get hit, too?"

Troy's glance at Angelica was as cold as ice.

She swallowed hard. "I'm going to tend to Xavier. He needs to get inside, get cleaned up and rest."

"Fine." He turned away.

Letting her know things were anything but fine.

The surgery took longer than Troy expected, and operating on his own pet threw professional objectivity right out the window. Armstrong's help was crucial, but even with it, the outcome was touch and go.

Discouraged, his leg on fire with the pain of standing without support for several hours, Troy cleaned up while Buck finished bandaging Bull. Troy watched the younger man easily manage the heavy dog in one arm while he opened the crate door with the other, and the anger he'd shoved aside during the delicate surgery rushed back in.

Since when was Angelica in touch with Buck? How often did they talk, get together? Why hadn't she mentioned the friendship if, in fact, it was innocent?

He could barely manage to thank Buck, and the other man's cheerful "Anytime, my man" rang as guilty in Troy's ears. When they walked out together, Buck held the door for him and then checked his phone and jogged off toward his Jeep and swung in. Leaving Troy to hobble toward the house on both crutches, wanting nothing more than some pain medication and a place to put his leg up.

Angelica greeted him at the door. "How is he?"

Just looking at her made his stomach roil. "The dog or your boyfriend?"

She paled. "What?"

He clenched his jaw. "Bull is resting peacefully, but it'll be a few days before we know how well he does. He did come out of the anesthesia, so he's at least survived that."

"Oh, that's wonderful." She backed away from the door to let him by. "But, Troy, what did you mean by that other crack?"

He spun, faced her down. "Why did you keep Armstrong's phone number? How long have you had something going on with him?"

Her forehead wrinkled. "I don't have anything going on with anybody."

To Troy's ears, her denial sounded forced. He squeezed his eyes shut and turned away from her. "I'm beat. I'm going to get some rest."

"I'll take care of the dogs," she said, her voice hesitant. "But I don't want to have this stand between us. I had Buck's phone number because I never deleted it from before. Not because I'm seeing him."

"Yeah, right." Troy had heard so many denials all his life. He remembered his mother's lies to his father, remembered the first time he'd seen her driving by with another man and realized that she wasn't telling the truth about her whereabouts.

Angelica herself had left him to sleep with another man.

It crushed him that Angelica was seeing Buck. He'd half expected something like this to happen, but not so soon. He'd never thought she would cheat on him even before the wedding.

In fact, he'd even thought she had feelings for him. He felt his shoulders slump, as if the bones that held up his body had turned to jelly. Women were treacherous and his own meter of awareness was obviously broken.

Fool that he was.

"Listen," she said now, stepping in front of him as he tried to leave the room. A high flush had risen to her cheeks, and her eyes sparked fire. "I don't appreciate what you're accusing me of. I have no feelings for Buck. I barely know the man."

He leaned against the wall as exhaustion set in. "You were all set to date him. The only obstacle was his drinking. Well, he's sober today, so go for him."

"I. Don't. Want. Him. I never did. And anyway, I'm getting married to you."

"Yeah, well, we both know how real that marriage is," he said bitterly. "It's a sham, for your convenience and Xavier's. You said you never dated, but obviously that wasn't true."

"You're not listening."

"I don't listen to lies."

She shook her head, staring at him, her brown eyes gone almost black. "You're insulting my integrity and I don't appreciate that. I'm committed to you until we decide different. Which it looks like you're doing right now."

"It's not me who made the decision to seek comfort elsewhere." He rubbed the back of his neck. "Tell me, when you act all scared about being touched, is that fake? Or are you just repulsed by me?"

"Is it... Oh man." Her hands went to her hips. "You are making me so mad, Troy Hinton. Just because your parents had their problems—and yeah, I know about that, I heard it from your sister—it doesn't mean you get free rein to accuse me of whatever other women have done to you."

"I'm not..." He paused. Maybe he was. He didn't know. "Look, I'm too tired to think. Can we just put this whole conversation on hold for now?"

"What, so you can build up even more of a case against me? No way." She was small but she was determined and she obviously wasn't budging. "I'm not letting you do this, Troy. I'm not letting you fall in hate with me."

"Why not? Wouldn't it be easier for you?"

She heaved out a sigh and looked up at the ceiling. "No, it wouldn't be easier and it wouldn't be right. Stop judging me!"

"I wasn't—"

"Yes, you were," she pressed on, stepping in closer. "To think I'm dating Buck in all my spare time—which if you haven't noticed, is nonexistent—is totally insulting. As well as ridiculous. So can it and apologize before I whack you one."

That unexpected image made him smile. "You're scaring me, Angelica."

"Mom will do it, too. What do you mean, Mom's dating Buck ? And how's Bull?"

They both froze. In the doorway stood Xavier, in sweats and a T-shirt, his hair sticking up in all directions. He swayed a little and grabbed on to the door frame.

Angelica knelt before him, steadying him with a hand on his shoulder. "Honey! I didn't know you were up from your rest."

"I heard you guys fighting. Is Bull okay?" He looked plaintively up at Troy.

Hard as it was to kneel on one leg with his casted leg stuck awkwardly out beside him, he got himself down to Xavier's level. "Bull is sleeping. The drugs we gave him during the surgery made him tired. But he's looking pretty good for an old guy."

Xavier wasn't to be placated with that. "Is he gonna die?"

Troy's heart clenched in his chest. This was a kid too familiar with death. "I can't promise you that he won't, because he's an old dog. The accident was hard on him, and surgery is, too. But I did my best, and we're going to take good care of him. Okay?"

"Can I see him?"

Troy glanced at Angelica. "How about we bring him inside in a couple of hours, once he's gotten some rest? Okay?"

Angelica and Xavier nodded, both looking serious, and Troy's chest clenched painfully. He cared for both of them way too much. He wanted to protect them, wanted to answer Xavier's questions, wanted to help him heal.

Wanted to trust Angelica.

Now that he'd come down from his angry high, now that he was looking at the sunshine on her black hair as she leaned forward to hug her son, he thought he must have been crazy to accuse her.

But at the same time, there was that nagging doubt.

"You better get some rest, Troy." Angelica's tone was guarded. "And we'll do the same, right, Zavey? We'll have a quiet day. Because tomorrow, we get to go meet your teacher and see your classroom. Just a couple of weeks until school starts."

Troy nudged Xavier with his crutch. "That's a big deal, buddy. You're going to have a blast."

Concern darkened Angelica's eyes and she was biting her lip. He knew she wanted Xavier to go to school, wanted him to have as normal a life as possible for as long as possible.

He headed toward the stairs but turned back to look at Angelica. She was ushering Xavier toward the door, but he was dawdling over a handheld video game. Angelica stopped, looking half patient and half exasperated, and then she squeezed her eyes shut. He saw her lips moving.

He felt like an utter cad. She was dealing with the worst thing a mother could face, the possible death of her child, and doing it beautifully, focusing on Xavier and his needs. Given his health issues, educating him at home would have been easier, but Xavier was a social kid and needed friends, so she'd called umpteen social workers and school administrators and the school nurse to figure out a way he could attend as much as possible and make up his work when he had to be out. She was super stressed out, and how had he supported her?

By calling her out for cheating, when she'd just been trying to help him. At least he thought so.

He scrubbed a hand over his face and headed up the stairs. Reopening their discussion would likely just result in more misunderstanding. He had to get a little rest.

And then he'd get up and be a better man. With God's help.

Chapter 8

As soon as the school secretary buzzed them in, Angelica marched into Xavier's new elementary school—her own alma mater—holding Xavier by one hand.

Immediately memories assailed her, brought on by the smell of strong cleaning chemicals and the sight of cheerful, bright alphabet letters hanging from the ceiling. She could almost feel the long patchwork skirt brushing her first-grade legs and taste the peanut-butter-and-sprouts sandwiches that had marked her as just a little different from the other kids.

Behind her, Gramps was breathing hard, and she paused to hold the office door open for him. Gramps had driven them there because he knew how important this was. They all wanted to see Xavier have a real childhood, and a big part of that was a regular school.

The other reason Gramps had driven her was that

Troy had taken the truck to drive himself and Bull into town today for a consultation with another vet. He wasn't supposed to drive with his cast, but he'd insisted that they keep this appointment for Xavier, that he could manage driving with his left foot.

She knew the real reason he didn't want her to drive him: he was still a little mad at her. Well, fine. She was mad at him, too. Things hadn't been the same since he had accused her of dating Buck on the sly, an idea that would be laughable except he so obviously took it seriously.

It made her feel hopeless about their relationship. If he was that quick to suspect her morals when she'd called Buck in to help him, how would he react to finding out about her assault?

And underneath her anger, a dark thread of shame twisted through her gut. She *had* gone out drinking. She'd even flirted. If she hadn't, if she'd stayed safely at home by herself, she wouldn't have been assaulted.

But she couldn't think about that now; she had to gear up to fight yet another battle for Xavier. Had to get the right teacher and the best classroom situation for him. "Hello, I'm here to see Dr. Kapp," she said to the plump, middle-aged secretary who was working the desk in the front office.

"Okay, and this must be Xavier," the woman said, smiling down at him. "Welcome to your new school! Dr. Kapp will be right out."

Xavier's grin was so wide it made his eyes crinkle and his cheeks go round as red apples.

Meanwhile, Angelica took deep breaths, trying not to be nervous. Dr. Kapp had always been strict, and she must be ancient now, probably even more set in her ways. How would she respond to Angelica, who'd been notorious in the town for having parents who bummed around in their ancient Volkswagen minivan, spent too much time in bars and sold weed?

While Gramps and Xavier looked at a low showcase of children's art, Angelica tried to forget about Troy and prepare for the battle ahead.

Please, Lord, help me remember. I'm not that mixed-up little hippie girl anymore. I'm Your child and You're here with me.

"Well, Angelica Camden! It's been a long time." Dr. Kapp's tone was dry. "So you have a son now."

Was that accusation in her voice? Angelica couldn't be sure, but she felt it. "Hello," she said, extending her hand to the woman whose close-cropped hair and dark slacks and jacket still made her look like an army general. *God's child. God's child.* "It *has* been a long time."

"I know you're here to talk about your son, but I think we have all the necessary information." Dr. Kapp's eyebrows went up, suggesting Angelica was wasting her time. "Was there something else before you meet Xavier's teacher and see the classroom?"

Angelica glanced back at Gramps for support, but he'd sat down heavily in one of the chairs in the waiting section of the office. Xavier had come over to press against her leg in an uncharacteristic display of neediness. So he was scared, too.

Angelica swallowed. "I'd like to talk to you about Xavier's placement in first grade." She'd rehearsed these words, but her voice still wobbled like the little girl she'd been. She drew in a deep breath. "I understand one of the first-grade teachers is a man, and I'd like for him to be in that class."

Dr. Kapp nodded. "A lot of parents want to choose their child's teacher, but we don't do things that way. I've placed Xavier in Ms. Hayashi's classroom. I think you'll like her."

"Go see if Gramps wants to play tic-tac-toe," Angelica said to Xavier, who was staring up at Dr. Kapp with a sort of awe.

Once he'd gotten out of earshot, she spoke quickly. "I'm a single mother, and that's why I'd like for him to have a male influence."

Dr. Kapp nodded. "That's understandable, but from what you said on the phone, Xavier may have some special needs. That's why we've placed him in Ms. Hayashi's class. She's dual-certified in special education, and I think she's the best choice for Xavier."

So Dr. Kapp wasn't just being autocratic. Angelica bit her lip. "Yes, the doctors said his chemo might have caused some cognitive delays, so a teacher who gets that makes a difference, for sure. I just...don't have many men in his life, and I think that's important for him."

Dr. Kapp nodded toward Gramps and Xavier, heads bent over Gramps's cell phone. "Looks like he has one good male influence, at least."

"Yes, and I'm so thankful. But—"

"Tell you what," Dr. Kapp interrupted. "Why don't I take you down to see Ms. Hayashi? She's here now, setting up her classroom. I'm sure she'll be glad to talk to you about Xavier, and then if you're still feeling dissatisfied, we can talk. I know it's a special situation, but I just have a hunch that Ms. Hayashi is going to be the right placement for Xavier."

Troy parked the truck in the elementary school parking lot. Man, it felt good to be in the driver's seat again, but the doctor had been right about how he shouldn't drive. He could tell he was overdoing it. He used his crutches to make his way to the school's front door.

As he waited to be buzzed in, feelings from his past flooded him. The fun of going to school, the escape from the tension in his family, the relief of making new friends who didn't know anything about his big fancy home. He started to walk into the office when he saw Angelica, her grandfather and Xavier following—could that be Kapp the cop, still running this place?—around a corner in the brightly painted hallway ahead, and he followed them. "Hey, sorry to be late."

"He's gonna be my dad!" Xavier said proudly to the school principal.

Troy's heart constricted at the boy's trusting comment. What had he, Troy, done to deserve that affection and trust? Nothing, but there it was, and it got to him. Made him want to earn it by being a really good dad to Xavier.

"Some say he always was the boy's dad," Gramps muttered, frowning at Troy.

Troy's fist clenched. Homer Camden was even older than Dr. Kapp, but someday he was going to get Troy put in jail for assault on a senior citizen.

"Gramps!" Angelica hissed, nodding sideways at Xavier, who fortunately had darted over to the wall to examine a fire alarm.

As the principal walked over to explain the fire

alarm and caution Xavier never to pull it unless there was a fire, Camden glared at Troy. "Just saying what I've heard around town," he said in a lower voice.

Troy glared back. What an idiot. "If you want to talk to me about something, we'll talk later where the boy won't hear."

"Let's do that." He muttered, "Sorry" to Angelica as he walked over to study the fire alarm with Xavier and the principal.

"How's Bull?" Angelica asked. "Is he going to be okay?"

"Yeah, did you bring him with you?" Back at Angelica's side, Xavier wrapped his arms around his mom's legs and looked worriedly up at Troy.

Troy hesitated. "He's…he's not doing that well. He might need another operation. He's staying at the office in town for now."

"Oh no!" Xavier's eyes filled with tears. "He's gonna have to get his leg cut off and it's my fault!"

Immediately Troy squatted down, barely stabilizing himself on one crutch, his bad leg awkwardly out in front. "If Bull's leg has to be amputated, we'll do everything we can to help him do okay with it. Most dogs are just fine with three legs. There's even a special name for three-legged dogs."

"What is it?"

"Tripod," he said, tapping his palm with three fingers of his other hand. "See? One, two, three."

"I have to talk to Ms. Hayashi," Angelica said. "Do you think—"

Troy got it. "Hey, buddy," he said to Xavier as he shoved himself painfully to his feet. "What do you think about seeing the gym and the lunchroom first?

Let Mom talk to your new teacher, and then we'll come back and look around the classroom. Okay?"

"Sure!" Xavier reached up and gripped Troy's hand where it rested on the handle of his crutch.

Troy looked at Homer Camden, red-faced and frowning, and for a split second, he got the image of a man who didn't know what to do with his feelings, who was jealous of a new man in Xavier's and Angelica's life, and who wanted only the best for them. He sighed. "Want to come along?"

Thank you, Angelica mouthed to him before disappearing into the classroom.

"Guess I can," Homer Camden groused. "If you can't handle the boy alone."

It was going to be a long half hour. But he'd do it for Angelica. He'd do almost anything for her, if she'd let him, even though he wasn't at all sure that was wise.

"Where's the lunchroom?" Xavier asked as the three of them headed down the hall.

"Straight down thataway," Camden said, pointing, before Troy could answer.

"Wait a minute," Troy said, "did you go to this school, too?"

Camden nodded. "I was a member of the first graduating class. Back then, it was the new K-eight building, and I was here for seventh and eighth grade."

"That's cool, Gramps!" Xavier grabbed the older man's hand and swung his arms between the two of them, practically pulling Troy off his crutches.

"Back in those days," Camden said, "a lot of farm kids only finished eighth grade, so it truly was a graduation."

"What about you?" Troy had never thought about the old man's schooling, or lack thereof.

"Oh, I finished high school," Gramps said, a note of pride in his voice. "I was always good at math and science. English, not so much."

"Me, too," Troy said as they entered the school lunchroom, where a summer of cleaning couldn't quite erase the smell of sour milk and peanut butter. "That's why vet school had more appeal than, say, lawyering."

"But don't get too friendly," Gramps said as Xavier ran around looking at the colorful posters and sitting in various chairs. "I want to know why you're taking such an interest in Angelica and her son. Is there something you want to tell me?"

"Well, you know about our engagement." He felt duplicitous still, talking about something that might not happen. But it might. He was willing to marry Angelica and be a father to Xavier; he'd meant it when he'd offered, and he would stick with it.

"Is that because you're Xavier's dad?" Camden asked bluntly.

Troy stopped, turned and faced the other man. "No. I don't know who Xavier's father is. I'd like to, but so far, Angelica hasn't been willing to tell me."

Camden studied him. "I'm supposed to believe that? When you were engaged and spending practically every evening together?"

"It's not up to me what you believe," Troy said, "but it's the truth. Angelica and I had decided to wait until marriage." He couldn't keep the bitterness out of his voice. "Why she decided to change that plan, and with whom, I have no idea. But it wasn't me."

Camden crossed his arms over his chest and shook

his head. "Guessin' that don't sit right," he said finally. "I always thought it was you. Thought you'd gotten her pregnant and then sent her away. But when you said you were marrying her now, you really threw me off."

Troy drew in a breath. "So you don't know what happened, who the father is?" He knew he shouldn't probe, should only discuss this with Angelica, but it felt like important information, and she wouldn't tell him. Maybe if he knew…

Camden shook his head. "Can't help you there."

"Come see this, Gramps!" Xavier was calling, and the two of them headed over just in time to stop him from squirting an entire container of ketchup into the sink. Plenty had gotten onto his shirt and shorts as well, and the two of them looked at each other with guilty expressions, obviously thinking the same thing: *we're going to be in trouble with Angelica*. A few paper towels later, they headed toward the gym.

"Do you know how to play basketball, Mr. Troy?"

"I sure do. I used to play at this school."

"Were you that tall then?"

Troy laughed. "No, son. I wasn't very tall at all."

"He was a pip-squeak. A lot smaller than you. I remember him in those days."

That hadn't occurred to Troy before, that Homer Camden had known him as a kid. On a whim, Troy put down his crutches. Camden grabbed a basketball, and they took turns lifting Xavier up to shoot baskets.

When they headed back toward the classroom, Xavier rested his hand on Troy's crutch again.

Which made Troy feel that all was right with the world. When had this boy put such a hold on his heart, enough to make him even see the good in Homer Camden?

* * *

When Xavier walked into the classroom between Troy and Gramps, tears sprang to Angelica's eyes. It felt as if all of her dreams were coming true.

She'd always wished her son could have a real father. And she'd hoped he could go to a regular school. It hadn't happened for kindergarten, because of all of his treatments, so this was his first opportunity.

"Hey, cool!" Xavier ran into the room and sat down at one of the desks. "I'm ready!"

"And is your name Sammy?" asked Ms. Hayashi.

Angelica was pretty sure she liked this teacher, who turned out to be the friend who'd come to the kennel with Daisy. She seemed very knowledgeable about children with medical issues, and her educational background was impeccable.

Her tight jeans, Harley-Davidson T-shirt and biker boots weren't everyone's idea of a first-grade teacher, even one who was at the school early to move books and set up her classroom. From Gramps's raised eyebrows, she could tell he thought the same. Angelica hoped the woman wouldn't intimidate Xavier.

But her son put his hands on his hips and spoke right up. "I'm not Sammy, I'm Xavier!"

"Aha. And do you know what letter your name starts with?" The woman squatted effortlessly in front of Xavier.

Xavier nodded eagerly. "An X, and I can write it, too!"

His enthusiasm made Angelica smile. They'd been practicing letters for months, and she'd taught him to write his name, but it had taken quite a while. His treatment had caused some cognitive issues that might or might not go away, according to the various nurses and social workers they'd dealt with.

"That's good. Can you find your desk?"

"How can I…"

The woman put a hand to her lips, took Xavier's hand and pointed to the sign on the front of the desk where he'd been sitting. "See? It's Ssssammy," she said, emphasizing the *S.* "What we need to do is to find your desk, the one that says "Xavier."

He frowned and nodded. "With an *X.*"

"Yes, like this." She held her fingers crossed.

Xavier did the same with his hands. "I remember. Your nails are cool. I like purple."

"Me, too. Let's find that *X.*"

So far, the woman hadn't even said hello to Troy or Gramps, but Angelica didn't care. She was impressed by Ms. Hayashi's educational focus and by how much learning was already taking place.

If only her son would remain healthy enough to benefit from it.

He'd woken up with a fever several mornings this week, which filled her with the starkest terror. Fear of relapse stalked every parent of a cancer kid. But, according to Dr. Lewis, all they could do was wait and see.

"Come see my new desk, Mr. Troy!"

Troy limped over, and Angelica followed, her arm around Gramps. Who didn't look as disgruntled as he had looked before. As Xavier showed with pride how the desk opened and closed, and Troy pretended amazement over the schoolbooks inside, Angelica snapped pictures and pondered.

She'd wanted Xavier to have a male role model. And maybe he already did.

Chapter 9

Angelica was paying bills the next Saturday morning—thanking God for the job that allowed her to—when she heard a tapping on the door. Her heart did a double thump. Since she hadn't heard a car drive up, it had to be Troy.

They hadn't talked since their visit to Xavier's classroom and the closeness that had come out of that. She didn't know what to think of their up-and-down relationship. One minute he was mad at her about Buck, and then the next day he was acting like the sweetest father Xavier could possibly have, making her fall hard for him.

"Hey." Outlined in the early morning sunlight, his well-worn jeans and faded T-shirt made him look as young as when they'd been engaged. But now his shoulders bulged with the muscles of someone who ran a farm and lifted heavy animals and equipment. Running her hands up those arms, over his shoulders, as she'd done back then…it would feel totally different now.

"Hey yourself." When her words came out low, husky, she looked away and cleared her throat. "What's up? Everything okay at the kennels?"

He blinked. "The kennels are fine, but I wondered if you could help me with Bull." He nodded downward, and for the first time she realized that the bulldog was sitting patiently beside him, his wrinkly face framed by his recovery collar.

"Hey, big guy!" Feeling strangely warm, she knelt down to pet Bull, and he obligingly pushed up into a crooked standing position and wagged his stub of a tail.

"Is he okay?" She looked up at Troy. Man, was he handsome!

"He's doing pretty well. I can't tell for sure until the stitches are out, and it's time to do that. Then we'll see how he gets around."

He was saying it all without taking his eyes off her, and the intensity in his gaze seemed to be about more than the dog.

She looked down, focusing on Bull, feeling confused. Between her own feelings and the way Troy was looking at her, she was starting to feel as though they had an actual relationship.

Except they didn't. It was all about business and Xavier. Because if Troy knew the truth about her and her past and why she'd left, he'd never have anything to do with her. And what kind of relationship could you build on secrets and shame?

Back to business. "I need to get Xavier up and give

him some breakfast," she said. "When were you thinking?"

He shrugged. "Whenever."

Something about the way he said it made her think of him rattling around his big house. Weekends could be so lonely when you were single. She knew it well, but at least she'd always had Xavier. "Would you... would you want to have breakfast with us first? I can make us something."

His face lit up. "Sure would. I'm strictly a cold cereal guy when I'm trusting my own cooking, but I do like breakfast food."

"Pancakes are my specialty." She didn't add that there'd been many nights when pancakes were all they could afford for dinner. "You go wake up Xavier. He'll love the surprise of it."

"Even better, how about if Bull and I wake him up together? We could probably even take the stitches out right here, if you don't mind my using your front porch as an exam room."

"Perfect." They smiled at each other as the sunlight came in the windows, their gazes connecting just a little too long. And then Angelica spun away and walked toward the kitchen, weak-kneed, her smile widening to where it almost hurt.

Half an hour later, she looked around the kitchen table and joy rose in her. Xavier was just starting to sprout a few patches of hair and his grin stretched wide. Troy sniffed appreciatively at the steaming platter of pancakes. Beneath the table, Bull sighed and flopped onto his side.

"Let's pray," she suggested, and they all took hands

while Xavier recited a short blessing. Then she dished up pancakes and warm syrup to all of them.

"Delicious," Troy said around a mouthful.

"Mom's a good cook."

He swallowed. "Obviously." Then, a few bites later: "I'm impressed that you sit down at the table for meals and start them with prayer."

Angelica chuckled. "I could let you go on thinking we do that at every meal, but the truth is, there are plenty of nights when we eat off the coffee table and watch *Fresh Prince* reruns."

"Yeah, that's fun!" Xavier shoved another bite into his mouth.

"And we don't always remember to pray, either. I'm not a perfect mom *or* a perfect Christian."

Troy put a hand over hers. "Perfectly imperfect."

Yeah, if only you knew.

Later, Troy went and got his exam bag and then called Bull out to the porch, putting his crutches aside and lifting the dog down the hard-to-maneuver step. In every painstaking move, she saw his care for the old bulldog.

She got Xavier involved in a new video game, then went outside and petted Bull while Troy gathered his materials for removing stitches. "Hey, buddy, you gonna get your fancy collar off, huh?"

As if answering her, Bull pawed at the recovery collar that formed a huge bell around his neck.

"I'm going to try him without it," Troy said. "It's been driving him crazy, and he can't get around that well with it on. Depends on whether he'll leave the leg alone."

He put his hand on the dog and turned to her. "Angelica, I have to apologize."

She tipped her head to the side. "For what?"

"For going off on you that day. You were right. This guy wouldn't have survived without my having Buck to help me. I owe you."

She lifted an eyebrow. "You *were* quick to judge."

"I know. And I'm sorry. I'm kind of a Neanderthal where you're concerned." He looked at her with a possessive intensity that flooded her with warmth.

Troy had grown, for sure. He could see when he was wrong and apologize. And he definitely had a softer heart these days. It looked as if he was blinking back tears when he gazed down at his old dog.

She didn't dare focus on what else his words evoked in her.

Troy removed Bull's stitches with skilled hands while she held the dog's head still and murmured soothing words. But as Troy examined the dog's leg more carefully, moving it back and forth, he frowned. "The range of movement isn't good," he said. "This is what my buddy the specialist warned me about. Once he starts to walk on it, I'm worried what will happen."

"Is there anything we can do?"

"Not right now," he said, still moving Bull's leg, intensely focused. "We'll have to watch him for a few more days, see how he does when he's free to move around."

After the stitches were removed, Angelica insisted on carrying Bull back to Troy's house. She'd noticed how badly Troy was limping, and it wouldn't do for him to ditch his crutches and carry Bull himself.

As she knelt beside Bull's crate, helping the dog settle in and petting him, Troy came up behind her and put a hand on her shoulder. After an initial flinch, she relaxed into his touch. Which felt amazing.

"So you were right about getting Buck's help and I was wrong," he said. "But I'm right about something else. Will you listen to me?"

She kept petting Bull, superaware of Troy's hand on her shoulder. "Okay."

"I want to take Xavier to a new doctor for his physical tomorrow."

She let go of Bull and scooted around to look at Troy. "What?"

"I found a new doctor for Xavier," he repeated. "We scored big-time. Great cancer doctor, hard to get, but he's an old friend of mine from college so I called in a favor. He's at the Cleveland Clinic, just about an hour and fifteen minutes away."

Before she could analyze her own response, it was out of her mouth. "No."

"What?" He looked startled.

"He likes the doctor we've started seeing here. I'd rather go to him. Anyway, it's just a simple physical for school and sports." She stood. "And I have to get back to Xavier."

He grabbed his crutches and held the door for her. "I'll walk with you if you'll listen."

"I listened. And then I said no." She started walking back toward the bunkhouse.

He followed. "Angelica, this is a really good doctor. Someone who specializes in leukemia."

"No."

"Wait." He turned toward her, leaning on his

crutches, and looked hard into her eyes. "Why not? Why really?"

She looked away from his intensity. Why didn't she want a great new cancer doctor for Xavier? She took in a deep breath and started walking again. "Because I'm scared."

He fell into step beside her. "Of what? It can only be good for Xavier."

She stared at the hard dirt beneath their feet. "What if this doesn't work out?"

"What are you talking about?"

She glanced over at him. The morning they'd spent together, the delight of Xavier's happiness, of Troy's appreciation for her cooking, all of it made this so hard to say. "Look, I know the chances of us—you and me, this so-called engagement—making it are fifty-fifty at best. So what if we don't? What if you decide you don't want to go through with the marriage, or even if we do go through with it, that you don't want to stay? What are Xavier and I supposed to do then?"

He stared at her and then, slowly, shook his head. "You don't trust me, do you?"

"It's not you necessarily." She shrugged. "But why would you stick with us? What's in it for you? People don't just do things out of the goodness of their hearts."

They'd reached the bunkhouse porch, and he waited while she climbed the steps, then hopped up behind her. "What world have you been living in? Around here, people do things to help others all the time."

"Sure, give them a ride or watch their dog when they go on vacation. But marry someone? Stand by a kid with serious health issues? That's way, way beyond the call of duty, Troy. I appreciate your willingness, and for Xavier's sake, I have to give it a try. But—"

He tugged her down onto the porch swing and then sat next to her, held out a hand to touch her chin, ran his thumb ever so lightly over her lips. "Really? It's just for Xavier's sake?"

She stared at him, willing herself to stay still and explore the mix of feelings that his touch evoked. But she couldn't handle it. She scooted away and stood, and at a safe distance, pacing, she switched back to a safer topic. "Xavier hates changing doctors. If our relationship doesn't work, I certainly can't afford a fancy specialist. So that's why I'd rather just stick with the doctor we've been going to since we moved here."

"So you'd rather go with safe and mediocre."

"Dr. Lewis comes highly recommended," she protested.

"By whom?"

"Gramps and his friends." At his expression, she flared up. "I know you don't like Gramps, but he's been in the area forever, and all of his friends have medical issues, as does he. They know doctors."

"Geriatric doctors, not pediatricians. Look, this is a great opportunity. He'll get the athletic physical times ten. We're really blessed to see this guy, Ange."

Ange. It was what he'd called her when they were engaged, and hearing it thrust her back to that time. His excitement did, too.

Back then, she would have joined in readily, would have shared his optimism; she'd have been eager to try something new and take a risk.

But now, given her life experiences since that time,

her stomach clenched. "I think Dr. Lewis will be just fine."

"Not really." He was getting serious now, leaning in, crossing his arms. "I asked around about Dr. Lewis. He's been in practice forty years. He isn't likely to be up on the latest research."

Angelica's spine stiffened and she felt her face getting hot. "I researched all the CHIP-eligible doctors within fifty miles. He's by far the best of those."

"Of those." His tone had gone gentle. "I'm not questioning that you did the best you could—"

"He seems really experienced. And Xavier liked him when we went when we first arrived in town."

He sighed. "Look, I just don't understand why you're not excited about this. It's a chance for your son to have the very best care around. Don't you want that?"

"Of course I do," she said, forcing herself not to strangle the guy. "But listen, would you? It's hard for Xavier to handle a new doctor. He's suffered through a lot of them. I don't want to make a change when it might not be permanent."

He leaned over and clamped a hand on her forearm. "I'm not going to fall through. I'm here for you!"

She stared at him, meeting his eyes, trying to read them. But something about his expression took her breath away and she pulled free and turned to look out over the fields, biting her lip.

God, what do I do?

She wanted to trust Troy. She wanted to trust God, and hadn't she been praying for better medical treatment? Hadn't she had her own issues with Dr. Lewis's wait-and-see attitude?

Xavier banged out the front door, sporting a T-shirt

Angelica hadn't seen before, and she pulled him toward her, hands on shoulders, to read it.

Rescue River Midget Soccer.

"Where'd you get this, buddy?"

He smiled winningly. "Becka gave it to me. It's her old one. But she said I can get a new one as soon as I'm 'ficial on the team."

Angelica's heart gave a little thump as she put her arms around him, noticing he was warm and sweaty. He must have been running around inside.

He wanted this so badly, and she did, too. But she worried about whether it was the right thing to do.

Here Troy was offering her an opportunity to get the best medical opinion, even on something so minor as whether a six-year-old could play soccer. Shouldn't she be grateful, and thanking God, rather than trying to escape their good fortune?

Even if it poked at her pride?

She took a deep breath. "Guess what! Mr. Troy found us a new doctor for you, a really good one. We're going to get you a super soccer checkup, to make sure you're ready to do your best."

The next day at the clinic, watching his friend and expert cancer doctor, Ravi Verma, examine Xavier's records and latest test results, Troy heaved a sigh of relief.

He had to admire the way Angelica was handling this. He knew he'd gone beyond the boundaries when he pulled strings to make the appointment, but he just couldn't stand to think that they were making do with a small-town doctor when the best medical care in the world was just another hour's drive away.

Obviously Angelica hadn't loved his approach, but she wasn't taking it out on Xavier. She'd pep-talked him through today's blood tests and played what seemed like a million games of tic-tac-toe as a distraction. Now she had an arm around her son as he leaned against her side.

She was a great mom. She was also gorgeous, her hair curlier than she usually wore it and tumbling over her shoulders, her sleeveless dress revealing shapely bronzed arms and legs.

Troy swallowed and shifted in his plastic chair. Man, this consultation room was small. And warm.

The doctor cleared his throat and turned to them. "There's so much that looks good on his chart and in the testing," he said, "but I'm afraid his blasts are up just a little."

"No!" Angelica's hand flew to her mouth, her eyes suddenly wide and desperate.

Troy pounded his fist on his knee. Just when things had been going so well. "What does that mean, Ravi?"

His friend held up a hand. "Maybe nothing, and I can see why my colleague Dr. Lewis wanted to wait—"

"He didn't even tell us about it!" Angelica sounded anguished.

"And that's common. The impulse not to alarm the patient about what might be a normal fluctuation."

"Might be...or might be something else?" Angelica's throat was working, and he saw her taking breath after breath, obviously trying to calm herself down. She stroked Xavier's back with one hand; her other hand gripped the chair arm with white knuckles. "What can we do about it?"

Ravi nodded. "Let's talk about possibilities. The first, of course, is to wait and see."

"Let's do that." Xavier buried his head in Angelica's skirt. He sounded miserable.

"Other options?" Troy heard the brusqueness in his own voice, but he couldn't seem to control his tone. Hadn't had the practice Angelica had.

"There is an experimental treatment for this kind of…probable relapse."

Angelica's shoulders slumped. "Probable relapse?"

Ravi's dark eyes flashed sympathy. "I'm afraid so. You see, his numbers have crept up again since his last test. Not much at all, so not necessarily significant, but from what I have seen in these cases…" He reached out and put a hand on Angelica's. "I think it might be best to treat it aggressively."

"Treat it how?" Angelica's voice was hoarse, and Troy could hear the tears right at the edge of it.

Xavier looked up at his mother. "Mom?"

"We'll figure it out, buddy." She smiled down reassuringly and stroked his hair with one hand. The other dug into the chair's upholstery so hard it looked as if she was about to rip it.

"The traditional protocol is radiation and chemo, quite intensive and quite…challenging on the patient."

Angelica pressed her lips together.

Troy leaned forward. "Is there another option?"

"Yes, the experimental treatment I mentioned. Cell therapy. Using the body's own immunological cells. Now, most of the participants in the trial are adults, but there is one other child, a girl of about twelve. It's possible I could talk my colleagues into allowing Xavier in, if he passes the tests."

"Isn't that going to be really expensive? We don't have good insurance."

"In an experimental trial, the patient's medications are fully funded. However…" He looked up at Angelica. "There may be some expenses not covered by our grant or your insurance."

"That's not a problem," Troy said. "Is this new treatment what you'd recommend?" he pressed.

Ravi looked at Xavier's bent head with eyes full of compassion. "If he were one of my own, this is the approach I would take."

Angelica opened her mouth and then closed it again. Shut her eyes briefly, and then turned back to Ravi. "How difficult is the treatment?"

"That is the wonder of it. It is noninvasive and not harmful as far as cancer treatments go because it uses the body's own cells. Of course, there are the usual tests and injections…" He reached down and patted Xavier's shoulder. "Nothing about cancer is easy for a child."

"I don't want a treatment." Xavier's head lifted to look at his mother. "I want to play soccer."

She lifted him into her lap and clasped him close. "I know, buddy. I want that, too."

Troy leaned toward the pair, not sure whether to touch Xavier or not. In the mysteries of sick children, he was a rank beginner. He had to bow to the expertise of Ravi, and especially of Angelica. At most, he was a mentor and a friend to the boy. "Buddy, this could make you well."

"It never did before." Xavier's expression held more discouragement than looked right on that sweet face. "Mom, I don't want a treatment."

"We'll talk about it and think about it. And pray about it." She straightened her back and squared her shoulders and Troy watched, impressed, as she took control of the situation. "Listen, I think Mr. Troy is feeling worried. And I also think I have a bag of chocolate candy in my purse. Could you get him some?"

Xavier sniffed and nodded and reached for her purse. She let him dig in it, watching him with the most intense expression of love and fierce care that he'd ever seen on a woman's face.

"Here it is!"

"Give Mr. Troy the first choice." She took back the purse and reached in herself, pulling out a creased sheet of paper. While Xavier fumbled through the bag of candy, patently ignoring her instruction to let Troy go first, Angelica skimmed down a list and started pelting Ravi with questions.

Troy imagined he could see the sweat and tears of their history with cancer on that well-worn paper. He didn't pray often enough, but now he thanked God for allowing him the honor of helping Angelica cope.

He focused on Xavier for a few minutes while the other two talked, bandying about terms and phrases he'd not heard even with his vet school history. Finally Angelica folded the paper back up, glanced over at Xavier and frowned. "Is there time for me to think about this?"

"Of course," Ravi said, "but it's best to get started early, before his numbers go up too high. If there is any chance you'll be interested in participating, we should start the paperwork now."

She closed her eyes for a moment, drew in a slow

breath and then opened her eyes and nodded. "Let's do it."

During the little flurry of activity that followed— forms to fill out, a visit from the office manager to pin down times and details, some protests from Xavier— Troy kept noticing Angelica's strength, her fierceness and her decision-making power. She'd grown so much since he knew her last, and while he'd been aware of it before, he was even more so now. She had his total respect.

And she deserved a break. When Xavier's protests turned into crying and the office manager started talking about initial tests that would be costly but not covered by the trial's grant, he nudged the boy toward her. "Why don't you two go out and get some fresh air, maybe hit the park across the street? I need to talk to my friend here for a minute. And I'll settle up some of the financial details with the office manager and then come on out."

"Can we go, Mom?"

She pressed her lips together and then nodded. "I'll be in touch," she said to Ravi. She mouthed a thank-you to Troy, and then the two of them left.

Troy stood, too, knowing his friend's time was valuable, but Ravi gestured him back into the chair. "You cannot escape without telling me about her."

"She's…pretty special. And so is the boy."

"I see that." Ravi nodded. "They've not had an easy road, I can tell from the charts. Lots of free clinics, lots of delays."

"Has it affected the outcome?"

"No, I think not. It has just been hard on both of them."

"What are his chances of getting into the trial?"

"Honestly? Fifty-fifty. We have to look more deeply into all his previous treatments and his other options. But I will do my best."

"Thank you." And Troy made a promise to himself: he *would* make sure they got in. And, God willing, the treatment would make Xavier well.

That night, Angelica was helping Lou Ann clean up the kitchen—they'd all eaten together again—while Troy and Xavier sat in the den building something complicated out of LEGO blocks. The sound of the two of them laughing was a pleasant, quiet backdrop to the clattering of pots and dishes, and Angelica didn't know she was sighing until Lou Ann called her on it. "What's going on in your mind, kiddo?"

Angelica smiled at the older woman. "I'm just… wishing this could go on forever."

"Which part? With Xavier, or with Troy?"

"Both."

"Xavier we pray about. Is there a problem with your engagement we should take to the Lord, too?"

Lou Ann didn't know that the engagement was for show, and normally Angelica felt that was right and would have continued the deception. But something in the older woman's sharp eyes told her that she'd guessed the truth. "Yes," she said slowly, "we could use some prayer. I just don't know that it will work, not really."

"Why's that?" Lou Ann carried the roaster over to the sink and started scrubbing it.

Angelica wiped at the counter aimlessly. "Well, because I...I don't know, I just don't believe it can happen."

Lou Ann shook her head. "Why the two of you can't see what's under your noses, that you love each other, I don't know."

"We don't love each other!" And then Angelica's hand flew to her mouth. If the fact that their engagement was a sham hadn't been out before, it was now.

"I think you have more feelings than you realize," the older woman said. "So what's holding you back, really?"

Angelica leaned against the counter, abandoning all pretense of working. "I...I just don't believe he'll love me. Don't believe I'm able to keep him."

"The man's crazy about you!"

Lou Ann's automatic, obviously sincere response made Angelica's breath catch. "You really think so?"

"Yep."

Lou Ann's certainty felt amazing, but Angelica couldn't let herself trust it. "That's because he doesn't know much about me. If he did, he'd feel differently."

Lou Ann pointed at her with the scrubber stick. "What did you do that's so all-fired awful?"

Angelica shook her head. "Nothing. I...I can't talk about it."

"If it's about Xavier's daddy," Lou Ann said with her usual shrewdness, "I think you should let it go. The past is the past."

"Not when you have a child by it," Angelica murmured, starting to scrub again.

"Look," Lou Ann said, "all of us have sinned. Every single one. If you'd look at the inside of my soul, it would be as stained and dirty as this greasy old pan."

"You? No way!"

"You'd be surprised," Lou Ann said. "For one thing, I wasn't always as old and wrinkled as I am now. I had my days of running around. Ask your grandfather sometime."

Angelica laughed. "Gramps already told me you were the belle of the high school ball. In fact, I think he has a crush on you still."

Lou Ann's cheeks turned a pretty shade of pink. "I doubt that. But the point is, we've all done things we're not proud of. I ran around with too many boys in my younger days, and I've also done my share of gossiping and coveting. Not to mention that I don't love my neighbor as well as I should."

When Angelica tried to protest, Lou Ann held out a hand. "Point is, we're all like that. We've all sinned and fallen short, that one—" she pointed the scrubber toward the den where Troy was "—included. So don't go thinking your sins, whatever they are, make you worse than anyone else. Without Jesus, we'd all be on the same sinking ship."

"I guess," Angelica said doubtfully. She knew that was doctrine, and in her head she pretty much believed it. In her heart, though, where it mattered, she felt worse than other people.

"I think you need to sit down and talk to the man," Lou Ann said. "The two of you spend all your time with Xavier, and you don't ever get any couple time to grow your relationship and get to know each other."

"But our connection…well, you've pretty much guessed that it's mainly about Xavier."

"But it shouldn't be," Lou Ann said firmly. "You two should build your own bond first, like putting on your oxygen mask in a plane before you help your kid. If Mom and Dad aren't happy, the kids won't be happy. Xavier needs to see that you two have a stable, committed relationship. That's what will help him."

Angelica sighed. "You're probably right." She'd been thinking about it a lot: the fact that their pretend engagement had grown out of their control and was now of a size to need some tending. Half the town knew they were engaged, and more important, her own feelings had grown beyond pretend to real. She didn't want to think about ending the engagement, partly because of what it would do to Xavier, but also because of what it would do to her.

"You need to get to know him as he is now, not just the way he was seven years ago. Things have changed. He writes articles in veterinary journals now, and other vets come to consult with him. He's way too busy. And on the home front, his dad's not getting any younger, and Troy needs to make his peace with him. You're the one with the big, immediate issues in the form of that special boy in there, but Troy has his own problems to solve. You need to figure out if you can help him do that."

"Sit down. Take a break." Angelica nudged Lou Ann aside and reached for the scrubber, attacking the worst of the pots and pans. "I've been selfish, haven't I?"

"Not at all. You're preoccupied, and that makes sense. But promise you'll talk to him soon. Maybe even tell him some of that history that's got you feeling so down on yourself."

Angelica sighed. The thought of bringing up their

engagement, of having that difficult talk, seemed over-whelming, but she could tell Lou Ann wasn't going to let it go. "All right," she said. "I'll try."

Chapter 10

Angelica strolled toward the field beside the barn, more relaxed than she had felt in a week.

She'd tried to work up the courage to talk to Troy about their relationship, even to tell him the truth about why she'd left him, but it hadn't happened. Finally this morning, she'd turned the whole thing over to God. If He wanted her to talk to Troy, He had to open up the opportunity, because she couldn't do it on her own strength.

Red-winged blackbirds trilled and wild roses added a sweet note to the usual farm fragrances of hay and the neighboring cattle. Beyond the barn, she could hear boys shouting and dogs barking as Troy's Kennel Kids tossed balls for the dogs.

Today—praise the Lord—she'd gotten word that Xavier was accepted into the clinical trial. He'd go for his treatment in a couple of days, and Dr. Ravi was reassuring about everything. The treatment wouldn't be difficult, and he was optimistic that the trial would work, told stories of patients' numbers improving and "positive preliminary findings."

Impulsively she lifted her hands to the sky, feeling the breeze kiss her arms. *Lord, thank You, thank You.*

She rounded the corner of the barn and froze.

One of the Kennel Kids, older and at least twice Xavier's size, loomed over him, fist raised threateningly.

"Hey!" Poised to run to her son, she felt a restraining hand on her shoulder.

"Let him try to handle it himself," Troy said.

She yanked away. "He can't fight that kid! Look at the size difference!"

"Just watch." Troy's voice was still mild, but there was a note of command that halted her. "Wendell always pulls his punches, so don't worry."

Clenching her fist, still primed to run to her son, she paused.

Xavier smiled up guilelessly at the other boy. "Hey, I'm sorry my ball hit you. My pitching stinks."

"Leave him alone, Wendell. He's just a kid." One of the other boys put an arm around Xavier.

The bigger boy drew in a breath, and then his fisted hand dropped. "Yeah, well, don't hit me again. Or else."

One of the puppies jumped into the mix, and as if no threat had ever existed, the group broke into a kaleidoscope of colorful balls and yipping puppies and running boys.

As her adrenaline slowly dissipated, Angelica

leaned against the wall of the barn and sank down to a sitting position.

"I want to go give Wendell some positive feedback. He's getting better about controlling his anger."

"I'm still working on that myself," she snapped at him, but halfheartedly. She knew it was good for Xavier to socialize with other kids, but these rough-around-the-edges boys scared her.

She watched Troy walk over and speak briefly with Wendell and then clap him on the back. Xavier, completely unmoved by his near brush with getting the tar kicked out of him, was rolling with one of the puppies.

Taking deep breaths, she willed herself to calm down. She hated the way Troy was high-handed with her, but after all, he was right, wasn't he? Xavier had handled the situation himself just fine and was fitting in nicely with the other boys. If she'd run in to save him, that might not be the case.

A few minutes later, Troy came back and sat down beside her. "You mad at me?"

"Yes and no." She watched as one of the other boys threw a ball back and forth with Xavier. The other boy was older; in fact, most of the boys were, but Xavier was holding his own. It reminded her of what a good athlete he could be.

If he got the chance.

And that was where Troy had been incredibly, incredibly helpful. "Listen," she said. "I don't necessarily like being told how to mother my kid, but there are times when you're right." She smiled up at him. "Dr. Ravi called today."

Troy's head jerked toward her, his face lighting up. "And?"

"And Xavier gets into the trial."

"That's fantastic!" He threw his arms around her.

No, no, no. She couldn't breathe, couldn't survive, couldn't stand it. She pushed hard at his brawny chest.

"Hey, fine, sorry!" He dropped his arms immediately and scooted backward, his eyebrows shooting up.

She gulped air. "It's fine. I'm sorry. I just..." Blinking rapidly, she came back from remembered darkness—something she'd had years of practice at doing—and offered Troy a shaky smile. "I'm so grateful that you made us see Dr. Ravi. He's wonderful. And I like that he's going forward aggressively with the treatment. I really, really want Xavier to have it. This could make all the difference."

"I'm glad." Troy continued to look a little puzzled. "But you're still mad at me?"

Mad wasn't the word. She knew she should launch into the talk she'd promised Lou Ann she'd have with Troy. She looked out across the fields and breathed deeply of the farm-scented air.

And changed the subject. "Look, I know I'm overprotective. It kind of comes with the territory of parenting a seriously ill child."

"Of course."

"And I was worried about that bigger kid hitting him. Xavier tends to bruise and bleed easily, or he did when he was in active disease. I try to make sure he doesn't fall a lot and all that."

"Should I have stopped them? I struggle with how much to intervene and how much to let them work it out themselves so they can build better social skills." He studied his hands, clasped between his upraised knees. "Thing is, a lot of these boys are out on their own much of the time. I spend such a small fraction of their lives with them. So I feel like they need to practice solving some of their conflicts themselves. We usually talk it over in group, after they've gotten some of their energy out." He shrugged. "I'm just a vet with a heart to help kids. I don't know sometimes if I'm doing it right."

"You do a great job," she said warmly.

"Thanks." And then he was looking at her again, and she spoke nervously to make the moment pass. "Parenting is like that for me. I never know if there's something I should do differently. Xavier's going to go to school, and he'll have to learn to handle the playground himself. I won't be there to intervene for him, so I guess that's something I'd better get used to."

"We can help each other out. We're a good partnership." He reached out and squeezed her shoulder.

She cringed away instinctively. And when she saw the hurt look on his face, she felt awful.

She opened her mouth to apologize and then closed it again. What was she going to say? How could she explain?

Nervously she pulled a bandanna out of her pocket and wiped off her suddenly sweaty neck and face. The thing was, she didn't know if she was going to get over this, ever. Being touched was hard for her. Oh, she could hug Xavier, did that all the time, and his childish affection was a balm to her spirit. When she stayed with Aunt Dot right after being assaulted, and indeed for years afterward until that wonderful woman had died a year ago, they'd shared hugs galore. And her girlfriends were always hugging on her and plenty of nurses had let her weep in their arms.

Female nurses.

It was only when a man hugged her that she freaked out.

Troy was regarding her seriously. His blue eyes showed hurt and some anger, too. "Look, I'm sorry," he said. "I guess I didn't realize how much you... Well, how much you don't want me near you. That's a problem. How are we..." He broke off, got awkwardly to his feet, favoring his hurt leg. "I better go check on the boys."

He limped off and she wanted to call him back, to apologize, to say she'd work on it, really she would. But the thing was, it had been seven years and she still wasn't over the assault.

She hadn't been motivated to get over it before because she hadn't dated anyone and she hadn't wanted a man around.

But Troy was doing so much for them. Moreover, when he touched her, she felt something uncurl within her, and that as much as anything made her shy away.

There'd been plenty of chemistry between them when they were engaged. Now, though, everything felt different.

She stared absently out at cornfields with tassels almost head high. Above her, the sky shone deep blue with puffy clouds.

She'd seen a counselor right along with her obstetrician, at her aunt's insistence, and the woman had been wonderful and had helped her a lot. But Angelica hadn't wanted to date. Hadn't wanted to open herself up to love—and the accompanying dangers and risks—again.

Still didn't, if the truth be told. She'd rather stay in her safe, comfortable little shell. But Troy was so good with Xavier, and Xavier needed a dad. Holding back like this was selfish of her. She had to fix this.

If she wanted to love again, a part of loving was hugging and kissing and all the intimate physicality created by the same God who'd made the corn and the sky and the sweaty little boys and jumping, bounding dogs in front of her.

She let her head drop into her hands. *Lord, I can't do this myself. Please help me heal. Help me learn to love.*

Slowly, as she listened for God's voice, as she breathed in the wonders of His creation, she felt herself relaxing. She didn't know if it would work for her. She certainly didn't want to tell Troy the reasons for her pain, because she knew he would judge her.

But maybe God would give her a pass on that. Maybe He'd let her have this relationship and let Xavier have a dad—a dad who could do amazing things with his connections, who could actually help Xavier heal—and she wouldn't have to tell Troy the sordid side of her past. Wouldn't have to tell him about her own culpability in what had happened to her.

Because no matter what her therapist had said, Angelica knew the truth. She'd gotten drunk and silly and flirty, and she'd been mad at Troy for not coming out to celebrate her birthday, and she'd been flattered when a handsome older man wanted to walk her home.

It wasn't pretty and it wasn't nice, and she'd regret it for the rest of her life.

God in His amazing excellence had turned it to good. God had brought her Xavier and he was the purpose of her life now, the thing that gave it meaning. And she, flawed as she was, loved him as fiercely as any mother could love any child, despite his bad beginning. God had done that much for them, overlooking her sins.

She could only hope and pray that He'd heal her enough to let her go forward with the marriage to Troy.

Troy strode away from Angelica and out toward the driveway. He just needed a minute to himself.

Apparently, though, he wasn't going to get it, because heading toward him was a police cruiser. Like any red-blooded American male who'd occasionally driven faster than he should, he tensed...until he realized that Dion was at the wheel.

Even seeing his friend didn't make him smile as he walked up to the driver's-side window.

"What's wrong with you, old man?"

Troy shrugged. He'd talk to Dion about almost anything, they were those kinds of friends, but there was a time and a place. "What brings you out my way? You're working nights. You should be home catching Zs."

"Yeah, had an issue." Dion jerked his head toward the backseat and lowered the rear window.

There, on a towel, was the saddest-looking white pit bull Troy had ever seen. Ears down, cringing against the backseat, quivering, skin and bones.

Troy's heart twisted.

"Found her chained to an abandoned house. You got your work cut out for you with this one."

Troy opened the rear car door and wasn't really surprised when the dog shrank against the back of the seat and bared her teeth. "Problem is, I've got the Kennel Kids here today."

"I know you do. I'm gonna help out for a bit while

you take care of this little mama. Those boys could use an hour with a cop who's not out to arrest them."

Troy focused in on the word *mama*. "She's pregnant?"

"Oh yeah. It rains, it pours."

Troy drew in a breath and let it out in a sigh. "Okay. Lemme run get a crate and—"

Shaking his head, Dion turned off the engine and got out. "Can't crate her, man. She freaks."

"How'd you get her into the cruiser?" As always, when there was a hurting animal nearby, Troy went into superfocus, forgetting everything else, trying to figure out how to help it. He braced his hands on the car roof and leaned in, studying the dog.

Dion gave his trademark low chuckle. "One of the guys had a sandwich left over from lunch."

"Gotcha. Be right back."

Minutes later, with the help of a piece of chicken, the dog was out of the cruiser and in one of the runs right beside where the boys were playing.

"See what you can do, my man," Dion said, then strode over to the group of boys in the field, who went silent at the sight of the tall, dark-skinned man in full uniform.

Troy watched for a minute. Angelica was with them, and he saw her greet Dion. The two of them spoke, and then Dion squatted down to pet one of the dogs.

A couple of the boys came closer. Dion greeted them and apparently made some kind of a joke, because the boys laughed.

So that would be okay. Dion was great with kids; in fact, some of these boys probably knew him pretty well already, though not for as innocent a reason as his visit here today.

Using treats, Troy tried to get the dog to relax and come to him, but she cowered as far away as possible. From this distance, he could see her distended belly and swollen teats. She'd probably give birth in a week or two.

Xavier, for one, would be excited. He loved the puppies best, and though he was having a blast with the ones already here, watching them grow and playing with them, new babies would thrill him beyond belief. For that reason, Troy was glad they had a mama dog, though he had to wonder about this one's story.

Right on schedule, his sister pulled into the driveway. She helped with the Kennel Kids whenever she could.

"C'mere, Lily." On an impulse he named the dog for her white coat, even if she was more gray than white at the moment. He threw a treat to within a few inches of her nose, and she made several moves toward it, then jerked back. Finally she dove far enough forward to grab the dog biscuit and retreat, and he praised her lavishly. Still when he moved toward her, she backed away, growling.

He settled in, back against the fence, watching the boys, Dion, Angelica and his sister.

Dion said something to Angelica and she laughed, and Troy felt a burning in his chest. Would Angelica go for his best friend?

A year older than Troy, Dion had been a little more suave with the ladies when they played football together in high school. But Troy had never felt jealous of the man…until this moment.

He tried to stifle the feeling, but that just made his heart rate go up, made him madder. Yeah, he was possessive, especially where Angelica was concerned. Nothing to be proud of, but the truth.

He watched Angelica and noticed that, while she was friendly to Dion, she kept a good few feet between them. Not like his sister, who often put an affectionate hand on Dion's arm or fist-bumped him after a joke.

Relief trickled in. Looked as though Angelica wasn't attracted.

He tossed another treat to the dog, and this time she dove for it and ate it immediately. He scooted a couple of feet closer, still staying low so he didn't look big and threatening to her. She let out a low growl but didn't attack.

He tossed another treat halfway between them, and the dog considered a moment, then crept forward to grab it.

He reached out toward the dog with a piece of food in his hand. This was a risk, as he might get bitten, but he figured it wasn't likely. He had a sense about this one. She wanted help.

A moment later, his instinct was rewarded when she accepted food out of his hand.

He fed her several more pieces and then reached toward her. She backed away, a low growl vibrating in her chest.

Righteous anger rose in him. He'd like to strangle the person who'd mistreated this sweet dog. Maybe ruined her for a home with a family. Fear did awful things to an animal.

Or a person.

It hit him like a two-by-four to the brain.

The dog was reacting the way Angelica reacted.

It was pretty obvious why, in the dog's case: people had treated her badly, and she'd learned to be afraid.

So who'd been mean to Angelica? What had they done? And when?

He jumped up, moved toward the dog and she lunged at him, teeth bared. He backed away immediately. He should know better than to approach a scared dog when he was feeling this agitated; she could sense it.

Had Angelica been abused or attacked?

No, not possible. He spun around and marched over to the kennels, grabbed a water bowl for the dog, filled it.

He had no idea what had gone on in Angelica's life in the years they'd been apart. She could very well have gotten into a bad relationship. And given that she'd apparently been poor, she could have lived in bad areas where risks were high and safety wasn't guaranteed.

He needed to talk to his social-worker sister. He took the water bowl back to the new dog's run and set it down, keeping a good distance from her. Then he beckoned to Daisy.

She came right over. "Hey, bro, what's happening with Xavier and Angelica? Did you find out about the cancer trial?"

"Xavier got in. We're pretty happy."

Hands on hips, she studied him. "Then what's eating you?"

"You know me too well. And you understand women, and I don't."

She raised her eyebrows. "What's up?"

He looked out at the cornfields. "If a woman was…

abused, say, or attacked…how would she react? Wouldn't she tell people what happened?"

Daisy cocked her head to one side. "Probably, but maybe not. Why?"

"Why wouldn't she tell?"

"Well…"

He could see her social work training kick in as she thought about it.

"Sometimes women are ashamed. Sometimes their attacker threatens them. Sometimes they're in denial, or they just want to bury it."

He nodded. "Okay, it makes sense that they might not want to report it, to have it be common knowledge. But if they have close family or friends who would help them…"

"Are you talking about a rape?"

The word slammed into him. And the doors of his mind slammed shut. That couldn't have happened. Not to Angelica. *Please, God, no.*

Daisy crossed her arms over her chest and narrowed her eyes at him. "Whatever you're thinking, you need to talk to that person about it. Not to me."

He nodded, because he couldn't speak.

"So go do it."

He drew in a breath, sighed it out. "Cone of silence?"

"Of course."

Slowly he walked over to where Dion leaned against a fence, talking to a rapt group of boys. Angelica knelt a short distance away beside the pen they'd made to keep Bull safe from too much activity but still included in the fun. She was rubbing the old dog's belly, praising him for how his leg was healing, telling him he'd feel better soon. She looked pensive and beautiful and she didn't hear him coming.

Deliberately he touched her shoulder, and just as he now expected, she jumped and frowned toward him.

He hated being right. "We have to talk," he said to her. "Soon."

Chapter 11

The next Saturday night, Angelica listened to the closing notes of the praise band and wished she felt the love the musicians had been singing about.

Sometime during the past month, coming to Saturday night services with Lou Ann, Troy and Xavier had become the highlight of her week. The focus on God's love, the sense of being part of a community of believers and the growing hope of a future here—all of it made church wonderful. But tonight, she'd been too jittery to enjoy it.

She felt Troy's gaze on her—again—and scooted toward the edge of the padded pew. "I've got to go get Xavier."

"No, that's okay." Lou Ann sidled past her and out of the pew. "I'll do it."

Oh. Rats.

Troy turned to greet the family next to them, and, hoping he hadn't heard her exchange with Lou Ann, she started edging out of the pew. Grabbing her purse, she stood and took a sideways step, then another.

Suddenly some kind of hook caught her wrist, and she looked down to see the crook of a wooden cane tugging at her.

She spun back toward him. "Troy! What are you doing?"

"I knew this thing was good for something," he said, holding up the cane he'd borrowed from Lou Ann and offering her a repentant grin. Then he scanned the room. "The place is emptying out. We can have some privacy. Do you mind staying a minute?"

Yes, I mind! She bit her lip, shook her head and sank back down onto the pew. It was probably better to stay here in the sanctuary than to go off somewhere by themselves. Somewhere she might feel that strange sense in her stomach again, that sense of...

Being attracted.

Yeah, that.

She hadn't felt it for years—in fact, she hadn't felt it since she was engaged to Troy—and it was making her crazy.

"We've got to talk about why you jump every time I touch you."

"Don't open that can of worms, Troy," she said quickly. Of all their possible topics of conversation, that was the one she most wanted to avoid.

He cocked his head to one side, studying her face. "Actually we've got to talk about a few things," he said finally. "One of which is this marriage. People are asking more and more about it. We can't put them off forever with some vague engagement plans in the future."

Early-evening sunshine slanted through stained-glass windows, and the breeze through the church's open back door felt cool against Angelica's neck. "I know. It's Xavier, too. He wants to know when the wedding will be."

"Is there going to be a wedding?" He watched her, his face impassive.

Her heart skipped a beat. "Do you want to back out?"

"Noooooo," he said. "But I'm seeing some implications I wasn't thinking about before." Deliberately he reached out and took her hand.

It felt as if every nerve, every sensation in her body was concentrated in her hand. Concentrated to notice how his hand was bigger, more calloused than hers. To notice the warmth and protection of being completely wrapped in him. Waves of what felt like electricity crackled through her veins.

He was watching her. It seemed he was always watching her. "You feel it?"

Heat rose to her cheeks as she nodded.

"So…we're going to have to figure out what to do with that."

Somehow even admitting she felt something for him—something like physical attraction—made her feel panicky and ashamed. She looked away from him, focusing on the polished light wooden pews, on the simple altar at the front of the church. Her hand still burned, enclosed by his larger one, and she pulled it away, hiding it in the folds of her dress.

"It's not wrong, you know. It's a mutual thing, a gift

from God, and He blesses it in the context of marriage." Troy's voice, though quiet, was sure.

Angelica wanted that quiet certainty so much. She wanted Troy's leadership in this area. Wanted to feel okay about her body and wanted to find the beauty in physical intimacy sanctioned by God. It had been so long since she felt anything but sadness and regret about the physical side of life. Here, in God's house, she wanted to hope. But did she dare? Was change possible after all these years? Could God bless her that much?

Xavier and Lou Ann came hurrying in through the side front door of the sanctuary. *Whew, relief.*

"Hey, you two." Lou Ann reached them right behind Xavier and leaned on the pew in front of them. "Some of the kids and parents are walking over to the Meadows for ice cream. Is it okay if I take Xavier along?"

"Please, Mom?" Xavier chimed in.

Angelica grabbed her purse. "I can take him," she said to Lou Ann.

"That's okay. I could use a rocky road ice-cream cone myself." Lou Ann reached over and put a hand on her shoulder, effectively holding her in the pew. She leaned down and whispered, "Besides, you need to talk to him."

"Do I have to?"

"Yes, you have to!" Lou Ann patted her arm. "I'll be praying for you."

"Thanks a lot!" She bit her lip and watched Lou Ann guide Xavier off, trying to remember what was most important: God was with her, always, and God forgave her, and God would help her get through this whole thing.

She drew in a breath, and the peace she'd been seeking during the service came rushing in. *Pneuma*. Holy Spirit. God.

She turned back to Troy and he took her hand again, and immediately that uncurling inside started. That opening; that vulnerability. She tried to pull away a little, but he held on. Not too tight, not forcing her, but letting her know he wanted to keep touching her.

Angelica let him do it, her eyes closed tight. She didn't want to like his touch. Didn't want to need him. It would be so much easier and safer not to open up.

He tightened his grip on her hand, ever so slightly. "I want you to tell me why you pull away all the time."

"I'm not sure—"

"Hey, hey, the engaged couple!" Pastor Ricky came over and clapped Troy on the shoulder, leaned down to hug Angelica, overwhelming her. She shrank back, right into Troy. *Aack*.

"Have you two set a date yet? Are you wanting to get married here? You'd better reserve it now if you're planning to do it any time soon. We're a busy place."

"We were just talking about that," Troy said.

"Make an appointment with me to start some premarital counseling, too." He made a few more minutes of small talk and then turned to another pair of parishioners and walked away with them.

"He's right," Troy said. "We've got to decide."

"I know." But inside, turmoil reigned.

Xavier needed a dad in the worst way, and Troy was the perfect man for the job. The three of them were already close.

Xavier needed it, needed Troy, but she herself was terrified.

Lord, help me. Her heart rate accelerated to the

pace of a hummingbird. She could barely breathe. She looked up at Troy, panicky.

"You can talk to me." He slid an arm along the back of the pew behind her, letting it rest ever so lightly around her shoulders. "What is it you need to tell me?"

She took deep, slow, breaths. The fact that she was shaking had to be obvious to Troy.

What part could she tell him? What part did she need to keep private? What part would come back to bite her?

Tell him the worst right away.

Like yanking off a Band-Aid. She moved to the edge of the pew, away from his arm, and pulled her hand from his. Clenching her fists, she turned her head toward him, looking right at his handsome face. "I was…I was raped."

"Raped? What? When?"

It was the first time she'd ever said that word, even to herself. Her vision seemed to blur around the edges, bringing her focus to just his mouth, his eyes. She had to grip the edge of the pew, waiting for the expression of disgust and horror to cross his face.

His mouth twisted.

There it was, the anger she'd expected. She looked away from his face and down at his hands. His enormous hands. They clenched into fists.

She shrank away. Was he going to hit her right here and now? Frantically she looked around for help.

"Tell me." He sounded as though he was gritting his teeth. But his voice was quiet, and when she looked at his hands, they'd relaxed a little. He wasn't moving any closer, either.

"Troy, I'm sorry…I was drinking. I should have been more careful."

"Man, I'd like to kill the jerk who did that to you. When did it happen?" His voice was still angry, and she couldn't blame him. At least it was a controlled anger, so she wasn't at immediate risk.

Even though it would destroy their relationship, she'd started down this path and she had to keep going. *God, help me.* "It was…after my twenty-first birthday celebration. Remember I went out to that bar?" She heard the urgent sound in her voice. Couldn't seem to calm down.

His expression changed. "I remember that night. I had to work and couldn't go." He pounded a fist lightly against the pew. "I should have been there to take care of you."

"I was drinking."

He took her hand in his. "It's not your fault. Man, I wish I'd been there." He shook his head slowly back and forth, his eyes far away, as if he were reliving that time.

Not her fault? She looked away, bit her lip. That was what her therapist and her aunt had said, but she'd never really believed it. Could Troy?

"Look," he said, "as far as any physical connection between us is concerned, you can have all the time you need. I'll be patient. I understand."

Tears filled her eyes. Was it possible that, even knowing this, Troy could still want her?

"So…wait. That's when Xavier was conceived?"

She nodded, staring down at her lap, kneading her skirt between her hands. He was being kinder than she had any right to expect. She blinked and drew in shuddery breaths as tension released from her body.

Telling him the truth was something she'd barely considered at the time because she was terrified of what his reaction would be. She'd had some vague image of yelling and rage and judgment, and the notion of Troy, her beloved fiancé, doing that had pushed her right out of town. Better to leave than to face that pain.

He didn't seem to be blaming her. She could hardly believe in it, couldn't imagine that his kindness would stay, but even the edge of it warmed her heart.

"Who did it, Angelica?" Troy's voice grew low, urgent. "Was it someone you knew? Someone we knew?"

And there it was, the part she didn't dare tell him.

"Did we know him?" Troy repeated.

Still looking down at her lap, she shook her head. Did it count as a lie if she didn't say it out loud?

Troy looked at Angelica with his heart aching for all the pain she'd been through and his fists clenching with anger at the jerk who'd done this to her. He tried to ignore the tiny suspicion that she wasn't telling the whole truth.

His mother had constantly lied to his father. He didn't want to believe it of Angelica, but her body language, her voice, her facial expressions—all of it suggested she was keeping something from him. "We were engaged. You should have told me."

"I blamed myself," she said in a quiet voice. "And I knew how much my chastity meant to you."

Her words hit him like a physical blow. "You think that would be more important than taking care of you? I would've helped you."

"Out of obligation," she said, glancing up at him and then away. "But you wouldn't have liked it."

"Was I that kind of a jerk?" He didn't think so, but look how he was feeling right now. Compassion, sure, but with the slightest shred of doubt in his heart.

He grabbed the Bible from the rack in front of them and held it. For something to do with his hands, but also to remind himself to take the high road and think the best. "I can't believe this happened to you," he said, turning the Good Book over and over in his hands, thinking out loud. "It was a crime committed against you. It's not your fault, and you shouldn't blame yourself." He put the Bible down beside him. "And if you didn't report the crime then…" He searched her face, saw her shake her head, looking at her lap again. "If you didn't say anything already, you should now. The man should be brought to justice. I'll talk to Dion. He knows everything about the law."

"No!" She scooted away from him, an expression of horror on her face. "I don't want to dig into it again. And anyway, it's not…it's not necessary."

"We gotta get the guy! Don't you want justice?"

She shook her head. "No. I don't want anything to do with the police."

"Are you protecting someone?"

"I just don't want to get the police involved. For all kinds of reasons."

Why wouldn't she tell him who did it? Was she telling the truth, that she didn't know the person?

And if she was lying, then how much did she really care for him?

He looked at her face and was shocked by the disappointment he saw there. Immediately he felt awful.

She needed support, she needed help. She needed a dad for Xavier, and speaking of that sweet kid…wow, he was the product of an assault. And she'd mothered him despite that, wonderfully.

Whatever mistakes she'd made in the past, he was going to provide what he could for her. He reached out to put his arm around her. Felt her stiffen, but remain still, letting him do it.

There was none of the tender promise of before, though. There was more of a cringe. He reached out involuntarily to stroke her shiny hair.

She pulled away and stood. "I'm going to leave you to think about this. It's a lot to take in, I know."

"Angelica—"

"We'll talk later, okay?" Her lips twisted and she hurried off toward the back of the sanctuary.

Leaving him to his dark thoughts and guilt and anger, a mixture that didn't seem to belong in this holy place.

Chapter 12

"I'm terrified," Angelica admitted to Lou Ann as they dug carrots from the garden. "They hated me before and they'll hate me even more now."

The older woman shifted her gardening stool to the next row. "Troy's family isn't that bad."

Hot sun warmed Angelica's head and bare arms, and the garden smells of dirt and tomato vines and marigolds tickled her nose. Around them, rows of green were starting to reveal the fruit of the season: red tomatoes, yellow squash, purple eggplant.

Later today, she and Troy and Xavier were going to join his family at the small country club's Labor Day picnic. Just the words *country club* made Angelica shudder.

Not only that, but her relationship with Troy had felt strained ever since last Saturday, when she'd revealed the truth about how Xavier was conceived. Although he'd responded better than she'd expected, she still felt questions in his eyes every time he looked at her. It made her want to avoid him, but they'd had the plan to go to the Labor Day picnic for weeks.

And she had to see whether she could stand it and whether his family could accept Xavier. Had to see whether to go forward with the marriage or run as fast as she could in the opposite direction.

The older woman sat back on her gardening stool. "You put way too much stock in what those people think."

"What they think about me isn't that important," Angelica said, "but I don't want them to reject Xavier."

Lou Ann used the back of her hand to push gray curls out of her eyes. "I've yet to meet a person who could dislike that child. What God didn't give him in health, He gave him double in charm."

"Which he knows how to use," Angelica said wryly. "But what he doesn't know is which fork to pick up at what time. I don't, either. We've neither of us ever been to a country club."

"He never took you when you were engaged?" Lou Ann asked, and when Angelica shook her head, the other woman waved a dismissive hand. "Honey, this isn't some ritzy East Coast place. This is a picnic in small-town Ohio. I've been to the country club dozens of times. It's just a golf course with a pool and some tennis courts. Ordinary people go there."

"People like me? I don't think so." She remembered the girls from high school who spent their summers at the club. They wore their perfect tans and tennis whites around town as status symbols. Angelica could only pretend not to see their sneers as she scooped their ice cream or rang up their snack purchases, working summers at the local Shop Star Market.

"You've got the wrong idea," Lou Ann said. "Rescue River's country club has always been a welcoming place. Never had a color barrier, never dug into your marital status, never turned away families based on their religion. They're open to anybody who can pay the fee, which isn't all that much these days. I've thought about joining just to have a nice place to swim."

Angelica tugged at a stubborn weed. "You may be right, but Troy's family can't stand me. Not only did I dump their son, but my grandfather threw a wrench in their plans to dominate the county with their giant farm. We've been feuding from way back."

"Isn't it time that ended?" Lou Ann pulled radishes while she spoke. "The Lord wants us to be forces of reconciliation. I know Troy believes in that. You should, too."

Angelica sat back in the grass, listening to crickets chirping as a breeze rustled the leaves of an oak tree nearby. God's peace. She smiled at Lou Ann. "You're my hero, you know that? I want to be you when I grow up."

"Oh, go on." Lou Ann's flush of pleasure belied her dismissive words.

"But I'm still scared."

"You know what Pastor Ricky would say. God doesn't give us a spirit of fear, but of power and love and self-control."

"Yeah." Angelica tried to feel it. Sometimes, more and more often these days, she felt God's strength and peace inside her.

But this Labor Day picnic had put her into a tail-spin. Steaks and burgers weren't the only thing likely to be grilled; she would be, too.

"Here's a little tip," Lou Ann said. "Pretend like they're people from another country, another culture. You're a representative of your culture, bringing your own special gifts. You're not expecting to be the same as them, just to visit. Like you're an ambassador to a foreign land."

Angelica cocked her head to one side, her fingers stilling in the warm, loose dirt. Slowly a smile came to her face. "That's a nice idea. If I'm an ambassador, I'm not under pressure to be just like them."

"Right. You just have to think, that's interesting, that's not how we do it in my culture, but that's okay."

"Yes! And in my culture, we'd bring a gift." Angelica reached for a sugar snap pea and popped it into her mouth, savoring the vegetable's sweet crunch.

Lou Ann smiled. "Atta girl. What would you bring?"

"Food, probably. But that's the last thing they need, especially at a country club bash."

Lou Ann tugged at a recalcitrant carrot and then held it up triumphantly. "Anyone would welcome fresh vegetables from a garden."

Angelica flashed forward to imagine herself and Xavier walking onto the country club grounds. The image improved when she threw in a basket of zucchini, tomatoes and carrots. She threw her arms around the older woman. "You're a genius!"

Troy pulled up to the bunkhouse and, on an impulse, tooted the horn in the same pattern he used when he'd dated Angelica years ago. It was a joke, because he'd always insisted on coming to the door even though she urged him not to. It used to be something of a race, with him hustling to get out of his car and up to the door before she could grab her things and burst outside.

He couldn't beat her now, though. By the time he'd grabbed his stupid cane and edged gingerly out of the truck—man, his leg ached today—Angelica had emerged from the bunkhouse. Her rolled-up jeans fit her like a dream, and her tanned, toned arms rocked the basket she was carrying, and Troy wanted to wrap his arms around her, she looked so cute.

"What do you have there?" Troy asked. He was proud of her, proud of bringing her to meet his family. Remeet them, actually; they'd all known each other forever. But Angelica was a different person now, and they all had a different relationship.

"Just a little something for your dad."

"For Dad, huh?" Troy tried to smile, but he wondered how that would be received. His father was notoriously difficult, and Troy had already warned Angelica that his dad's moodiness had gotten worse. None of them could go a whole evening without causing him to yell or cuss or storm out of the house.

Lou Ann came out bringing Xavier, fresh-scrubbed and grinning.

Troy gave him a high five. "You ready for some fun, buddy? They have a blow-up bounce house and a ball pit and face painting."

"Face painting is for girls," Xavier said scornfully.

"I just now saw your outfit," Lou Ann said to Angelica, then turned to Troy. "Have they changed their rules about denim?"

Angelica's face fell. "Aren't you supposed to wear jeans?"

"It's no problem," Troy said. "They did away with that rule a couple of years ago."

"I didn't even think of it," Angelica said uneasily.

He put a protective arm around her shoulder. "You'll be fine. You look great!" But the truth was, he was on edge himself. It wasn't just his dad's bad moods; his older brother wasn't much better. Dad and Samuel, the two wealthiest men in the community, could be an intimidating pair.

"It'll be fine," he repeated. And hoped it was true.

When they got to the club, they were greeted with the smell of steaks and burgers grilling and the sound of a brass quartet playing patriotic songs. The whole place was set up like a carnival, with music and clowns and inflatables, and kids ran in small packs from one attraction to the next.

"This is so cool, Mom!" Xavier's eyes were wide, as if he'd never seen anything like this before. And knowing how poor they'd been, maybe he hadn't.

"It really is." She was a little wide-eyed herself.

He took Xavier by one hand and Angelica by the other and urged them forward. "We'll find you someone fun to play with," he told Xavier. "Samuel's girl, Mindy."

"A girl?"

"Girls can be fun!" He squeezed Angelica's hand, trying to help her relax, and looked around for his brother's daughter. Truthfully he worried about the girl. With an overprotective, suspicious father who tended to stay isolated, she often seemed lonely. "Hey, Sam!" He waved to his brother, gestured him over.

Sam walked toward them, frowning, holding Mindy's hand.

"Hey," Troy greeted his brother, glaring to remind him to be polite. "You remember Angelica, right?"

Sam gave him a quick nod and turned to Angelica. "Angelica. It's been a long time."

"And this is Xavier, Angelica's son."

"Say hello," she prompted gently.

But Xavier was staring at Mindy. "What happened to your other hand?"

"Xavier!" Angelica sounded mortified.

"I was born without it," Mindy said matter-of-factly. "What happened to your hair?"

"Leukemia, but it's gonna be gone soon and then I'll have hair."

Mindy nodded. "Want to go see the ball pit? It's cool."

"Sure!" And they were off.

"I'm so sorry he said that," Angelica said to his brother. "He should know better."

"No problem," Sam said, but to Troy's experienced ear, the irritation in his brother's voice was evident. He hated for anyone to comment on his daughter's disability. Plus, the man was frazzled; since his wife's death, he'd had his hands full trying to run his business empire and care for his daughter.

"Kids will be kids," Troy said as a general reminder to everybody, especially his brother.

"That's true," Sam said. "I'm sorry Mindy commented on your son's hair. Are things going okay with his treatment?"

"I'm hopeful," Angelica said quietly. "Lots of people are praying for him."

They strolled behind the two running children. Troy kept putting his arm around Angelica while trying not to actually touch her. He was being an idiot, but there'd been awkwardness between them ever since their botched conversation the other night, when she told him about her attack. He wished he hadn't pushed her to reveal her assailant, but he wanted to know because the guy deserved punishment. He also needed to be off the street.

Xavier and Mindy were chattering away as they zigzagged from craft table to ball toss. The adults, on the other hand, were too quiet. "Angelica brought some vegetables for Dad," Troy told Sam, trying to keep this reunion from being a total fail.

His brother nodded. "Too bad Dad hates vegetables."

"Oh." Angelica's face fell. "They're fresh from the garden back at Troy's house. I've been helping Lou Ann take care of it. Does he even hate fresh tomatoes?"

"Pretty much. But," Sam added grudgingly, "his doctor told him he needs to eat better, so maybe this will help."

"We made some zucchini bread, too. Maybe he'll like that, at least."

"I'm sure he will," Troy said firmly.

Sam didn't answer, and after a raised-eyebrow glance at him, Angelica shrugged and got very busy with examining the Popsicle-stick crafts at the kids' stand and checking out the tissue-paper flowers some of the older girls were making. The brass quintet started playing old-fashioned songs, of the "Camptown Races" sort, and the smell of grilled sausage and onions grew stronger, making Troy's mouth water.

"Where's Dad?" he asked to kill the awkward silence.

"I'll get him," Sam said. "Watch Mindy, would you?"

"Sure."

As Sam left, Angelica looked up at Troy. "He hates me. I can tell."

"Well, he doesn't *hate* you. He doesn't hate anyone. He's a good guy underneath. But he's had people take advantage of him a lot, and his wife's death was really traumatic. So bear with him. He's protective of his family, and he thinks you hurt me."

"I did hurt you," she said softly. After a minute's hesitation, she reached out and lightly grasped his forearm, and the touch seemed to travel straight to his heart. "I never apologized about that. I shouldn't have left like I did, Troy. I should have trusted you more, and it was wrong of me to leave without any explanation. You can maybe understand how desperate I was, but still, I realize now that it was a mistake."

"Thanks for saying that." Seven years later, he found that the apology still mattered. His throat tightened. "I appreciate hearing those words from you. But I'm sorry, too."

"For what?" She looked up at him through her long lashes, and she was so pretty he just wanted to grab her into his arms. But you didn't do that with Angelica.

"For being the type of person who'd judge a woman for something that wasn't her fault." He saw Mindy stumble, watched Xavier reach out a hand to steady her. "Life's taught me not to be so rigid about everything."

"Isn't that the truth?" She laughed a little, looking

off toward the cornfields in the distance. "We all learn as we get older."

"Well, most of us." He nudged her and nodded toward his father, who was being urged out of his seat by Sam and Daisy. "Some are a little more thickheaded and it takes longer."

"Here we go," she said, obviously trying to be funny, but he could hear the dread in her voice.

"Just don't let anything he says get to you. I've got your back."

"Thanks." She tightened her grip on his arm and then let go. Today was the first time Angelica had initiated touching him since they met again, and he had to hope that it meant there was some promise for them together.

Xavier and Mindy shouted for them, and they turned to watch the two kids skim down the inflatable slide together. Around them, people were starting to gather at tables covered by checkered tablecloths. Parents were trying to get their kids to come to supper, helped along by the smell of hot dogs and cotton candy.

The warm sun and music and patriotic decorations brought back memories of his parents in happier days, of playing baseball and Frisbee with his brother and sister here at the club, of eating and laughing together before everything had started to go wrong in his family.

Behind them, he heard his father's grousing voice. "I don't want to walk all the way over there. I just got comfortable sitting down and—"

"Come on, Dad." It was Daisy, and when he turned to look he saw that she was urging their father along by herself; Sam had apparently bailed on supervising this meeting. "Troy's fiancée is here," Daisy continued determinedly, "and you need to welcome her. Hi, Angelica!"

Angelica offered a big smile. "It's good to see you, Daisy. Hi, Mr. Hinton."

"Hello." His father didn't say anything rude, thankfully; that probably meant he hadn't had much to drink yet. But he looked Angelica up and down with a frown.

"Dad, Angelica brought you some vegetables from the garden."

She rolled her eyes at him, subtly, and he realized he was trying too hard.

"Humph." His father looked at the basket dismissively. "Green stuff."

Troy opened his mouth to smooth things over, but Angelica took a step in front of him, effectively nudging him out of her way. "Sam said you don't like vegetables, but there's some zucchini bread I made from Lou Ann Miller's recipe. I hope you like it." She held out the basket.

"Thank you." His father took it begrudgingly. "That woman always won the prize at picnics when we were teenagers. Even back then, she was a good cook."

Angelica smiled. "She still is. Maybe you could come visit sometime."

Troy gritted his teeth. He avoided inviting his dad over because the man was so difficult. He didn't like what Troy was doing with his life—being a vet, especially doing rescue. The Hinton sons should be making money hand over fist in the world of agricultural high finance, according to his dad.

"So you've taken to being a hostess at Troy's house, have you?" his father asked.

"Dad!" Daisy scolded before Troy could intervene. "Angelica has every right. She's marrying Troy."

As Angelica followed the group toward the long dining tables, Daisy's words rang in her ears like chimes foretelling her fate. *"She's marrying Troy."*

"Hi, Angelica!" A blonde in spike-heeled sandals approached, with mirror-image blond girls holding each hand. Ugh. She'd wanted a distraction, but not necessarily in the form of Nora Templeton—one of the country-club girls who'd been meanest when they were in high school together. Was her voice really prissy? Or was Angelica just defensive?

"Hi, Nora," she said, holding out a hand.

"Let Mommy shake hands, Stella," Nora said, pulling loose from one of her daughters to hold out a perfectly manicured hand.

Which made Angelica wonder if she'd gotten all the dirt out from under her own nails since her marathon gardening session that morning.

"Run along and play a minute." Nora shooed her daughters away. "How are you? I heard you were back in town."

"Yes." As Nora's daughters high-fived each other and ran off toward the dessert table, Angelica debated how much to tell. "My son and I wanted to spend more time with my grandpa."

"That's sweet. I see your grandpa sometimes at the Towers when I visit my aunt." She leaned closer. "Your son looks a lot like his daddy."

Angelica's world blurred as she stared at the other woman. Did Nora know Jeremy, her assailant, then? Who else did?

"He's got that same dark hair and sweet smile."

Around them, people stood in clusters or found seats at family-sized tables. Troy's friend Dion was sitting down with an older couple, and he saw her and gave a friendly wave.

Angelica fought to stay in the present and analyze Nora's words. Did she mean Jeremy? Had Jeremy talked about what had happened, then, after threatening her with a worse assault if she ever said a word?

Nora's eyes grew round. "Did I say something wrong? I just assumed Troy's your son's father."

Angelica's breath whooshed out. Troy. Nora thought Troy was Xavier's dad.

"If it's supposed to be a secret, I won't say anything to anyone. But I think it's just so sweet that you two are finally getting married."

Angelica stared at the other woman blankly while her mind raced. Should she just let this happen, let the misperception remain? Was that fair to Troy? To Xavier?

"Mom! Stella rubbed cake in my face and we didn't even eat dinner yet!"

"Girls! Stop that!" Nora looked apologetically at Angelica. "They're not always such brats. See you around!" She rushed off, leaving Angelica in a haze of self-doubt.

Oh, she'd been stupid, thinking she could bring Xavier here to live without putting this small, close-knit community on alert. Everyone had to be doing the math in their heads, figuring out that Xavier was of an age to have been conceived during her former engagement to Troy.

"Come on, Angelica." Daisy's voice brought her

back from the brink. "They're about ready to serve dinner, and Dad likes to be first in line."

"Make me sound like a cad," her father grumbled.

The savory tang of barbecue sauce and the slightly burned scent of kettle corn filled the air as they straggled toward long tables heaped with potato salad, watermelon and enormous silver chafing dishes of baked beans.

Lou Ann had been right: the crowd included all skin colors, just like the town. There was even a man wearing a turban at one table and a group of women in brightly colored saris at another. Cooks and servers in pristine white aprons and chefs' hats shouted instructions to one another, punctuated by the laughter of family groups and the shouts of children.

Angelica ran a hand over Xavier's bald head and felt the tiniest hint of stubble. A bubble of joy rose in her chest, reminding her of what was really important.

As Angelica helped Xavier load his plate for dinner, Troy's father stood next to her in line. "I told my son not to get together with you," he said in what was apparently supposed to be a whisper, but was probably audible to everyone up and down the long serving buffet.

"Oh?" Ignoring the stares and nudges around them, she scooped some baked ziti onto Xavier's plate. "Why's that?"

"Because you dumped him before," Mr. Hinton said. "Fool me once, shame on you, fool me twice, shame on me."

Heat rose to her cheeks, but she just nodded. What could she say? She had left Troy, it was true.

"What's that man talking about, Mom?" Xavier asked in a stage whisper.

"Ancient history," she said.

"Actually history about the same age as you are."

The server behind the grill was openly staring. "Shrimp or steak, ma'am?"

"Xavier," she said, "take this plate over where Mindy's sitting. I'll be right there."

As soon as Xavier left, she turned to Mr. Hinton, hands on hips. "Any issues you have with me, you're welcome to tell me. But don't involve my son. None of this is his fault, and he has a lot to deal with right now."

Mr. Hinton narrowed his eyes at her. "Your son is part of the issue. Is he related to me?"

She cocked her head to one side.

"I mean, is my son his father?"

Light dawned. "No, of course not! Troy would never…" She trailed off. Mr. Hinton believed that, too? She'd known on some level that acquaintances like Nora might think Xavier was Troy's son. But she was shocked to realize that his own father suspected it.

Keeping Xavier's parentage a secret was hurting Troy. But revealing it would hurt Xavier.

Lou Ann's words came back to her. As a Christian, she was supposed to be all about reconciliation.

She turned to Mr. Hinton, gently took his plate and put it down on the buffet table and nudged him off to the side, ignoring the raised eyebrows of family members and bystanders around them. She pulled him by the hand to a bench out of earshot of the crowd and sat down, patting the seat beside her.

He gave her a grouchy look and then sat.

Aware that she didn't have long before he left in a hissy fit, she talked fast. "Look, I can understand why you're upset with me. And I can understand why you want to know whether Xavier is a blood relative. The answer is no. He's not."

Mr. Hinton crossed his arms and glared at her. "All the more reason for me to be angry, then. Isn't that right? Isn't my son opening himself up to a lying, cheating woman by getting back together with you?"

His voice had risen and people were staring; conversations in the area had died down. She'd *thought* this area was secluded enough to keep their conversation private, but apparently, with the volume of Mr. Hinton's hard-of-hearing voice, it wasn't.

It was her worst nightmare come true: she was a spectacle at the country club, looked down on by the other guests.

What's the right thing to do, Lord? The prayer shot straight up through the tears that she couldn't keep from forming in her eyes.

An arm came around her shoulder, and Troy sat beside her, pulling her to his side. His strength held her up where she felt like collapsing.

"Dad," Daisy said as she hurried over to clutch her father's shoulder, leaning over him from the other side. "Why are you making a scene? You know this isn't right."

"No." Angelica straightened her spine, pulled away from Troy, and stood. "He's not doing anything but protecting his son. That's totally understandable."

"Thank you!" Mr. Hinton's exasperated words almost made her smile.

"But, Mr. Hinton," she said, reaching out to clasp his arm. "That's what I need to do, too. Xavier's story is his own to tell, and he's too young to understand it and share it yet. So I'm just going to have to ask you to take it on faith that, when the time is right, you'll know the right amount about his parentage."

"That's about as convoluted as a story can get," Mr. Hinton complained, but his voice wasn't as loud and angry as it had been before.

"Dad. I know enough to understand what happened," Troy said. "None of it is Angelica's fault, and I'd just ask you to accept Xavier without any questions right now. That's what I'm planning to do."

"And that's what this family is about," Daisy said firmly. "We accept kids. All kids."

Angelica took deep breaths and shot up a prayer of thanks. Troy had supported her. And it looked as though Daisy was coming around to her side, too.

Mr. Hinton was a tougher case, but he was just trying to protect his child and his family. That was something she could understand.

"Come on," she said, and took the risk of clasping his hand. "Let's go get back in line before the food's all gone."

He cleared his throat. "Finally somebody said something that makes sense." As they walked together to the line, he leaned down to mutter in her ear, "You tell Lou Ann that nothing on the dessert table here holds a candle to her zucchini bread."

"Wait. You've been sampling dessert already?"

"Life's short. Eat dessert first. Right?"

"I think I'm going to follow that philosophy," Angelica said, grabbing a big piece of chocolate cake.

"You're not my favorite person in the world," Mr. Hinton said to her. "But I reckon I can back off of hassling you. Xavier's not accountable for your problems.

And come to think of it, you're not accountable for your grandfather's."

Angelica gave the old man a sidearm hug and then sidled away before he could either embrace her or reject her.

"Humph." He glared at her and bustled off.

It wasn't a warm welcome, but Angelica felt that progress had been made. And she shot up a prayer of thanks and wonder to God, who was clearly the author of the peace and reconciliation she'd just felt.

Chapter 13

After dinner, they all moved over to sit near the band. Xavier was fighting tiredness, but losing the battle, so Angelica talked him into lying down for a little rest on the blanket beside her. He resisted, but in minutes, he was asleep.

The gentle music prompted a few older couples onto the makeshift dance floor, where moonlight illuminated them in a soft glow. Most of the younger kids were quieting down or already asleep, while the teenagers paired off at the edges of the crowd. Nearby, most of the Hintons were spreading blankets and settling in to listen to the music.

She wanted this for Xavier. She wanted the community and the family and the security represented by life here.

She'd never thought she could have it. When she

left seven years ago, running scared, she'd thought her connection with this community was severed. Now she had a chance to regain it, stronger than when she was young, to regain it as part of a connected, loving family.

She wanted it so badly, but was she just setting herself up for disappointment?

"Aw, he's so sweet," Daisy said, coming over to settle in the grass beside her. "He got along really well with everyone, didn't he?"

"I was pleased. But he's a great kid that way. He's always had an ease and charm with people that I can only envy."

Daisy cocked her head to one side, studying Xavier. "I wonder where he gets that."

The comment echoed in Angelica's head. Where did Xavier get his charm and people skills?

The thought pushed her toward his genetics, toward Jeremy and his superficial charm, but she shoved that idea away. "My aunt helped out with him so much when he was small. She was an amazing woman, and I'm sure he picked up some of her better traits."

"I'm sure he's picked up some of your great traits," Daisy said, patting her knee. "I really admire what you've done, raising him even though…" She stopped.

"Even thought what?"

"Look," Daisy said, "I'm guessing Xavier is the product of some kind of an assault. Remember, I'm a social worker. I see stuff like this all the time. I can tell you're wary of men in a way that suggests you've been treated badly, and I know you didn't use to be like that, so…" She spread her hands expressively.

Angelica stared at the woman, feeling defeated. Daisy had guessed most of the story of her past. As much as Angelica wanted to hide it, it was written and apparent in the existence of Xavier.

"I'm sorry." Daisy patted Angelica's arm. "There I go blurting stuff out again. I should learn to put a sock in it."

Angelica let out a rueful sigh. "For sure, I don't want to talk about my past troubles. But am I going to be able to escape it? Is it wrong for me to want to keep it all private?"

"From me, it's okay," Daisy said. "I have no right to your private information. But I would think that Troy would want to know whatever information is available about Xavier's father."

"That's what I'm afraid of." Troy was the last person she wanted to tell. The trust developing between them was a beautiful thing, but fragile. Revealing the name of her attacker might downright destroy it. After all, Troy had looked up to Jeremy. Would he believe that a guy he admired, a guy who'd mentored him, who'd been a town athletic star, had done something so awful to Angelica?

Or would he turn on her instead?

"But maybe not," Daisy went on, lying back to stare up at the emerging stars. "Maybe he won't need to know. Troy is a rescuer at heart. He's taken in animals since he was a little kid, and in those cases you don't know what happened. But you deal with the results."

"Gee, thanks, Daisy." She whacked the woman on the calf, welcoming the distraction from her own uneasy thoughts. "Did you just compare me to a rescue dog?"

Daisy grinned. "If the shoe fits…"

"If the dog coat fits…" Angelica played along. She

was glad that she and Daisy could joke. But what the woman had said bothered her. Why did Troy want to be with her, anyway? Why was he willing to put up with not knowing Xavier's background?

Was it because he saw her, not as an equal human being, but as a creature to be rescued?

"Today's the day, buddy!" Troy turned in the passenger seat to give Xavier a high five. "I get my cast off, and you get to start playing soccer on the team."

"Just to try it," Angelica warned as she swung the truck around the corner. "Remember, when we go to your checkup on Thursday, Dr. Ravi is going to let us know if soccer is the right thing for you to do."

Xavier's jaw jutted out, and Troy could almost see his decision to ignore his mom. He looked down, grabbed the soccer ball from the seat beside him and clutched it to his chest. "Hey, Mr. Troy, do you think you could be one of the coaches?"

"I don't know much about soccer, buddy." But the idea tickled his fancy. What a great way that would be to connect with Xavier. And to help kids. Coaches had been a huge part of his own childhood, giving him the encouragement his dad hadn't.

Xavier was bouncing up and down in the car seat. "You played football before. You could learn about soccer. Please?"

"We'll see, buddy. I have to get the okay from my doctor. Just like you."

"Really?" Xavier's eyes went round as quarters. "I didn't think grown-ups had any rules."

Troy and Angelica exchanged amused glances, and Troy reached back to pat Xavier's shoulder. "We have more rules than you know. And if we're smart, we follow the rules. We listen to doctors."

Xavier frowned and nodded, obviously thinking over this new concept.

Angelica flashed Troy a grateful smile as she pulled up to the door of the hospital. *Thanks*, she mouthed.

Looking at her made his heart catch fire. She was everything to him, and once he got this wretched cast off, he'd feel whole again and as if he could take control. She wouldn't have to drive him and he would be able to be a full partner to her and Xavier. They'd be able to set a wedding date and move forward with their lives, with a real marriage.

"Let me know if you need a ride when you're done."

"This should be pretty quick. Afterward, I'll just stroll over to the park and you guys should still be doing practice."

He gave in to a sudden urge, leaned over and dropped a kiss on her cheek. Her hair's fruity scent and the sound of her breathy little sigh made him want to linger, and only his awareness of Xavier in the backseat held him to propriety.

Especially when she didn't pull back.

He felt ten feet tall. They were making real progress as a couple. What a great day.

"What was that for?" she asked while Xavier giggled from the backseat.

"Just feeling good about everything."

He walked into the hospital easily, barely using his cane. After checking in and waiting impatiently in a roomful of people, the nurse put him in a room to wait for X-rays.

The technician came in and told Troy to hop up on

the exam table. "First I'll cut the cast off and then we'll x-ray everything." He was bent over an electronic tablet, recording and filling things in. Finally he looked up. "Hey, I know you."

Troy studied the bearded man, who looked a little younger than Troy. "You do look a little familiar." Then it clicked into place: this was the man they'd seen outside the Senior Towers, that day they'd done the weeding. The one Angelica hadn't liked. His friend's younger brother.

"I'm Logan Filmore." He held out his name tag as if to prove it. "I was a couple years behind you in school, but I watched you play football with my brother."

"Right, right!" Troy reached out, shook the man's hand. "I'm sorry for your loss." Logan's brother had died in a car accident about five years ago. "The whole town came out for Jeremy's funeral. What a loss."

"Yeah." Logan frowned as he positioned Troy on the x-ray table. "I keep hearing that from everyone now that I've moved back permanently."

They made small talk as Logan took pictures of Troy's leg in every position. When the ordeal seemed to be almost over, Logan looked at Troy with a serious expression. "I hate to bring this up, but I heard that you're pretty intense with Angelica Camden. Is that true?"

"Yeah." Troy smiled to remember their exchange in the car. "In fact, we're getting married pretty soon."

"That's great." Logan moved the X-ray machine to another position. "Now, lie still for this one. It's a full 360 and takes a few minutes to get warmed up." He made a tiny adjustment to Troy's leg. "So, you feel okay about everything that happened before?"

Something in the man's tone made Troy's stomach clench. "What do you mean?"

"I mean, about her leaving town pregnant, staying away. You…" He shook his head. "I don't know if I could do that, raise another man's child."

Heat rose inside Troy but he tamped it down. "That's between me and Angelica. And anyway, a kid's a kid."

Logan took a step back, palms out like stop signs. "For sure. Didn't mean anything by it."

"No problem." He'd have to learn to deal with nosy people. It came with the territory of marrying a woman with a kid and a bit of mystery in her past.

"Anyway, I'm glad to see my nephew get a good home. After Jeremy passed, I always thought I should do something, but since Jeremy said she didn't want it…"

His *nephew*? Icy shock froze Troy's body. "Want what?"

"Well, any help with the baby. I guess she felt like, since it was just a one-night stand, he didn't owe her anything."

"Just a one-night stand." Troy repeated the words parrotlike, feeling about as dumb as an animal. "What do you mean? Are you saying Xavier is Jeremy's son?"

"Yeah. Oh man, didn't you know?" Logan's eyebrows shot up. "I thought sure she would've told you. Or you would've asked." He slapped the heel of his hand to his forehead. "Man, I feel like a fool. I'm sorry. What a way to find out."

Troy just lay there on his back under a giant machine, his heart pounding like sledgehammer blows, sweat dripping from his face into his ears. *He* was the one who felt like a fool.

"Okay, ready? Lie still now."

Troy forced himself to obey while the machine moved its slow path up and down his leg. Inside, anger licked slow flames through his body. It took massive self-control not to jump up and slug Logan, though none of this was his fault.

It wasn't Troy's fault, either, nor Xavier's.

It was Angelica's fault. Angelica, and the guy Troy had always looked up to, the guy who'd stayed after practice to help him when he was a scrawny freshman, the guy who'd argued his case when the coach thought Troy was too focused on his studies to play first string.

Troy's mind reeled. Angelica had called it a rape, and he'd 99 percent believed her. So why did Logan think Jeremy was Xavier's dad?

And why did he have details about Angelica not wanting Jeremy's help? Wouldn't she have wanted it?

Well, but if it had been a one-night stand...

Because Jeremy wouldn't rape anyone. Would he?

He felt as if a million little dwarves were hammering at his brain. He wanted out of this conversation. This room. This whole wretched situation.

"Why do you think Xavier is Jeremy's child?" he ground out after the infernal machine had done its work and Logan was back in the room, a sheaf of X-rays in hand.

"Because he told me." Logan crossed his arms over his chest, looking off into space. "Man, that was one of the last times I saw my brother, right before I went overseas. We were out drinking one night and got to talking. He told me they'd hooked up." Logan's gaze flickered down, and he must have seen the turmoil on Troy's face. "Oh man, I'm sorry to break that news.

Especially to a guy who's having this kind of trouble with his leg."

"What?" What did his leg have to do with anything? Who cared about his leg now?

"Here, sit up. Take a look." Logan pinned Troy's X-rays up on a light board and pointed. "That didn't heal worth nothing, man. It's all wrong. I don't know if they'll rebreak it or just leave it." He studied the light board, cocking his head to one side. "I don't think I ever saw a break heal that bad before, dude. My sympathy." He went to the door. "Sit tight. Doc will be in any minute. And hey, sorry to be the bearer of bad news."

Angelica sat on the grass watching Xavier joyously joining in the soccer practice. She still felt a little out of place with the other parents, all of whom seemed to have known each other for years. People were friendly, but Angelica knew she was still an outsider. Had always been an outsider, even when she was a kid.

"Good kick, Xavier!" one of the other children yelled.

Coach Linda, Becka's mom, waved to her. "Your son's a natural! Hope he can stay on the team!"

She watched as her son, completely new to soccer, raced to the ball and took it down the field in short, perfect kicks. Or whatever you'd call it…dribbling, maybe? She was way short on soccer terminology.

She so wanted for Xavier to fit in, and truthfully she wanted to fit in with the community, too. During her early years with Xavier, scrambling with work and day care, sometimes struggling to find a place to live before she'd settled in with her aunt, she'd looked enviously at families watching their kids play sports, kids with not only parents but grandparents and aunts and uncles to cheer them on. Families that could afford the right uniforms, could get their kids private lessons or coaching. She'd never even had the chance to dream of such a thing for her and Xavier, but now, hesitantly, she was starting to hope it could happen. They could be a part of things. They could have love, and a community, and a future.

When Nora, the woman from the country club, came up to her with a clipboard, Angelica smiled at her, determined to keep her walls down, to make a fresh start. "Hi," she said, extending her hand. "Are your girls on the team? I'm hoping Xavier can join."

"I heard. He seems really good." The woman settled down on the bench beside Angelica. "I'm head of the parents' organization. We do fund-raising and plan the end-of-season banquet for the kids, so I wanted to get you involved."

Pleasure surged inside Angelica. "Great. I'm pretty new to all this, but I'm glad to help however I can."

"Let me get your contact information." Nora pulled out her iPhone.

As she punched in Angelica's address, she smiled. "So you're living with Troy already, are you?"

Angelica swallowed. *She doesn't mean anything by it. Don't take it personally.* "No, we're not living together exactly. Xavier and I live on the farm, in the guesthouse."

"Oh, I'm sorry! I just assumed, since you have the same address… Great job, Nora, foot in mouth as usual. Never mind."

"It's okay. I work at the kennels," Angelica said,

hearing the stiffness in her own voice. "That's why we live there."

"Oh! I misunderstood." The woman leaned in confidingly. "You know, ever since I got divorced, people have been trying to match me up with Troy."

Angelica looked sideways at the woman's perfect haircut and designer shorts. She was tall with an hourglass figure. What had Troy thought of her? Had they gone out?

Nora waved her hand airily. "It didn't work out. He's a great guy, though."

"Yes, he is," Angelica said guardedly. Why hadn't it ever occurred to her that Troy had other options he was closing off by being involved with her? That he could date, or even marry, someone like Nora, the gorgeous, well-off, country-club-bred head of the parents' group?

"So, I notice Xavier doesn't have a uniform yet," the woman continued. "They cost fifty dollars. And we ask that parents make a donation of fifty dollars to the group, for parties and snacks and special events."

Angelica swallowed. "Um, okay. I might need to do one thing per paycheck, if that's okay. Money's a little tight."

The woman laughed. "You're kidding, right? Troy has all the money in the world."

I want to fit in, God, but do I have to be nice to this busybody? "Like I said, we'll take it one thing at a time. I'd like to get him the uniform first, but if you need the parents' fee right away—"

"Oh no, it's fine." The woman shrugged, palms up. "You pay when you're ready. Or when you tie the knot! I know Troy's good for it."

That rankled, and then another truth dawned as

Angelica realized how her engagement to Troy must look to much of the town. Here she was, in her ancient cutoffs, and Xavier in his mismatched holey T-shirt and thrift-store gym shorts, and apparently Troy was known as one of the richest men in town. Just like when they'd been engaged before. They were two people from opposite sides of the tracks. They didn't fit.

Did everyone think she was marrying Troy for his money?

Angelica's phone buzzed, and when she saw Dr. Ravi's office number on the caller ID, she wrinkled her nose apologetically at Nora. "Sorry, I have to take this." When the woman didn't get up to move, Angelica stood and walked out of earshot. "Hello?"

"Angelica, it's Dr. Ravi. I got your message about Xavier playing soccer, and I wanted to tell you I think it's wonderful."

"Really? He's cleared to play?"

"Not only that, but all the signs about the treatment are very, very positive. Of course, definitive cures aren't part of the language of cancer doctors, but we are looking at very, very good numbers."

"Oh, Dr. Ravi, thank you! That's wonderful!"

"I agree." In his voice, she could hear his sincere happiness. "One never likes to make promises, but if I were you, I would be planning a long, healthy future for that young man."

Angelica half walked, half skipped back to the bench and sat down, vaguely conscious that there were a couple of other moms there with Nora now. She couldn't even remember why she'd felt upset with Nora.

What an incredible gift from God. She looked up

at the sky, grinning her gratitude. Wow, just wow. She felt like shouting.

"Could you give me your email and cell phone information for our parents' directory?" Nora was looking at her, eyebrows raised.

"Um, yes, I… You know what, can we do this later? I just got some really, really good medical news. Xavier! Hey, Zavey!"

Xavier came trotting over. "Mom, did you see me score a goal?"

She reached out widespread arms and caught him in them, holding him so tight that he started to struggle. Reluctantly she let him go but held his shoulders to look into his eyes. "Guess what?"

"Mom, can I go back and play more?"

Her smile felt so broad that her cheeks hurt. "You sure can. In fact, Dr. Ravi says you're cleared to play, and that the treatment seems to be working."

His eyes and his mouth both went wide and round. "You mean I'm getting well?"

"Looks like it, kiddo."

"And I can be on the team? And have my own shirt?"

"Absolutely. Just as soon as I get my next paycheck, you'll have a uniform, buddy."

He took off his hat and threw it high in the air, and the other moms seemed to draw in a collective sigh at the sight of his cancer-bald head.

"You know," Nora said, "I'm sure that, between us, we can get him a uniform right away. Can't we, ladies?"

The others nodded, and one of them, an acquaintance from years ago, reached out to give Angelica an impulsive hug. "We're so glad you moved back. It'll be great to get to know you again."

"Yes, and with Xavier playing, maybe our team will win a game every once in a while," chimed in one of the other moms, and they all laughed.

"Hey, there's Dad!" Xavier pointed down the street. "Can I go tell him, Mom? Can I?"

She was so happy that it didn't even bother her that Xavier had called Troy "Dad" in front of all these mothers, who, no matter how nice, were likely to gossip about it. She looked in the direction Xavier was pointing and saw Troy walking toward them, along the sidewalk. A part of her wanted to tell Troy the great news about Xavier herself, but she couldn't deny Xavier the delight of telling. After all, it was his news. "Go for it, honey. Just don't knock him down. He looks a little bit tired."

Angelica watched Xavier running toward Troy, soccer ball under one arm, and happiness flooded her heart. It almost seemed in slow motion, like a dream: she was surrounded by other moms who seemed, suddenly, like supportive friends. The warm, late-afternoon air kissed her cheeks, tinged with the scent of just-mown grass. Giant trees shaded them all, testimony to how long this park had been here, how deeply the community was grounded in history.

She wanted this, especially for Xavier, so much she could taste it. And here it was within their grasp.

Xavier got to Troy, shouting, "Mr. Troy! Dad! Guess what!"

Troy kept walking. Limping, actually, and he still had his cane.

Angelica's heart faltered.

"Mr. Troy, hey! Don't you hear me?" Xavier grabbed Troy's leg.

Troy stumbled a little.

Angelica sprang from the bench and strode toward them, ignoring the concerned exclamations of the other mothers.

"Hey, Mr. Troy, guess what!"

Finally Troy stopped and turned to Xavier. "What?" His voice was oddly flat.

"I can play soccer! And I'm gonna get all better!"

Knowing Troy so well, Angelica could see him pull his mind from whatever faraway place it had been. He turned and bent down awkwardly, slowly. "That's great news, buddy." He was clearly trying to show enthusiasm. Trying, and failing.

To which her excited son was oblivious. "So that means you can be my coach, right? Can you, Dad? Can you?"

"We could use a few extra coaches, Troy," Coach Linda called from among the group of mothers. "Hint, hint."

Troy looked toward them, forehead wrinkled, frowning. "No," he said. "No, I can't do that."

"Whaddya mean you can't, Dad? You gotta coach me! You said you would."

Angelica reached the pair then and, breathless, knelt down beside Xavier. "Give Mr. Troy a minute here, buddy." She studied Troy's face.

He was looking from her to Xavier with the strangest expression she'd ever seen. Eyes hooded, corners of his mouth turned down. She couldn't read it and for some reason, it scared her.

"What's wrong?" she asked, putting a protective arm around Xavier.

"Mr. Troy, watch what I learned already!" Xavier threw the soccer ball he'd been carrying up into the air and bounced it off his head. Then he dribbled it in a circle, then kicked it up into his hands again.

His ability to handle the ball took Angelica's breath away. He was well, or pretty close, and he was going to be able to develop this amazing talent. She clasped her hands to her chest, almost as if she could hold the joy inside.

"Don't you want to coach me now?"

Troy looked at the two of them for a minute more. Then, without another word, he turned and started limping toward the truck.

She felt Xavier's shoulders slump.

"Troy!" she said. "Come back here and tell us what's going on."

He didn't answer, didn't look at her, just kept walking. And now she could see that he had a pronounced limp from some new, big kind of bandage around his leg, beneath his long pants.

"Troy!" When he didn't answer, she put her hands on her son's shoulders. "Remember how tired and cranky you can get from going to the doctor?"

Xavier nodded. But his lower lip was wobbling. He was so vulnerable, and she could have kicked Troy right in his bad leg for hurting her son's feelings. "Well, I think that's how Mr. Troy is feeling now."

"Did he have a treatment?" Xavier asked. "Does he have cancer, like me?"

"He doesn't have cancer, but I think he must have had a treatment that hurt or something. So we'll talk

to him later. Right now I think your team needs you."
Gently, she turned him back toward the playing field.
She waved to Coach Linda, ignoring the curious stares
of the other mothers. "Hey, Coach, Xavier's coming
back in to play some, okay?"

"We can use him," Linda called, and as Xavier ran
toward her, she reached out an arm to put around his
shoulders.

Angelica watched long enough to see the pair head
back toward the field. Both of them glanced back a
couple of times, Xavier still looking a little crestfallen.

She marched after Troy.

"Hey, what's going on?"

He didn't stop, but she caught up with him easily.

"Troy! What happened at the doctor's? Did you get
bad news?"

He got to the truck and looked at it. Shut his eyes
as though he was in physical pain. Then walked to the
passenger door and opened it.

"Troy! I thought you… What happened?"

He closed the door and sat in the truck, staring
straight ahead.

She reached out and pulled the door open before he
could lock her out. "Look, I get that you've had some
bad news, but let me in, okay? Tell me what's going
on. We're a team, remember? We're engaged! We're
getting married!"

"No, we're not."

The three words, spoken in that same flat tone he'd
used with Xavier, pricked a hole in her anger. She felt
her energy start to flow out of her, like a tire with a
slow leak. "What do you mean? Talk to me."

He didn't.

"What happened? Why aren't we getting married now? Troy, no matter what happened to you, which I'd appreciate being told about, you can't just shut me out. And I don't like your ignoring Xavier that way. You really hurt his feelings."

"And of course I wouldn't want to hurt the feelings of Jeremy's son."

Jeremy's son.

A core of ice formed inside her. He knew. Troy knew the truth.

Jeremy's son.

She never thought of Xavier that way. Xavier was her son. God's son. Soon, she'd thought, he would be Troy's son.

Though Jeremy Filmore had had a role in his conception, a role she'd spent a lot of years blocking out, it had ended there.

Hearing Troy say that name made her feel like throwing up. She staggered and leaned against the side of the truck. It was hot, but somehow the sun's warmth didn't penetrate the icy cold she felt inside.

Her worst nightmare. Troy had found out her assailant, who wasn't some stranger he could hate from a distance, but his own good friend, someone they'd both known. "What did you hear?" she asked in a dull voice.

"Well, for one thing, I heard that my leg is permanently screwed up. That I'll have to wear this boot for six months and I won't be able to drive or exercise. After that, I have to have some surgery that might or might not allow me to walk without a cane."

She didn't answer, couldn't. She could barely focus on what he was saying, only realizing that it had something to do with his leg not healing.

That awful name kept echoing through her head. *Jeremy. Jeremy. Jeremy.*

It whirled her back to a night she'd spent years trying to forget. To a very handsome and charming older guy who'd flattered her at her birthday celebration, walked her partway home, then dragged her into his apartment and spent what seemed like hours hurting her in ways she'd had no idea a man could hurt a woman.

Her screams had been ineffectual; the other apartments had been empty. Her pleas had fallen on deaf ears, even made him laugh.

What he'd done to her physically was horrible enough. But his name-calling, his degradation of her as a woman, his comments about her past, her unworthiness, her asking for it... All of those words had stuck to her like poison glue, growing inside her right along with the baby growing in her womb. The ugly descriptions of herself had expanded until they were all she could see, all she could feel.

Only the tireless nurturing of her aunt, and intensive sessions with a skilled therapist, had been able to pull her out of the deep depression she'd sunk into.

"You cheated on me," Troy said now. "And you lied to me."

Cheater. Liar. Even though the words Jeremy had uttered had been much stronger and more degrading, the echo in the voice of her beloved Troy made her double over, the hurt was so sudden and so strong.

She knelt in the dirt beside the truck, holding her stomach.

"Don't even try to defend yourself. I won't believe a word you say."

His flat, angry, judgmental certainty slammed into her. It was just the way she'd figured he would react; it was the reason she'd thrown clothes into a bag and left town the day she learned she was pregnant.

Now, though, her automatic reaction was different. To her own surprise, she didn't feel like running. She felt her shoulders go back as she glared at him. "Did you just tell me not to say anything?"

"Yeah," he said, leaning out of the truck, breathing hard. "That's exactly what I told you."

Gravel dug into her knees. What was she doing on her knees? Holding on to the side of the truck for support, she climbed to her feet. "Don't you ever tell me I can't say what's on my mind. I spent a lot of years keeping silent, and I'm tired of it. I don't deserve what happened to me, and I don't deserve for you to blame me for what someone else did to me."

He looked at her with huge sags under his eyes, as if he'd aged ten years. "You wanted to be with him. Right?"

Whoa! Just like Jeremy! Her hands went to her hips as heat flushed through her body. "You can stop right now with telling me what I did and didn't want. No woman would want what happened to me, and any man who says otherwise is messed up." She walked closer to him, her heart pounding in her ears. "You hear me? Totally. Messed. Up." With each word, she jabbed a pointing finger at him. "If that's what you're thinking, you can get out of my life."

He swung his legs down with a painful wince. "I'm going, just as soon as I can get a ride. And you can get out of mine. I want your bags packed and you…" He trailed off, swallowed hard. "You and Xavier…off my property. By tomorrow."

Chapter 14

Troy watched the woman he'd thought he loved draw in a rasping breath, then clench her jaw. "I'll drive you home," she said. "Let me get Xavier."

She turned before he could answer and marched down toward the playing field. Her back was straight, shoulders squared.

He stared after her, then squeezed his eyes shut and looked away. His heart rebelled against the sudden change he was asking of it: stop loving her, start hating her. Stop believing in her, realize that she'd been lying this whole time.

She *had* been lying, right? Because she'd said she hadn't known her assailant, but when he'd confronted her with Jeremy's name, she'd tacitly acknowledged him as Xavier's father.

But why would she have lied about it being Jeremy?

The answer had to be that she'd gone with him willingly. Just as Jeremy's brother had said.

Sliding out of the truck, he landed painfully on his bad leg, and the metal cane the doctor had lent him—the old man's cane with four little feet on the end—crashed to the ground.

A teenage girl on a skateboard swooped down, picked it up, then skidded in a circle to hand it back to him.

He wasn't even man enough to pick up his wretched cane for himself.

Angelica came back, pulling an obviously reluctant and angry Xavier by the hand. "Mom!" he was whining, almost crying. "I don't want to go."

"Get in the truck," she ordered.

"But—"

"Now." Her voice was harsh.

Tears spilled from Xavier's eyes, and his lower lip pouted out, but he climbed into the truck.

"Mr. Troy!" Xavier said as soon as they were all in. "Mama says we have to move away. But that's not true, is it?"

Troy looked over at Angelica and saw a muscle twitch in her cheek. Her jaw was set and obviously she wasn't about to answer.

Troy was already regretting his hasty order that they leave. He turned back to Xavier, looked at his hopeful face.

Looked into Jeremy's eyes. How had he not noticed that before? "I'm sorry, but yes. You do have to leave."

"Why?" Xavier's face screwed up. "I love it here. I hate moving."

Troy looked over at Angelica and saw a single tear trickle down her cheek.

Well, sure, she was upset. Her game was up.

"Mom, you promised we wouldn't have to move again!"

Angelica cleared her throat. "I'm sorry, honey. I made a promise I couldn't keep."

"Seems you make a habit of that," Troy muttered.

Angelica's body gave the slightest little jerk, as if she'd been hit.

The truth hurt. He tried to work up some more righteous anger about that, but he was finding it hard to do.

What she'd done was wrong, but it had happened a long time ago.

But she's been lying to you just in the past few weeks.

But she'd seemed to genuinely care about him. Hadn't she? "Look," he said, "maybe I've overreacted. I…I need to take a breath, think about this. I don't want to throw the two of you out on the street…"

"We've been there before." She spun the truck around a corner too fast, making the tires squeal. "We'll manage."

"I don't want you to just manage. I need to pray about this, get right with God, figure things out. I was blindsided, but we all make mistakes. I…maybe I can work through it and learn to forgive you."

"Don't strain yourself." She pulled the truck into the long driveway and squealed to a jerky stop in front of his house. "Here you go."

There were a couple of unfamiliar cars parked in front of the house, and he couldn't deal with strangers.

Didn't want to talk to anyone but Angelica. "I…Look. Let's talk before you go."

"I think you've said all you need to say. I know what you think about me. I know how much respect you have for me. All I want now is to pack my things and be gone."

"Mom! You should listen to Mr. Troy! Maybe we won't have to leave."

"Are you getting out?" she asked him through clenched teeth.

"No. Angelica—"

She pulled out fast enough to make the wheels spit gravel, drove past the kennels and down to the bunk-house. She skidded to a halt and slammed the truck into park. "C'mom, Xavier. Out." As soon as the sobbing boy had obeyed, she faced Troy. "By tonight, we'll be gone." She slammed the truck's door and walked into the bunkhouse, back stiff, one arm around Xavier.

Troy sat in the truck, his legs and arms too heavy to move. He stared out at the cornfields and wondered what he could do now.

His life had been snatched out from under him. Instead of being active, doing everything himself, he'd need help. With the kennels. With his practice. Even with driving, for pity's sake. Instead of getting married to the woman he loved, instead of becoming dad to the child he'd come to care deeply for, he'd be alone.

Alone, with a big empty space in his heart.

He knew he shouldn't be sitting here feeling sorry for himself, but he couldn't seem to make himself move. He didn't know what to do next.

Well, he did know: he should pray, put it in God's hands.

He let his face fall forward into his hands. *God...* He didn't know how to ask or what to say. Even looking at the bunkhouse and knowing that Xavier and Angelica were inside packing made his throat tighten up and his heart ache.

Help, he prayed.

The word echoed in his mind, as if God was saying it back to him.

There was nothing to do but try to help them. He'd help them load their stuff into the truck, as much as a crippled guy could. Find someone to drive them to the station. He'd pay for tickets wherever they wanted to go.

Where would they go, though?

And what about follow-ups to Xavier's treatments? What would Angelica do for a job? She'd worried that this would happen, that the "us" wouldn't work out and that she'd be alone, unable to afford the rest of the cost of treatment. He'd waved her concern aside.

Had she suspected he'd find out the truth about her?

What *was* the truth about her? He pounded the seat beside him. Why had she cheated on him? Why had she given herself to Jeremy?

"Mr. Troy! Mr. Troy! Come in here!"

At first he thought he was imagining the sound, but no; it was Xavier pounding on the truck's door. He lowered the window and looked out. "You okay, kiddo?"

"I am, but Lily's not! She's having her puppies! And Mom says she's in trouble!"

Troy grabbed the bag he always kept in the backseat and swung out of the vehicle.

"Come on! Mom said you wouldn't still be here, but I knew you would!"

They hurried into the bunkhouse together and there in a dark corner of the living room was Angelica, leaning over Lily.

Her dark hair was pulled back with a rubber band and she was doing something with a towel.

"What's going on?"

"She's having trouble with this last one." The anger was gone from her voice, replaced by worry. "She can't get it out. I've been trying to help her, but I'm afraid of hurting the puppy."

"Let me see." He squatted down and saw the puppy's hindquarters protruding from Lily, who was whimpering and bending, trying to lick at the new puppy while three other pups pushed at her teats.

"Get a couple towels," he told Xavier, and to Angelica, "Get the surgical scissors out of my bag while I try to ease the pup out."

It took several minutes, and when the puppy was finally born he saw why: it was half again as big as the other puppies. Lily sank back, too exhausted for the usual maternal duties, so Troy carefully removed the sac and cut the cord and rubbed the puppy vigorously in a clean towel until he was sure it was breathing on its own.

"Poor thing," Angelica cooed, stroking Lily's ears and head. "You did a good job."

The pup was breathing well, so Troy tucked it against Lily's tummy, where it rooted blindly until it found a teat to latch on to.

Lily lifted her head feebly and licked the new puppy a couple of times, then dropped her head back to the floor.

"You can rest now," Angelica said to the tired dog. "We'll help you."

A small hand tugged at his shoulder as Xavier peered past him to look at Lily. "Is she gonna die? Why's she bleeding?"

He'd half forgotten that Xavier was there. "She's doing great. There's always a little blood when a dog gives birth, but she should be just fine."

"The puppies look…yucky."

Troy glanced over at Angelica, not sure how much detail she wanted her son to know. She shrugged, so he gave Xavier a barebones account of placentas and amniotic fluid and umbilical cords.

Fortunately the boy took it in stride. "Is she gonna have more?"

"I feel one more little bump, so she'll probably have one more." He smiled at Xavier. "It'll be okay. Just takes a while."

"Can I watch?"

Troy looked over at Angelica, eyebrows raised.

"Sure, I guess." She stood up, stretched with her hands on her lower back, then walked over to the small bookcase. And started putting books in boxes.

Troy's heart dove down to his boots. For a minute there, he'd forgotten their conflict, forgotten that he'd kicked her out, forgotten they weren't a couple anymore. He opened his mouth to say something and then shut it again.

Should he take back his request that she leave? Beg her to stay? If she stayed, what would they do? Because the fact remained, she'd betrayed him.

Lily whimpered, and he looked down at her and petted and soothed her.

And then it hit him. Again. His revelation about how Angelica had cringed and held back from the physical.

If she'd consented to the relationship with Jeremy, then why did she act like an abused animal when a man tried to touch her?

Her phone buzzed just then, and he watched her as she answered it, wondering what to believe. Saw her frown and look despairingly at the half-filled box of books. "Are you sure you can't manage it? I'm kind of busy here."

She listened again.

"Okay. No, of course I can help." She clicked off the phone and sighed. "Lou Ann needs me to help her with something up at the house. Says she needs a woman, that you won't do. Can you..."

"I'll stay with Lily. And Xavier can stay with me." He felt so good being able to do something for her. Lord help him, he wanted to take care of her. Still.

"All right. I'll be as quick as possible. I still want to get going by nightfall."

"Angelica—"

"No time to talk." And she was out the door.

Angelica stalked into the house with her fists clenched and teeth gritted tight against the tears that wanted to pour out of her. "Lou Ann!" she called past the lump in her throat.

"Out here," came a voice from the backyard.

She walked through the kitchen, trying not to look at the table where she and Xavier had shared so many meals with Troy. The counter where they'd leaned together, talking. The window through which she'd watched him playing ball with her son.

The whole place was soaked in memories, and if she and Xavier weren't going to have Troy, if this wasn't going to work, then it was best for them to get out of here now.

She walked through the back door.

"Surprise!"

The sounds of female laughter, the pretty white tablecloth over a round table decorated with flowers, the banner congratulating her and Troy…all of it was totally overwhelming.

She looked around at Lou Ann; Daisy; Xavier's teacher, Susan Hayashi; Miss Minnie Falcon from the Senior Towers; and her two best friends from Boston, Imani and Ruth. She burst into tears.

Immediately the women surrounded her. "It's a surprise shower!"

"We're so happy for you!"

"Aw, she's so emotional!"

"Wait a minute." Lou Ann broke through the squealing circle of women to step right in front of Angelica and look at her face. "Honey, what's wrong?"

Something in her voice made the rest of the women quiet down. Angelica looked into Lou Ann's calm brown eyes and bit her lip. "It's not going to work. Xavier and I are leaving."

"What?" The older woman looked shocked, and around her, gasps and words of dismay echoed in Angelica's ears.

"Come on, sit down and tell us about it," her friend Imani said.

"I think I'll head over to see Troy." The deep voice belonged to Dion, and he waved a hand and headed for the front of the house.

"Go on, we'll catch up with you later," Lou Ann said. "He was helping us set up the canopy," she explained to Angelica.

"What did you mean, you're leaving?" Daisy asked.

So, haltingly, hesitatingly, Angelica explained what had driven her and Troy apart. What was the point in hiding it all now? And they'd be gone, so if any gossip came from this good group of women—which she doubted—it wouldn't hurt Xavier.

"But God's good," she finished, choking out the words. "It looks like Xavier's going to get well."

Hugs and tears and murmurs of support surrounded her.

"Men can be such idiots." Daisy pulled her chair closer to Angelica and squeezed her hand. "My brother most of all."

"That jerk Jeremy most of all," her friend Ruth said.

"So I don't *need* to marry Troy anymore, to help Xavier," Angelica explained, her voice still scratchy. "I mean, of course, he still wants a dad. But he's got time now, and he's got his health. And I can't be with someone who doesn't trust me."

"But what do you *want*?" Imani took her hand. "If Xavier weren't in the equation, would you love Troy? Do you want to be married to him?"

Angelica shut her eyes, and a slide show of memories played through her head.

The first time he'd asked her out, when she'd thought he must be joking, that no one as handsome and rich and popular as Troy could possibly want someone like her.

Riding horses together. Going to her first super-fancy restaurant. Looking up to see his marriage proposal in skywriting, in front of the whole town.

Back then, she'd been in love in a naive way. Impressed with him, infatuated with him. And down on herself, seeing no alternatives.

Now things were different. She'd gotten through the past six years by relying on God's strength. With His help, she'd mothered Xavier through the worst moments a child could have and come out stronger. She'd built friendships like those with Ruth and Imani, who'd come all the way from Boston to celebrate a milestone. Now she could add Daisy and Lou Ann to that circle of lifetime friends.

Now she didn't *need* Troy. But the thought of life without him was colorless, plain, lonely.

Now her images of him were different. She thought of him not only helping her get rid of a drunken Buck but also giving her cola and comfort and a shoulder to cry on afterward. She thought of him bent over Bull in the road, caring for the wounded animal and still remembering her son's feelings. Thought of him admitting he'd been wrong to accuse her of still dating Buck, apologizing, going on to find Dr. Ravi for Xavier.

"If he could accept my past without thinking less of me, then yeah." She looked around at the circle of concerned, supportive faces. "Yeah. I still love him."

"All right," Lou Ann said. "Then we've got to find a way to make this right."

A sharp rap on the door made Troy's heart thump in double time: *Angelica*. Maybe she'd decided not to go. Maybe she wanted to talk to him.

He didn't know why he was so eager for that when

she'd betrayed him with Jeremy. *If* she'd betrayed him. Because now that his initial anger was fading, he was having a hard time believing that of her.

"I know you're in there, my man," came Dion's deep voice.

"Come on in." Although he was glad to see his friend, needed a friend, Troy couldn't hide his disappointment.

Dion walked in looking anything but friendly. "Angelica's a mess. What did you do to her?"

Troy gave a tiny headshake, nodding toward Xavier. "We're watching Lily. She just had her last pup, and we're making sure she's okay."

"I'm helping," Xavier chimed in, bumping his shoulder against Troy. "Right, Mr. Troy?"

"Yep." Troy could barely choke out the word. How was he going to let this kid go?

Dion narrowed his eyes at Troy and flipped on the television to an old Western, complete with flaming arrows, bareback-riding Navajos and gun-toting cowboys. "Take a look, Xavier. You ever seen a cowboy show before?"

"Angelica wouldn't let…" Troy broke off. A little old-fashioned violence wouldn't hurt the kid. Xavier was immediately engrossed, leaving Dion and Troy free to move to an out-of-earshot spot at the kitchen table.

"What happened?" Dion glared at him.

Troy sighed, laced his hands together. "I found out who Xavier's dad is."

Dion looked at him expectantly.

"Jeremy Filmore."

Dion reared back and stared. "No kidding?"

Troy nodded. "No wonder she didn't want me to know, right? She could hardly claim assault with Jeremy." As he spoke, his anger came bubbling back.

"What do you mean? Does she say he attacked her?"

Troy nodded impatiently. "That's what she says, but I knew Jeremy. He wouldn't have done that."

Dion drummed his fingers on the table, frowning. "You sure about that, man?"

"You're not?"

"He had a pretty bad drinking problem." Dion studied the ceiling. "And he wasn't above clashing with the law. I broke up a few bar fights he started."

"True." And Troy had heard a few rumors, come to think of it, about how awful Jeremy had been to his wife.

"Not only that," Dion said, "but I was on duty for the car crash he died in. He was dead drunk. We didn't publicize that, and it was never in the paper—what would have been the point, when he was the only one involved, except to make his kids feel bad? But I can tell you it's so. I have the police reports to prove it."

"Wow." Jeremy, who'd had such potential, been a powerhouse of a football player, had died drunk. "So, what are you saying?"

"I'm saying that if Jeremy was drinking, he turned into an idiot. One who didn't have the ability to control himself."

"Even to the point of forcing himself on a woman?" The thought of Jeremy doing that to Angelica tapped in to a primal kind of outrage, but Troy fought to stay calm, to think. "Would he go that far, just because he wanted her?"

Dion shook his head. "It's about rage, not desire. They drill that into us at the police academy."

"But why would he be mad at Angelica? It just doesn't compute." Slowly he shook his head. "But it doesn't compute that she's lying, either."

"He was mad at women, period. Remember the so-called jokes he used to tell?"

"Yeah." Troy turned his cane over and over in his hand. "I guess I didn't spend much time with him once we were done with school."

"There could be another reason he kept his distance." The sound of televised gunshots and war whoops punctuated Dion's words. "He could have felt guilty about what he'd done."

"Getting her pregnant?"

"By force."

Troy pounded his fist on his knee.

"You have some apologizing to do."

Troy heaved out a sigh. "I screwed everything up."

"You might have, but pray Father God forgive you, and He will. Might even help you to make things right."

Troy nodded, staring down at the floor.

"And pray fast," Dion said. "Because there's a lot of estrogen coming our way."

Troy looked out the window Dion was looking out of. Marching in a line toward them, arms linked, were seven or eight women, his sister, Daisy, included. Angelica was at the center, and she looked shell-shocked. The rest of the ladies just looked angry and determined.

Man, was he in for it! But at least Angelica was still here.

Just before the women got within earshot, Angelica pulled away. The other women gathered around her and seemed to be urging her forward, but she shook her head vehemently. Then she broke away from the women and climbed into his truck.

Daisy marched over and yanked open the truck door. She and Angelica exchanged words, and then Angelica slid over to the passenger seat.

Daisy climbed into the driver's seat and they drove away, leaving clouds of dust behind them.

It was a mark of how upset Troy was that he didn't even care that his reckless sister was driving his vehicle.

He just wanted to be in there with Angelica.

The women watched her go and then headed toward the bunkhouse, looking more serious and less angry now.

"You better go out there and face them," Dion advised.

Xavier pushed in between them to look out the window. "Those ladies look mad."

"I know. But they're not mad at you, buddy." He spoke the reassuring words automatically, but his mind wasn't on Xavier. Mostly he wanted to know where Angelica had gone.

As the women reached the bunkhouse, he went out the front door and stood on the porch, arms crossed.

"You stay in here with me, Little Bit," he heard Dion say behind him.

The women stood in a line in front of Troy. "Come down here," said a dark-skinned woman he'd never seen before.

Troy used his cane to make his way halfway down the front steps.

"You've hurt that girl something terrible," Lou Ann said.

The dark-skinned woman added, "You accused her of stuff she didn't do."

"She'd never have cheated on you."

"I…yeah." Troy sat down on the edge of the porch and let his head sink into his hands. He was only now realizing the enormity of what he'd done. He'd made a terrible mistake, maybe lost the best part of his life— Xavier and Angelica. He looked up. "Where'd Angelica go?"

The women consulted and murmured among themselves for a couple of minutes. "We think she went out Highway 93," Lou Ann said finally.

Dion came out behind him, clapped a hand on his shoulder. "If you want to follow her, I can drive you. But not if you're going to make a fool of yourself again."

"No promises. I've already been an idiot. But I want to tell her how sorry I am."

That seemed to make the women happy; there were a couple of approving nods. "Take him out there, Dion," Lou Ann said, "but keep an eye on him."

Angelica knelt at the white roadside cross. *Jeremy Filmore* was painted on the horizontal board; *In loving memory* on the vertical one.

It wasn't his grave, but this was where he'd had his fatal accident. Somehow it had seemed to make more sense to come here, to this place she'd driven by dozens of times, getting mad and hating him with each pass. Never before had she stopped, gotten out of the car and studied it.

Now she saw the plastic flowers, the kids' football, the baby shoe and picture that decorated the cross, all looking surprisingly new, given that he'd died almost five years ago.

It reminded her that Jeremy had had a life, kids, people who loved him enough to keep up a memorial.

How could he be loved when he'd done something so awful?

Her legs went weak and she sank to her knees as regret overcame her. If only she hadn't been drunk that night. If only he hadn't. If only a friend had walked home with them. If only Troy had come out with her.

She'd never understand the why of it, no way. Why had God let it happen, something so awful?

She sat back and hugged her knees to her chest, aching as she remembered the years of hating herself, all the loose, ugly clothes she'd taken to wearing, scared of provoking unwanted male attention. Afraid of being the tramp Jeremy had accused her of being.

"I wasted the best years of my life hating you!" she cried out, pounding the ground, as if Jeremy lay beneath the memorial, as if he could still feel pain. She wanted to hurt him as he'd hurt her. Wanted to make him feel ashamed and awful. Wanted him to lose the love of his life, the way she'd lost Troy, twice now.

"Hey," Daisy said, getting out of the truck. "You okay?"

Angelica kept her eyes closed, her whole body tense as a coiled spring. "I hate him," she said. "I can't make myself stop hating him. I can't forgive him. I thought I could, but I can't."

Daisy knelt and put an arm around her. "He was

awful. A complete jerk. No one deserves to be treated the way you were treated."

"I hate him, hate him, hate him! I want him to suffer like I did. I want him to lose everything."

"Can't blame you there. Stinks that he lived in the community like a good person, and meanwhile, you felt like you had to leave."

"Yeah."

A breeze kicked up, and a few leaves fell around them. Fall was coming. Maybe it was already here.

Something was tugging at her. She thought about the years since the assault. "I hurt a lot in the past seven years."

"I know you must have."

"But I also had Xavier and got closer to God and… and grew up. Where Jeremy…he must have always had this in the back of his mind, what he did."

"Nah." Daisy let out a snort. "Guys like that are jerks. He didn't suffer."

"I think he did suffer. I think that's one reason he drank so much."

"Don't try to humanize him. It's okay to hate the guy who assaulted you!"

Angelica hugged Daisy; half laughing through her tears. "You're wonderful. But I don't actually think that it *is* okay to hate."

Daisy rolled her eyes. "Don't go all holy on me."

"I'm not very holy at all." Angelica shifted from her knees to a more comfortable sitting position. "I've always felt guilty myself, because I…" Tears rose to her eyes again. "Because I dressed up pretty and flirted with all the guys at the bar. Including Jeremy." She could barely squeeze the words out past the lump in her throat.

"Oh, give me a break. Men flirt every day and no woman commits assault on them. It wasn't fair, what happened to you." Daisy squeezed her shoulder. "And you totally didn't deserve it."

"You don't think so?"

"No! You'd probably make different decisions today, and you'd probably see more red flags with Jeremy." Daisy's voice went into social-worker mode. "Our brains keep developing and learn from experience. But no way—no *way*—did you deserve to be raped. Whether you flirt or dress up or get drunk, no means no." She squeezed Angelica's shoulder. "And you have to forgive yourself for being a silly twenty-one-year-old."

Daisy's words washed over her like a balm.

If she could forgive herself—the way God forgave her—then maybe she could forgive Jeremy. And get on with her life.

But it wasn't easy. "I'm still mad at myself. And even though I'm figuring it out, I still feel pretty hostile toward Jeremy."

Daisy was weaving a handful of clovers into a long chain. "I have a terrible temper," she said. "Pastor Ricky always tells me that forgiveness is a decision, not a feeling."

Forgiveness is a decision, not a feeling. The words echoed in her mind with the ring of truth.

Behind them, a truck lumbered by, adding a whiff of diesel to the air.

Forgiveness is a decision, not a feeling.

Angelica reached out a finger to the baby shoe that

hung on the crossbar. "I know, I've known all along, that God worked it for good by giving me Xavier." She drew in a breath. "Okay. I forgive you, Jeremy."

"And yourself?" Daisy prompted.

"I forgive…I forgive myself, too."

No fireworks exploded, and no church bells rang. But a tiny flower of peace took seed in Angelica's heart. For now, it was enough.

"Now, don't go ballistic," Dion warned Troy. "I think I see Angelica and Daisy up there."

"Why are they out of the car on the highway?"

"They're by a roadside memorial." Dion paused, then added, "For Jeremy Filmore."

Troy's hands balled into fists as Dion slowed the truck to a crawl and drove slowly past Daisy and Angelica. "If this doesn't show she's got feelings for him—"

"I'm sure she does have feelings." Dion pulled the truck off the road and turned off the ignition. "Wouldn't you hate the guy that did what he did?"

"That's not what I—" And Troy stopped. He was doing it again, being a jerk. He had to stop jumping to conclusions about Angelica, about how she felt and what she was doing. It wasn't fair to her or to him or to Xavier.

He sat there and watched while Daisy and Angelica held hands and prayed together. Man, his sister was a good person.

And so was Angelica. Talking with Dion had confirmed what his heart had already suspected: No way would she cheat on him.

He was a fool.

Troy dropped his head into his hands. If Angelica was praying, he should do that, too. She was amazing, always plunging forward and trying to do the right thing, to make a change, to live the way she was supposed to despite the horrible circumstances life always seemed to be throwing at her.

And he, what did he do?

He got his feelings hurt and suffered a minor disability and he fell apart.

He'd tried to fix her life and Xavier's on his own, giving her a job, letting them live on his place, getting medical help, even the marriage proposal. Looking back, it seemed as if he'd been waving his arms around uselessly, acting like some comic-book hero, trying to fix problems way too big for him.

For the first time in his life, he saw—just dimly— that there might be another way. The way that gave Dion his uncanny peacefulness. The way that made Angelica able to kneel by that jerk Jeremy's memorial and pray, after all she'd suffered.

He wanted, needed, that ability to let God in, to trust Him. Most of all, to ask Him for help. To recognize that he himself wasn't God and that God could do better than he could on his own poor human strength.

I'm sorry, God. Help me do better.

It was a simple prayer, but when he lifted his head, he felt some kind of peace. And when he looked over at Dion, he saw his friend smile. "What do you say I take Daisy home so you and Angelica can have some time?" he asked.

"That's a good idea."

Troy got out of the truck then and limped over to the two women. When he got there, Daisy stood and studied his face. Then, nodding as if satisfied, she walked back toward Dion's truck.

Leaving Troy to kneel beside Angelica.

She finished her prayer, turned and looked at him. Eyes full of wisdom but guarded against the pain he might inflict.

He reached out hesitantly and touched her dark hair. She didn't flinch away. Just studied his face.

A car whizzed by behind them. Another. The sound faded away into the horizon, and quiet fell.

He looked down at the cross for Jeremy. A man who'd done something so horrendous to the woman he loved. Reflexively his fist clenched. "I could kill him."

Angelica reached out and put her hand over his. "He's gone. Leave it to God." Her voice shook a little, and when he looked away from Jeremy's cross and into her eyes, he saw that they were shiny with tears.

One overflowed, rolled down her cheek. "You kicked us out. You didn't believe me."

"I'm so sorry." He relaxed his fist and reached out slowly to thumb the tears away. "I love you. I never stopped loving you. Can you forgive me?"

There was a moment's silence. Long enough for him to feel the cooling breeze against his back and smell the sweet, pungent zing of ozone. It was going to rain.

"I don't know." She knelt there, her face still wet with tears, and studied him seriously. As though she was trying to read him. "I love you, too, Troy. But I can't live with being distrusted, and I can't live with someone who thinks I'm a bad person inside."

"You're the best person I know!" The words burst out of him and he realized they were the exact truth. She'd gone through so much, and with such faith, and there was humility and wisdom and dignity in every move she made, every word she spoke. "Look, I screwed up, and I screwed up bad. I want to spend the rest of my life making it up to you. Even that won't be enough, but I want to try."

"Really?"

"Yeah, really." He touched her hand, tentatively, carefully. "I can't guarantee I'll never make another mistake, but I can guarantee it won't be about who you are inside."

She didn't look convinced.

He blundered on. "Like, I tend to be jealous."

She lifted an eyebrow. "No kidding. Right?"

"It's just, I know how incredible you are, and I see other men seeing it, and it makes me crazy."

Her lips tightened. "I'm not flattered by that, Troy. It's not a good thing."

"I know. I'm willing to do whatever I need to do to fix this. Read self-help books. Get counseling. Join Dion's men's group at church."

"That," she said instantly. "That's what you need. Other men to rein you in when you go all macho."

"I'll call him tomorrow." He took both of her hands in his. "Look, Angelica, I'm nowhere near as good of a person as you are. But I need you to know that I'll do everything in my power to protect you and Xavier. I'll take care of you and love you for the rest of my days. And I will never, ever tell you to leave again."

She looked steadily into his eyes as if she was reading him, judging him. And she had the right. She had to protect her son.

Finally her face broke into a smile. "I'm not a better person than you are. I've made plenty of mistakes and I'm sure I'll make more."

"Does this mean..." He trailed off, hardly daring to hope.

To his shock, she laughed, a pure, joyous sound. "You caught me on the right day," she said. "I'm on a forgiveness roll."

He took her face in his hands and was blown away by the sheer goodness of who she was. "I don't deserve you. You're...you're amazing, inside and out. I..." He ran out of words. *Way to go, Hinton. Smooth with the ladies, as always.*

She lifted her eyebrows, a tiny smile quirking the corner of her mouth. "Does this mean... What does this mean?"

She looked at peace about whether he wanted to marry her or not, whether they had a future or not. She had that glow of faith. She'd always had it, but it glowed brighter now.

He had so much to learn from her. And what could he, with his gimpy leg and his ignorant rages and his general guy immaturity, offer her?

Little enough, but if he could ease her parenting burdens and listen to her problems and protect her from anyone—anyone!—who so much as looked sideways at her, he wanted to do it. Would devote his life to doing it.

"It means," he said, "that I want you to marry me. For real. Forever. I want to help you and support you and be Xavier's dad. And I want it for the rest of our lives, through thickheadedness and illness and whatever else life throws at us. If you'll have me."

She looked at him with love glowing in her eyes. "Of course I will."

And as they embraced, the sky opened up and a warm, gentle rain started to fall, offering God's blessing on their new beginning.

Chapter 15

"That was awesome, Mom!"

Angelica turned toward her son's excited voice, only slightly slowed down by her wedding dress. Pure white. Traditional. What she'd always wanted.

"What was awesome, honey? The wedding?"

"No, the ride in a Hummer!"

Of course, her healthy, normal son had loved their unorthodox ride back from the church more than fidgeting through the wedding ceremony and receiving line.

Now they were back at the farm for the reception, which Lou Ann had insisted on orchestrating. There were two canopies set up, in case the warm October sunshine turned to rain, and Angelica could smell the good hearty dinner that was on buffet tables for the guests.

A small wedding, but meaningful. Just what she'd hoped for…and for many years hadn't dreamed possible for herself.

Since forgiving Jeremy that day by the side of the road, since feeling the sincerity of Troy's love and belief in her, she'd felt light enough to fly.

Gramps hustled over to give her a hug. "Did I tell you how beautiful you look?"

"About a dozen times, but it's okay." She kissed his grizzled cheek. "Thank you for walking me down the aisle. You've been wonderful today. I'm so grateful."

"Not sure about the rest of those Hintons, but Troy is all right." Troy had tried to talk Gramps into moving out of the Senior Towers and into the bunkhouse. When Gramps had refused, insisting on staying with his friends, Troy had helped him move into a bigger apartment at the Towers, paying the difference in rent secretly to save the old man's pride.

That was part of what she loved about Troy: he was willing to change, to break from the long-held Hinton animosity toward Gramps, to embrace her family with all its flaws.

Lou Ann had ridden from the church with Troy's father. As she emerged, radiant in a maroon dress and hat, from Mr. Hinton's vintage Cadillac, Gramps sniffed. "I'm gonna go over there and make sure he's not bothering Lou Ann. He always did have a crush on her."

People were all arriving now, and Angelica watched Lou Ann rush away from both men with an eye roll, hurrying on to direct the caterers and welcome guests. Angelica hadn't wanted a big fancy reception, but thanks to Lou Ann, everything was simple and perfect, from the centerpieces—a pretty mix of sunflowers, orange dahlias and autumn leaves—to the bluegrass band strumming lively music.

"Hey, Mom, look!" Xavier came out of the kennels, his suit knees dusty. "I have a 'prise for you!"

"You'll want to watch this," Troy said, coming up behind her. He wrapped his arms around her middle and she swayed back against him. He made her dizzy... in a good way. A very good way.

"Mom, pay attention!" Xavier stood frowning, hands on hips.

Troy chuckled into her ear, and Angelica laughed with self-conscious delight. It amazed her that she could feel so attracted to Troy, that it was easy and good to be close to him. No more cringing, no more fear. She trusted him completely.

She was getting back the girl she'd been, with God's help. He truly did make all things new.

She eased herself over to Troy's side, where she could breathe a little more easily. "What's the surprise, sweetie?" she called to her son.

"Lily's dressed up for the wedding!" Xavier yelled, so loud that everyone turned to see.

The rescued pit bull, her collar decorated with yellow roses, emerged from the barn with a line of puppies behind her. Amid the happy murmur of the guests, Xavier's voice rang out again. "Look what else!"

He whistled, and Bull came running full tilt from the barn.

Angelica did a double take. How was Bull moving so fast?

And then she realized that his back legs were supported by a doggie wheelchair, also decorated with yellow and white flowers. As he zigzagged after Xavier, Angelica pressed her hands to her mouth, amazed.

"We've been practicing with him for a couple of weeks," Troy said. "Xavier was determined that Bull could come to the wedding and play."

And trust Troy to make it happen, to take the time to work with Xavier and the dog and to keep the surprise for her.

"Come and get it, everyone!" Lou Ann called, and people flowed toward the tables to eat, stopping to greet them on the way. And there were hugs. So many hugs.

As she and Troy stood there arm in arm, welcoming their guests, Angelica lifted her face to the afternoon sunshine and thanked God for all He'd done for them.

Xavier barreled up toward them, and at the same time, both Troy and Angelica reached out to hold him. "Our whole family," Angelica said, rubbing her son's head, roughened by newly sprouted hair. Joy bubbled up inside her, rich and full and satisfying.

"Well…" Troy said, sounding guilty.

"Mom? There's one other thing. Dad and I have been talking about it."

"What?" She stepped out of Troy's embrace to frown in mock exasperation at her two men. "Are you guys conspiring against me?"

"What's 'spiring?"

"Hatching a secret plan, buddy. And…kinda. Tell her, Zavey."

Her son reached out and took one of her hands and one of Troy's. "I want a little sister."

"Oh, Zavey Davey…" She looked up at Troy as her mind flashed back to a family she'd seen in the park.

Mom, Dad and two children, one an adorable little girl. She hadn't thought it was possible God could be so good to her, but now she knew He could.

The last of her old doubts about the future faded away at the sight of Troy's smile. "What do you think?"

"I think it's a distinct possibility." He gave her a quick wink and reached out to pull her back into his arms.

* * * * *

WE HOPE YOU ENJOYED
THIS BOOK FROM

LOVE INSPIRED
INSPIRATIONAL ROMANCE

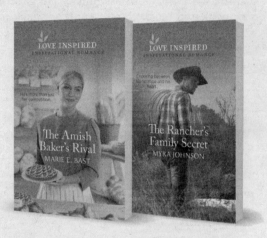

Uplifting stories of faith, forgiveness and hope.

Fall in love with stories where faith helps
guide you through life's challenges, and discover
the promise of a new beginning.

6 NEW BOOKS AVAILABLE EVERY MONTH!

HARLEQUIN

Save $1.00

on the purchase of ANY Harlequin book
from the imprints below.

*Heartfelt or thrilling, passionate or
uplifting—our romances have it all.*

PRESENTS INTRIGUE

DESIRE ROMANTIC SUSPENSE SPECIAL EDITION

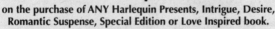

LOVE INSPIRED

Save $1.00

on the purchase of ANY Harlequin Presents, Intrigue, Desire,
Romantic Suspense, Special Edition or Love Inspired book.

Valid from December 1, 2020 to November 30, 2021.

LOVE INSPIRED

INSPIRATIONAL ROMANCE

UPLIFTING STORIES OF FAITH, FORGIVENESS AND HOPE.

Join our social communities to connect with other readers who share your love!

Sign up for the Love Inspired newsletter at **LoveInspired.com** to be the first to find out about upcoming titles, special promotions and exclusive content.

CONNECT WITH US AT:

f Facebook.com/LoveInspiredBooks

🐦 Twitter.com/LoveInspiredBks

Facebook.com/groups/HarlequinConnection